Science: A Third Level Course

Ecology   Block A   Energy flow through ecosystems

Introduction to Block A

Unit 1
Primary production - the process

Unit 2
Primary production in ecosystems

Unit 3
Consumers in ecosytems

Prepared by an Open University Course Team

THE OPEN UNIVERSITY PRESS

S323 Course Team

Chairman and General Editor

M. E. Varley

Authors

Mary K. Bell (*Staff Tutor*)
E. A. Bowers (*Staff Tutor*)
N. R. Chalmers
Irene Ridge
C. Turner (*Staff Tutor*)
M. E. Varley

Editor

Eve Braley-Smith

Other Members
N. Cleminson (*BBC*)
S. H. Cousins
R. D. Harding (*Course Assistant*)
S. W. Hurry
A. R. Kaye (*IET*)
E. Milner (*BBC*)
R. M. Morris (*Technology*)
S. P. R. Rose
J. Stevenson (*BBC*)

Consultants

J. M. Anderson
M. Burgis
K. Southern

The Open University Press,
Walton Hall, Milton Keynes.

First published 1974.
Copyright © 1974 The Open University.

Designed by the Media Development Group of the Open University.

Printed in Great Britain by
Martin Cadbury, a specialized division of Santype International,
Worcester and London.

ISBN 0 335 04150 7

This text forms part of an Open University course. The complete list of units in the course appears at the end of this text.

For general availability of supporting material referred to in this text, please write to the Director of Marketing, The Open University, P.O. Box 81, Walton Hall, Milton Keynes, MK7 6AT.

Further information on Open University courses may be obtained from the Admissions Office, The Open University, P.O. Box 48, Walton Hall, Milton Keynes, MK7 6AB.

1.1

Introduction to Block A

Contents

1.0 What is an ecosystem?

The mandate of ecologists is to study the interactions of all living organisms on Earth with each other and with their physical environment. This is a daunting task and would be almost impossible if there were no means of breaking the field of study into more manageable units. There are many different ways of trying to classify the Earth and its organisms into smaller units. For instance, environments can be divided into aquatic and terrestrial with further subdivisions of each, or they can be classified on the basis of latitude (and climate) as polar, temperate and tropical, or according to the geographical divisions of the Earth; all these systems of classification are useful in various ways because they allow ecologists to concentrate on parts of the Earth system and comparison of the parts reveals something about the functioning of the whole. The scale of environments is discussed in Block 1 of S2–3*; you should refer to Table 1 of that Block to remind yourself of the terminology used for geomorphological, climatic and biological features of the Earth.

The interaction of living organisms with their environments is very much a two-way process: organisms affect and are in turn affected by their physical surroundings. Professor Arthur Tansley, a British botanist, proposed in 1935 that the term 'ecosystem' should be used to describe 'not only the organism-complex but also the whole complex of physical factors forming what we call the environment' (Tansley, 1935).

ecosystem

The concept of this interaction system of living organisms and physical and chemical factors of their habitats has proved extremely valuable and the *ecosystem* has become a basic unit of ecological study. Since the term was first introduced it has acquired a broader meaning. It is probably most useful when applied at the level of 'communities' (which is how Tansley used it) but an ecosystem may be as small as a microstand[1]** (a dead log, for example) or large as a biome[1] or biogeographical realm[1] or even the biosphere,[1] each with its associated environment. The only constraint is that the unit being studied as an ecosystem should be reasonably self-sustaining.

* The Open University (1972) S2–3 *Environment*, The Open University Press.

** Superscripts refer to other Open University Courses (see p. 9).

A single goldfish in a bowl cannot be regarded as an ecosystem, as all energy input (feeding) and waste removal (bowl cleaning) are carried out by man. But a self-sustaining aquarium containing waterweeds, algae, snails and fish can be usefully studied as an ecosystem to find out how these organisms interact with and depend upon each other and the surrounding water.

It seems to be characteristic of all ecosystems that organisms can be grouped according to their methods of feeding or obtaining energy; a particular group is referred to as a *trophic level* (trophic meaning 'relating to nutrition'). For example, green plants obtain energy from the sun and are described as primary producers which occupy the first trophic level; herbivorous animals feed on living plants and are described as primary consumers which occupy the second trophic level. Each box in Figure 1 represents a trophic level and the arrangement and relative sizes of the boxes shows the *trophic structure* of a hypothetical ecosystem: all ecosystems possess a characteristic trophic structure.

trophic level

producers
consumers

Some organisms do not fit conveniently into a single trophic level. Consider the grizzly bear for example, which will eat small animals, fish, roots or berries, whichever is easiest to get: his assignment to a particular trophic level will probably depend on whichever source of food the investigator regards as the major source in a given situation. Sometimes an organism may feed on two or three trophic levels at the same time, the most obvious example being man!

Recall from S100² and from *Ecological Energetics* (Phillipson, 1966) that there is a flow of energy through ecosystems; this flow is illustrated by the black arrows in Figure 1.

energy flow

You should be able to answer the following questions from your study of S100 and by inspection of Figure 1:

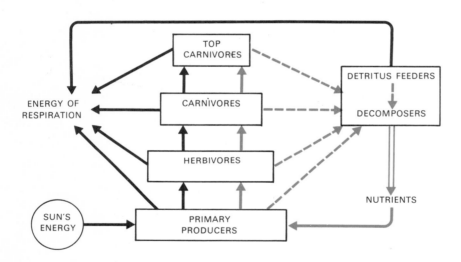

Figure 1

QUESTION   What are the external sources of energy in ecosystems?

ANSWER   In most ecosystems, the only external source of energy is the Sun (see Fig. 1). In some ecosystems, however, energy enters in the form of live organisms or dead or decomposed organisms from another ecosystem.

QUESTION   By what process is solar radiation converted into organic matter? Is a high proportion of the incident solar energy used in this process?

ANSWER   Photosynthesis carried out by primary producers uses a small proportion of the available sunlight. This is discussed in more detail in Unit 1.

QUESTION   What are the sources of energy for organisms other than green plants?

ANSWER   These organisms depend on living plants (herbivores) or animals (small carnivores and top carnivores) or on dead organisms or waste and excretory products (detritivores and decomposers). This is discussed further in Units 3 and 4. Some bacteria use light, and others simple inorganic compounds, as a source of energy: this is discussed in Unit 1.

4

QUESTION   How is energy 'used' by organisms?

ANSWER   For synthesizing new compounds (anabolic processes) for growth and reproduction and also for cell maintenance, for movement and (in some) for maintaining body temperature. Energy for these processes can be made available through the breakdown of complex organic molecules in respiration (a catabolic process), but not all the energy released in this way is utilized by the organism: a proportion is always 'lost' and dissipated as heat.

So there is a constant flow of energy through the ecosystem from primary producers to top carnivores and decomposers and a constant loss of energy as a result of respiration.

Recall from S100[3] that certain chemical elements 'cycle' through ecosystems as indicated by the red arrows in Figure 1.

nutrient cycling

QUESTION   Which elements could be represented by these red arrows?

ANSWER   'Mineral nutrients' such as nitrogen and phosphorus. Primary producers take up these elements in the form of soluble mineral salts from surrounding soil or water; herbivores and carnivores obtain nitrogen and phosphorus mainly as organic compounds in their food (but may need supplements of raw minerals such as salt ($NaCl$) for humans or copper licks for cattle). The dead organisms together with their waste and excretory products are broken down by decomposers (chiefly bacteria and fungi) which release mineral nutrients in a form available for re-use by primary producers.

QUESTION   Is there a carbon cycle? If so, describe it.

ANSWER   Yes. Carbon is released into the atmosphere as carbon dioxide as a result of respiration of plants, animals and decomposers: this CO_2 is taken up by green plants during photosynthesis and the carbon passes on to animals when they eat these plants.[3]

QUESTION   Are there similar cycles for oxygen and hydrogen?

ANSWER   Hydrogen and oxygen cycle through the atmosphere (as H_2O and O_2) as well as through decomposers; as H_2O, they are involved in the hydrological cycle. You did not study these cycles in detail in S100.

In this Block we shall concentrate on ecosystems from the point of view of trophic structure and the flow of energy and cycling of nutrients, but there are other aspects of the structure of ecosystems that are relevant. You will recall that species within communities of organisms show specializations of habits and activities.[4]

QUESTION   What is the term used to describe the 'place' in the community of a species with particular specialized habits?

ANSWER   Niche. This term was coined by the British zoologist Charles Elton (Elton, 1927). In some communities, the niches are very specialized and there is a great number of them; these communities include large numbers of species of organisms. Ecosystems with these complex communities are described as 'mature' in contrast to 'immature' ecosystems with relatively few species, mostly occupying wide niches.

niche

The use of the terms 'mature' and 'immature' to describe ecosystems implies that they change with time and progress in predictable directions. This pheno-menon of change in communities (and so in ecosystems) is called 'succession'. You will recall that you have already studied 'hydroseres'.[5]

succession

QUESTION   What is a hydrosere?

ANSWER   Plant successions in aquatic environments are called hydroseres. In lowland Britain, the general progression is from open lake, through reed swamp, to sedge fen, to fen woods.

QUESTION   What is the term used to describe the final stage of the succession (if it is reached)?

ANSWER   The climax community. Recall that this is often determined by climate (the climatic climax) and sometimes by soil conditions (the edaphic climax).

climax

Various theories have been advanced about the changes in ecosystems that accompany succession; some of these will be discussed in later Units.

If you consider an ecosystem such as a forest or a lake, then the interactions between the living and non-living components are clearly very complex. Why then are ecosystems adopted as units of study and what sorts of questions are asked about them? In the first place, there is the intrinsic scientific interest: ecologists would like to know how these complex biological systems work. In the second place, '. . . to enable us to have sufficient insight into the workings of ecosystems to be able to manipulate them with confidence and predict the consequences of our actions' (Mann, 1969). In other words, we want to know how to increase food production for human consumption and what will be the long-term effects of disrupting and polluting natural ecosystems.

A young American, Raymond I. Lindeman, laid the practical and theoretical foundations for the study of ecosystems from the point of view of energy flow. In his paper 'The trophic-dynamic aspect of ecology' (Lindeman, 1942) written shortly before his death at the age of 27, Lindeman suggested for the first time that organisms within ecosystems should be grouped according to their methods of feeding or obtaining energy (trophic level) and that the basic object of study should be the flow of energy between trophic levels. The questions asked are, therefore: How much energy enters a given trophic level in a given period of time (a year or a growing season for example)? What proportion of this energy is lost due to respiration? How much is lost to other trophic levels by grazing, predation or parasitism? How much is lost to decomposers? How much accumulates as living matter (biomass)? From such information, the efficiency with which the organisms in a particular trophic level use the available energy for growth or reproduction can be calculated. Such knowledge can have important implications. For example, if studies on the large grazers of the East African

Lindeman

TABLE 1   Terms relating to production and energy.

Term	Definition	Symbol
Biomass	The total amount of living substance of a group of organisms on a unit area at a given time—it may be measured in terms of weight (wet or dry) or as energy units or as nitrogen equivalents. The average biomass is sometimes called 'standing crop' for animals but, for plants, the term 'standing crop' is sometimes restricted to the biomass above ground.	B
Consumption (animals)	Total intake of energy by an organism in a given time. It is used chiefly for animals; the equivalent for plants is the total amount of light reaching the organism in a given time.	C
Gross production (plants) / Assimilation (animals)	Total energy fixed or absorbed by an organism (=physiologically useful energy) in a given time.	A
Respiration	That part of gross production or assimilated energy converted through respiration to heat or mechanical energy, or used in life processes.	R
Net production (plants) / Production (animals)	The increase in biomass or total energy content in a given time; it is the difference between A and R. Production includes reproductive products.	P
Yield	Sometimes applied only to that part of production which is used by man. It can be used more generally to describe that part of production which is consumed by animals in a given time; this is the same as the amount of a crop harvested over a given time.	Y
Productivity	The *rate* of energy absorption or accumulation per unit biomass in unit time.	$P:B$

plains (mainly antelope and zebra) show that these animals convert grass to meat much more efficiently than do the cows kept by local tribes, it follows that, for maximum meat production on the plains, farming antelopes might be a better proposition than farming cows!

Lindeman's 'trophic-dynamic model' relating to energy flow between trophic levels has remained the most popular framework for comparing the productivity of ecosystems and, partly because of this, the cycling of nutrients has been somewhat neglected. But it has become increasingly clear that nutrient supply may be a critical factor, limiting the production of organic matter, so that, in order to understand fully the functioning of ecosystems, we need to consider also the factors regulating nutrient cycling.

In Block A you will study in turn the various trophic levels—primary producers, consumers (herbivores and carnivores), detritivores and decomposers—how they obtain and lose energy, how productivity is regulated and what role each plays in nutrient cycling. The experimental methods used to study ecosystems will be emphasized because, in order to evaluate results, you need to understand the limitations of methods used to obtain them.

A number of scientific terms relating to production and energy flow occur throughout Block A. These are listed and defined in Table 1 together with the symbols used to represent them. You may find from your reading of set papers and other literature that other authors use slightly different definitions and different symbols, so bear this in mind and refer to Table 1 if in any doubt.

2.0 The International Biological Programme (IBP)

There is a radio programme about IBP

The idea for the International Biological Programme was discussed in 1959 by Sir Rudolf Peters, President of the International Council of Scientific Unions (ICSU) and Professor Montalenti, President of the International Union of Biological Sciences (IUBS), and a general plan was approved by ICSU in November 1963. Here is a quotation from a report submitted to the ICSU meeting:

> As a consequence of the rapid rate of increase in the numbers and needs of the human populations of the world and their demands on the natural environment, there is an urgent need for greatly increased biological research.
>
> It is proposed that there shall be an International Biological Programme (IBP) entitled *The Biological Basis of Productivity and Human Welfare*, with the objectives of ensuring a world-wide study of: (1) organic production on the land, in fresh waters, and in the seas, so that adequate estimates may be made of the potential yield of new as well as existing natural resources, and (2) human adaptability to the changing conditions.
>
> In proposing such a programme it is considered essential that it shall be limited to basic biological studies related to productivity and human welfare, which will benefit from international collaboration and are urgent because of the rapid rate of the changes taking place in all environments throughout the world.

The Programme was divided into seven sections:

Productivity of Terrestrial Communities (PT).

Production Processes (PP).

Conservation of Terrestrial Communities (CT).

Productivity of Freshwater Communities (PF).

Productivity of Marine Communities (PM).

Human Adaptability (HA).

Use and Management of Biological Resources (UM).

It was envisaged that there should be two and a half years of preparation (Phase I) followed by five years of operations (Phase II) and recently it has been recognized that there must be a period of synthesis (Phase III). For most of the world, including the UK, the IBP is now (1973) in Phase III but in the USA problems about funding led to delay and the IBP is early in Phase II. One of the objectives of the programme was international cooperation with a special view to standardization of methods so that results could be compared and also with the intention of spreading research projects over a range of geographical areas, climatic types, and environments; it was hoped that there would be studies of complete ecosystems representing the variety of environments in the world. A positive result of IBP has been the publication of a series of *IBP Handbooks* on methods recommended for use in different types of communities; preparation of these has involved scientists of many nationalities meeting as small committees and comparing their ideas and methods. Sometimes these meetings have been held concurrently with larger meetings where scientists gave review papers, published later as books; similar meetings are being held during the synthesis phase and eventually 'Synthesis Volumes' will be published by the seven IBP sections.

Some of the authors of this Course have been concerned with parts of IBP and all have been able to benefit from the *IBP Handbooks* and reviews. We would have liked to be able to include in Block A of our Course the results of IBP but unfortunately, in 1973, the synthesis stage is not complete. It may be that very exciting new ideas will emerge from the syntheses—if so, you should become aware of them through scientific journals as well as through technical reports and papers (if you have access to these). We shall have to rely on Supplementary Papers to keep our Course up to date.

3.0 Why begin with production ecology?

Why are we beginning this Course by studying energy flow and nutrient cycling? We could have started with the distribution of organisms in relation to physico-chemical factors of the environment or with the total numbers of species (the species diversity) in different parts of the world or with several other aspects of ecology. We have chosen to begin with production ecology for three main reasons:

1 This approach stresses the interdependence of different types of organisms and so provides a conceptual framework for sorting out the organisms in any community. For instance, there cannot be herbivores present unless there are plants growing in the habitat, and the types of food available impose limits on the feeding habits and numbers of animals that can live in a community.

2 Energy studies are concerned with rates—rates of uptake of solar energy or food, rates of dissipation of heat, rates of accumulation of biomass, and so on. Having to think in terms of rates emphasizes the dynamic aspect of communities: that balance may exist at any one time or over a period of time but that changes in relative rates will lead to changes in the position of balance and so to changes in the communities. This is the phenomenon of succession.

3 Productivity is of direct interest because human food supplies depend on the energy-flow processes of ecosystems. This will be discussed fully in Block D, but you should realize as you read Block A that understanding of the principles that govern energy flow and nutrient cycling is of very basic importance to the management of ecosystems for the benefit of mankind.

The five Units that make up Block A are not all of equal length but represent logical divisions of the subject-matter. Units 3 and 4 are long Units whereas Units 1 and 5 are short and Unit 2 is average; you should bear this in mind when you plan your other activities. We expect that you will start to read *ABE** while studying this Block; there are references in Units to specific topics that you should look up in ABE but you should also start to read it and the associated text. The equivalent of three to four hours of your time while you study Block A should be devoted to ABE.

* The Open University (1973) S321/323 *The Analysis of Biological Experiments*, The Open University Press. This is part of the supplementary material for this Course.

Units of measurement

In this Course, as in all Open University Science Courses, we use SI units. These are defined in *Science Data Book* (R. M. Tennent, 1971); refer to pp. 37–9, 49–50, 80–1. Quantities of heat are expressed as *joules* (symbol J) in SI Units. The units used in much of the biological literature on energy flow are *calories* (cal) or *kilocalories* (kcal or Cal) which are not SI Units; to convert into joules, multiply calories by 4·186 and kilocalories by $4·186 \times 10^3$ (use 4·2 or $4·2 \times 10^3$ respectively as an approximation in most cases). In these texts, we have converted all data into joules but the set papers use calories; when reading other books, you should make a mental note of the units that are being used so that you can make meaningful comparisons of figures.

The following information about units of measurement may be helpful to you in interpreting data:

Units of area
1 hectare (ha) $= 10\,000$ m^2
1 acre $\qquad = 4\,050$ m^2 (not used in the Units)

Units of weight
1 tonne (metric ton) $= 1\,000$ kg
1 kilogram $\qquad = 1\,000$ g
1 pound $\qquad = 454$ g (not used in the Units)
1 tonne ha$^{-1} = 0·1$ kg m$^{-2} = 100$ g m^{-2}
and lb acre^{-1} is roughly equivalent to kg ha^{-1}.

When converting dry weights of organisms into units of energy (joules), the dry weight of terrestrial plants (grams) is multiplied by (18.8×10^3) and for aquatic algae the factor is (20.5×10^3). These factors are the average energy value in joules of 1 g of tissue.

References to other Open University Courses

1 S2–3, Block 1, Table 1.

2 S100, Unit 20, Section 20.1.1, Objectives 2 and 4.

3 S100, Unit 20, Section 20.1.2, Objective 3.

4 S100, Unit 20, Section 20.2.1.

5 S2–3, Block 4, Section 2.5, Objective 2.

References cited in the text

Elton, C. S. (1927) *Animal Ecology*, Sidgwick & Jackson.

Lindeman, R. L. (1942) The trophic-dynamic aspect of ecology, *Ecology*, **23**, 339–418.

Mann, K. H. (1969) The dynamics of aquatic ecosystems, *Adv. in Ecol. Res.*, **6**, 1–81.

Phillipson, J. (1966) *Ecological Energetics*, Arnold.

Tansley, A. G. (1935) The use and abuse of vegetational concepts and terms, *Ecology*, **16**, 284–307.

Tennent, R. M. (ed.) (1971) *Science Data Book*, Oliver & Boyd.

Recommended books for Block A

You will find lists of books and papers recommended for particular Units in Block A listed at the end of each Unit. The following books provide background reading for the whole of the Block:

Krebs, C. J. (1972) *Ecology* (*The Experimental Analysis of Distribution and Abundance*), Harper & Row.

Odum, E. P. (1969) *Fundamentals of Ecology*, 3rd ed., W. B. Saunders.

Short general texts with particular emphasis on ecosystems and productivity:

Kormondy, E. J. (1969) *Concepts of Ecology*, Prentice-Hall.

Whittaker, R. H. (1970) *Communities and Ecosystems*, Macmillan.

Specialized books on productivity:

Phillipson, J. (1966) *Ecological Energetics*, Arnold.

Russell-Hunter, W. D. (1970) *Aquatic Productivity* (*An Introduction to Some Basic Aspects of Biological Oceanography and Limnology*), Macmillan.

IBP Handbooks (1968–73) Blackwell Scientific Publications. (There are some 24 handbooks in this series, mostly quite short; they are concerned largely with experimental methods in production ecology.)

Unit 1

Primary production—the process

Contents

Study guide

Units 1 and 2 are concerned with primary producers and primary production in ecosystems. Unit 1 is mainly about photosynthesis in plants and bacteria but considers also nitrogen fixation in both autotrophes and heterotrophes.

Before starting the Unit do the Pretest (p. 5) to check that you remember the terms and concepts introduced in earlier prerequisite courses. Questions 1–5 relate to Block A as a whole and questions 6 and 7 to Unit 1.

The Set Paper for Unit 1 is 'Photosynthesis under natural conditions' by L. T. Evans (from *Penguin Science Survey 1968: Biology*). This will be referred to in the Unit text as *Evans* and directions are given on when to read particular sections of the paper. It is a scientific essay which describes and comments on other people's research and is not a report of the author's own research. You may prefer to read straight through Evans before starting the Unit but, if so, read it through again at the end of Section 1.5 and answer the questions there to check your understanding of the paper.

The light available to primary producers and their ability to intercept and absorb it are considered in Section 1.1; omit Section 1.1.2 if short of time. Sections 1.2 and 1.3 are concerned with the factors limiting photosynthesis for different plants in different environments and Section 1.4 with the biochemical mechanisms of light trapping and carbon fixation. For students who took S2–1* (*Biochemistry*), much of Section 1.4 can be treated as revision, but Section 1.4.2b (photorespiration) will be new to all students. Leafy green plants can be grouped broadly into two classes, those with a high and those with a low capacity for primary production and, on the basis of information supplied in Sections 1.1–1.4 and in *Evans*, you should be able to describe the morphological, physiological and biochemical characteristics of plants in these classes (Section 1.5).

Photosynthesis is a very flexible process with many variations on a basic theme. Some of these variations and their ecological significance are considered (Sections 1.6 and 1.7) for bacteria and for blue-green algae, with special emphasis on photosynthetic nitrogen fixation, a process where trapped light energy is used to convert atmospheric nitrogen to nitrates. Discussion of N fixation is extended to include the heterotrophic bacteria, organisms which fix nitrogen using complex organic molecules as a source of energy. If short of time, omit Section 1.7.2 on methods of measuring nitrogen fixation.

Home Experiment 1 relates chiefly to this Unit, Section 1.1, and is a study of light interception by different types of leaves, using a light-probe. It will probably be most useful for you to do this experiment while working through Units 1 or 2 but, if you cannot find suitable leaves, then delay the experiment until the end of Block A.

---

* The Open University (1972) S2–1 *Biochemistry*, The Open University Press.

Table A1

List of scientific terms, concepts and principles in Unit 1

Developed in this Unit or its set paper	Page No.	Developed in a later Unit	Unit No.
ecosystem	*Intro. A*	nitrogen cycle	4
trophic level	*Intro. A*	bacteria and mineral cycling	4
accessory pigments	8		
leaf area index	9	role of microbes in the detritus food chain	4
	Evans 75		
sun and shade leaves	9	integrated energy flow models for whole ecosystems	5
limiting factors of photosynthesis	11		
	Evans 74		
light saturation	11		
	Evans 83		
photo-oxidation	12		
light reactions of photosynthesis	15		
dark reactions of photosynthesis (carbon fixation)	16		
C–3 pathway (Calvin cycle)	18		
photorespiration	19		
C–4 pathway (Hatch–Slack path)	20		
high- and low-capacity producers	21		
bacterial photosynthesis	22		
chemosynthesis	23		
nitrogenase	25		
biological nitrogen fixation:	25		
by autotrophes	26		
by heterotrophes	26		

Table A2

Units and Sections of Open University Science Courses taken as prerequisites

Course	Unit	Section
S100*	15	15.4
		15.5
		15.6
		15.7
		15.8
	18	Appendices 2,3
	20	20.0
		20.1
	34	34.2.1
S22–**	1	1.2
	3	3.8
		3.9

* The Open University (1971) S100 *Science: A Foundation Course*, The Open University Press.

** The Open University (1972) S22– *Comparative Physiology*, The Open University Press.

Objectives

After studying this Unit, you should be able to:

1 Define correctly and distinguish between true and false statements concerning each of the terms and concepts listed in Table A1.

2 Given relevant information about the total solar energy incident in different parts of the Earth, the losses of solar energy by reflection, transmission or absorption, and the region of the spectrum that can be utilized in photosynthesis, calculate the energy available for photosynthesis and the efficiency of utilization in different terrestrial and aquatic environments.
(Tested in ITQ and SAQ 1.)

3 Assess the factors which determine the efficiency of light-interception by plants.
(Tested in SAQs 2 and 9.)

4 Assess the major factors which determine the rate of photosynthesis for individuals and for whole plant communities in different environments.
(Tested in SAQs 4, 9 and 10.)

5 Describe (either by simple equations and flow-diagrams or in words) the light reactions for photosynthesis in higher plants, and recognize the major inputs and products of the reactions.
(Tested in SAQs 4, 5 and 6.)

6 Recognize the different roles of the light and dark reactions in photosynthesis.
(Tested in ITQs and SAQs 9 and 10.)

7 Describe by simple flow-diagrams the C–3 and C–4 pathways for carbon fixation, and correlate these pathways with other morphological and physiological characteristics relating to the productive capacity of plants.
(Tested in ITQs and SAQs 6, 7 and 8.)

8 Compare bacterial photosynthesis and chemosynthesis with green plant photosynthesis, and assess the ecological importance of the first two processes.
(Tested in ITQs and SAQ 11.)

9 Recognize that ATP and 'reducing power' produced by light reactions may be utilized in processes other than carbon fixation, and illustrate this with reference to photosynthetic nitrogen fixation.
(Tested in SAQ 12.)

10 Demonstrate, with appropriate examples, the ecological importance of both photosynthetic and heterotrophic nitrogen fixation.
(Tested in SAQ 12.)

Pretest

(Questions 1–5 relate to the whole of Block 1.)

1   What is the basic difference between autotrophes and heterotrophes? Classify each of the organisms (a–f) as:
(i)   either autotrophes or heterotrophes, and
(ii)   either primary producers, consumers or decomposers.

(a)   Mushrooms (fungi).
(b)   Beech trees.
(c)   Earthworms.
(d)   Bacteria living in the gut of man.
(e)   *Fucus* (brown alga living on the sea-shore).
(f)   Houseflies (maggots).

2   What process, common to all living organisms, results in a continuous loss of energy?

3   Plants need a supply of mineral nutrients for growth. How do plants obtain nitrogen and phosphorus and how is the supply maintained?

4   (a) What is the name of the gradual process of change which occurs in unstable ecosystems? (b) What is the name of the final, most stable stage?

5   In the classification of living organisms, what is the name given to those which lack membrane-bound sub-cellular organelles? Name two groups of organisms of this type.

(Questions 6 and 7 relate to Unit 1.)

6   In what organelles of higher green plants does photosynthesis take place?
(a)   nuclei   (c)   chloroplasts
(b)   mitochondria and chloroplasts   (d)   chloroplasts, nuclei and
                                                              mitochondria.

7   How does most of the carbon dioxide used in photosynthesis reach the cells within a leaf?
(a)   By diffusion across the epidermal cells.
(b)   By diffusion through stomatal pores on the leaf surface.
(c)   From cell respiration in the leaf.
(d)   In aqueous solution in the xylem of leaf veins.

(Questions 8 and 9 relate to Unit 2.)

8   For a stratified lake, name: (a) the upper zone; (b) the lower zone; (c) the boundary layer between (a) and (b).

9   Below are pairs of contrasting characteristics which apply to freshwater lakes. Select from the list the features typical of *oligotrophic* and *eutrophic* lakes:

Water	(A) deep	(B) shallow
Bottom	(C) muddy	(D) stony
Water	(E) oxygenated throughout	(F) deoxygenated in hypolimnion during summer
Plant nutrients	(G) plentiful	(H) scarce
Primary producers	(J) large numbers	(K) few

Answers to the Pretest are on p. 34.

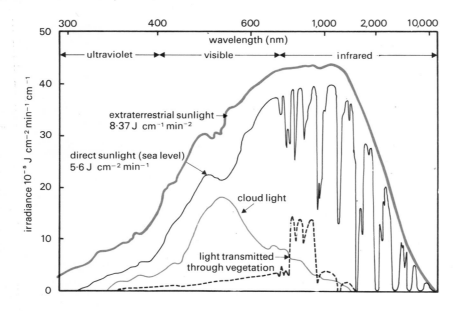

Figure 1 Wavelength distribution of extraterrestrial sunlight, sunlight reaching sea level on a clear day, sunlight reaching sea level on a cloudy day, and sunlight penetrating a stand of vegetation (Gates, 1965)

1.0 Introduction

The only external source of energy for the Earth is solar radiation and the only way that organisms can convert this radiation into chemical energy is by photo-synthesis. In the great majority of ecosystems the ultimate food source, the energy base, is provided by green plants which use solar energy, CO_2, water and mineral nutrients for growth. We shall consider, therefore, the efficiency with which solar radiation is trapped by plants, the factors which limit the rate of photosynthesis, and the mechanics of the process itself—how light is converted to chemical energy in one series of reactions and how this energy is used, to fix carbon dioxide for example, in other series of reactions. Bacteria and blue-green algae show considerable variation both in the ways of trapping energy and in the ways of using trapped energy, and these variations have important ecological implications.

Primary production is simply the accumulation of organic matter by primary producers; in green plants, the energy for this accumulation is the light trapped in photosynthesis, the carbon is derived from carbon dioxide fixed in photo-synthesis, and the other chemical substances needed are absorbed from the atmosphere or in solution from the soil. So to understand primary production you need first to know something about the underlying process, photosynthesis.

1.1 Light and plants

Study comment The important points to learn from this Section are:
1 The factors which determine the quantity and quality of light available to autotrophes.
2 The factors which determine the efficiency of light interception by plants.
Concentrate on Sections 1.1.1 and 1.1.3 if you are short of time.

1.1.1 Solar energy

Energy from the Sun reaches the outer atmosphere of the Earth at an average rate of around 8.4 J cm^{-2} min^{-1} (the solar flux). A hotplate of 100 cm^{-2} delivering energy at this rate to a well-lagged kettle containing 100 cm^3 of water at 20 °C would take about 40 minutes to boil the water.

ITQ 1 Bearing in mind that the Earth revolves on its axis as it orbits round the Sun, what will determine the actual solar flux at any given spot?

Read the answer to ITQ 1 (p. 34).

As solar radiation passes through the Earth's atmosphere, some 10–20 per cent is absorbed by gases, water vapour or dust and converted to heat energy; a further 30–40 per cent may be reflected back into space by clouds or dust so that, even at noon on a clear day, a maximum of only 67 per cent of the original radiation reaches the Earth's surface (and 50 per cent is a more usual value). Figure 1 shows the wavelength or spectral distribution of this radiation before and after passing through the Earth's atmosphere. It is quite clear that atmos-pheric absorption and reflectance affects not only the quantity but also the quality of radiation reaching the Earth's surface. About 40 per cent of this radiation is reflected by bare ground or water surfaces and the rest is available for absorption by green plants.

energy losses in the atmosphere

Read about this in Evans, pp. 81–2, ABSORPTION OF RADIATION.

Note Diffuse sky light means the light reaching Earth after passing through a cloud layer which causes light scattering.

Evans stresses the high efficiency with which plants absorb the radiation active in photosynthesis, but note (a) that he discusses only leafy terrestrial plants and (b) that of the active radiation absorbed not all is used in photosynthesis (some is converted directly to heat, for example).

In fact, a yearly average of only 0·2–0·3 per cent of the total light energy available to plants is fixed in photosynthesis. Table 1 summarizes the relationship between the input of solar energy, its absorption and its use in photosynthesis by plants.

TABLE 1 Percentage of solar energy reaching the Earth's surface during one year.

	Absorbed by plants %	Used in photosynthesis %
Maximum possible	50	5
Average for favourable conditions	50	1
Average for all ecosystems	<50	0·2
Average for deserts or open oceans	≪50	0·1

< means 'less than' and ≪ 'much less than'.

ITQ 2 Use the information in Table 1 to calculate the maximum possible percentage of absorbed light energy that can be converted to organic matter by plants.

ITQ 3 Suggest a reason for the low light absorption in deserts or the open oceans.

Read the answers to ITQs 2 and 3.

Now you could attempt SAQ 1 on p. 32.

1.1.2 Aquatic plants

For aquatic plants the situation is more complex, because water selectively absorbs the red and orange wavelengths of light which include those most strongly absorbed by the major photosynthetic pigment, chlorophyll a, and used in photosynthesis. Light becomes progressively more blue-green in colour as it penetrates through water, with the greatest penetration attained by blue light (wavelength 400–500 nm) in perfectly clear water and by greenish-yellow light of wavelength 500–550 nm in water containing suspended organic matter (including plants). Chloroplasts contain certain 'accessory' pigments which can absorb light in these wavebands and then pass on the absorbed energy to chlorophyll a for use in photosynthesis. Figure 2 shows the absorption spectra of various pigments (their relative absorption of light of different wavelengths) and Table 2 the pigment composition of some aquatic algae.

accessory pigments

Figure 2 Absorption spectra of chloroplast pigments.

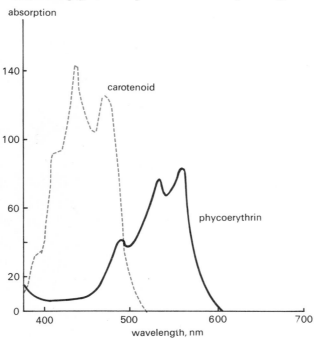

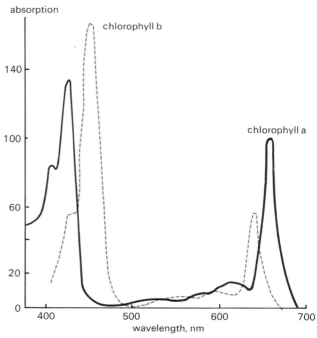

TABLE 2   Pigment composition of some aquatic algae.

Photosynthetic pigment	Green algae	Brown algae and diatoms	Red algae
Chlorophyll a	×	×	×
Chlorophyll b	×		
Fucoxanthin		×	
Phycoerythrin			×

There is some correlation between the average depth of submergence of aquatic algae and their pigment composition.

QUESTION   Where would you expect to find aquatic green algae?

ANSWER   In very shallow water or attached to rocks on upper shores.

In large areas of deeper water (lakes or oceans) where the planktonic (free-floating) algae may sink or be carried down by water currents, most species contain fucoxanthin and so do the large species attached to rocks in the middle shore zone. The red algae, which are all attached species, are found chiefly along the lower shore line or in off-shore water.

1.1.3   Plant structure and the interception of light

Since individual leaves of green plants absorb photosynthetically active radiation with a high degree of efficiency, then the total energy absorbed by whole plants, or plant communities, must depend on the numbers, arrangements, structure and length of life of the leaves. There is a more detailed discussion of light interception in *Evans*.

Now read Evans, pp. 78–81, INTERCEPTION OF RADIATION, *but note before reading:* the terms 'leaf area index' and 'net assimilation rate' occur in this section. The leaf area index, L, of a plant or crop is the ratio of its total leaf area to the ground area occupied and it gives some measure of the efficiency of light interception. For plants such as beech trees which cast a very dense shade, L may be as high as 8. The net assimilation rate, NAR, is the average rate of increase of organic matter per unit leaf weight. Remember that leaves gain organic matter through photosynthesis but continually lose it through respiration, and the difference between the gains and losses gives the NAR.

leaf area index

net assimilation rate

QUESTION   Apart from L, what other factors will affect light interception by leaves? Use the information given in Evans and try to think of additional factors yourself.

ANSWER   Evans describes (p. 81) how *leaf angle* affects light interception; in addition, leaf *arrangement*, which affects self-shading, is important. When viewed from directly above, the leaves of many plants are seen to be arranged in a 'mosaic' which gives minimal self-shading and allows the maximum number of leaves to receive light directly (see Fig. 3).

Leaf thickness and the number of layers of chlorophyll-containing cells also affect light interception; leaves normally exposed to strong sunlight are often smaller in total area but thicker than leaves normally exposed to low-intensity light. Furthermore, strong light may damage cells (see Section 1.2.1) and many plants are able to *vary the angle* of leaves and thus reduce interception in strong light, when their leaves adopt an 'edge-on' position parallel to the incident light; in weak-to-moderate light, interception is greatest when their leaves adopt a position at right angles to the incident light. Average leaf area is frequently greater in shady conditions and, on the basis of these leaf characteristics (thickness, angle and area), it is often possible to distinguish 'sun' and 'shade' leaves on a single plant or sun- and shade-adapted individuals within a population.

Figure 3 Leaf mosaic of walnut (*Juglans regia*)

9

Increasing crop yields by increasing light interception is now a major concern of crop physiologists and plant breeders. Some crops have horizontal or drooping leaves (Fig. 4) and in maize with leaves arranged in this way an acre of ground is covered by about 4 acres of leaves.

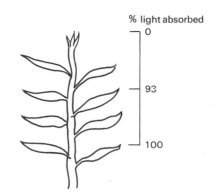

Figure 4 Plant with horizontal leaves.

QUESTION   What is the leaf area index of this crop?

ANSWER   4 $\left(\frac{4}{1}\right)$

This is with rather wide spacing of plants so that the leaves of one do not overlap those of another, and so do not cause extra shading of lower leaves.

QUESTION   Supposing that the planting density were increased so that the leaf area index of the maize were increased to 8, would you expect this to affect the crop yield and, if so, how?

ANSWER   It would probably *not* increase crop yield because the increased plant density would result in greater shading of lower by upper leaves. These shaded leaves would, therefore, produce less or, in extreme cases, might consume more in respiration than they produced by photosynthesis, thus becoming a 'drain' on the plants. The yield of individual plants would then fall and the total crop yield would probably be about the same as for the widely spaced plants.

It is possible, by selective plant-breeding, to alter plant shape and the angle at which leaves are held.

QUESTION   Suggest a suitable plant shape which would give a leaf area index of 8 for the crop without excessive self-shading of lower leaves.

ANSWER   A 'narrower' plant with more upright leaves does the trick (Fig. 5). Light now penetrates more deeply into the stand with a high degree of interception but without the severe self-shading of lower leaves; therefore, planting density can be increased without decreasing the yield per plant and total crop yield rises.

This upright-leaf stratagem has been an important factor in increasing yields of the new 'miracle' wheat and rice varieties, and plant breeders in the United States are now trying to produce the same shape for maize plants.

Now you could attempt SAQ 2.

1.2   Effects of environmental factors on the rate of photosynthesis

Study comment   The idea of limiting factors, as applied to photosynthesis, is introduced and the ways in which light, temperature and CO_2 supply can limit the rate of photosynthesis are discussed. If short of time, omit reading *Evans*, pp. 74–7.

We have seen that atmospheric conditions (such as cloudiness) affect the light supply and that plant anatomy, morphology and accessory pigments affect light interception. But is light the only environmental factor governing the rate of photosynthesis? For green plants, photosynthesis is usually summarized[1] * as:

$$6CO_2 + 6H_2O \xrightarrow{\text{light}} C_6H_{12}O_6 + 6O_2$$
$$\text{glucose}$$

This is a process in which light energy absorbed by chlorophyll pigments is used to reduce carbon dioxide to organic compounds (usually carbohydrates); oxygen is released as a by-product of the reaction.

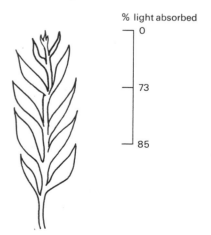

Figure 5 Plant with angled leaves.

* Superscript numbers refer to references to other Open University Science Courses which are considered to be prerequisites to this Course (see p. 30).

Pioneer work on the rate-limiting factors for photosynthesis was carried out in the early 1900s by F. F. Blackman and his methods using enclosed single leaves and his principle of limiting factors are discussed in *Evans*, p. 74, ENCLOSED LEAVES.

Now read Evans, pp. 74–7, COLLECTING THE DATA.

This describes various ways of measuring photosynthesis in the laboratory and in the field so that rate-limiting factors can be investigated. In Unit 2 there is a more detailed discussion of methods of measuring primary production, including ways of measuring photosynthesis. Read rapidly through the section 'MICRO-METEOROLOGICAL METHODS' (since there is further discussion of this technique in Unit 2). After reading *Evans*, answer the following ITQs to test your understanding of the text.

> **ITQ 4** State one advantage and one disadvantage of the leaf enclosure method for measuring photosynthesis.

> **ITQ 5** What two parameters are used to measure the growth rate of a leafy plant?
>
> *Read the answers to ITQs 4 and 5.*

limiting factors

1.2.1 Light intensity and temperature

Consider the relationship between light intensity and the rate of photosynthesis for a single leaf of sugar beet.

Turn to Evans, p. 80, and look at Figure 19.

Note The broken line in Figure 19 relates to the efficiency of photosynthesis,

$$\left(\frac{\text{light used in photosynthesis}}{\text{total light available}} \right)$$

and the solid line to the rate of photosynthesis.

> **ITQ 6** When does the light intensity limit the rate of photosynthesis in this leaf?
>
> *Read the answer to ITQ 6.*

As you can see in *Evans*, Figure 19, the efficiency of light utilization in photosynthesis falls dramatically as light intensity increases.

Now read Evans, p. 83, LIGHT SATURATION OF UPPER LEAVES.

light saturation

Evans' explanation of light saturation will be easier to follow after reading Section 1.5 of this Unit, but note particularly his comments on subtropical grasses and his Figure 20: corn or maize (*Zea mays*), sugarcane (*Saccharum officinarum*) and cocksfoot (*Dactylis glomerata*) are all grasses.

> **ITQ 7** Which of the two environments described below (A and B) permits the more efficient use of light in photosynthesis for plants 1–5?
> (A) Generally cloudy weather with long warm summer days.
> (B) Generally hot cloudless weather with bright sunlight and short day-length.
>
> 1 sugar beet   4 red clover
> 2 sugarcane   5 wheat
> 3 sorghum
>
> *Read the answer to ITQ 7.*

Much more is now known about these species which do not show light saturation of photosynthesis. They are all herbs (no shrubs or trees), many are grasses or sedges, and the uncultivated species grow mainly in open unshaded habitats where both light intensity and temperature are normally high. The effects of temperature on the rate of photosynthesis are described in *Evans*.

temperature

Now read Evans, pp. 85–8, TEMPERATURE.

The effect of increasing temperature on growth rate and photosynthesis of the tropical species mentioned above is different from that of species in temperate regions.

11

QUESTION   From your reading of *Evans* which species in Figure 21 (p. 87) is from a tropical or subtropical environment and which from a temperate environment? (Both species are grasses.)

ANSWER   *Paspalum* is a subtropical species: there is no inhibition of growth or photosynthesis at high temperatures. Ryegrass (*Lolium perenne*) is a temperate grass, and temperature inhibition is clearly shown in *Evans*, Figure 21.

ITQ 8   From your reading of *Evans*, what are the main features of plants showing the 'warm climate strategy' for photosynthesis?

Read the answer to ITQ 8.

Although in most plants low light intensity may be rate limiting for photosynthesis, prolonged exposure to high intensities may also inhibit the process. An excess of light energy can lead to the formation of potentially damaging substances and cause oxidation of pigments, although the precise mechanisms involved are still not fully understood. Shade species, normally growing in low light intensities, and marine phytoplankton are particularly susceptible to this light inhibition. This is one of the reasons why, on clear sunny days, the maximum rate of photosynthesis often occurs 1–2 m below the surface of the sea rather than immediately below the surface where light intensity is highest.

Some light damage is reversible and can be repaired in the dark. Some, however, is due to an irreversible oxidation of pigments (*photo-oxidation*) which is also dependent on the presence of oxygen and leads to breakdown of photosynthetic pigments similar to the fading of dyes in strong light. Certain mutant strains of algae which are deficient in carotenoids (orange pigments found in chloroplasts) are susceptible to photo-oxidation even in weak light, and it is thought that a major role of carotenoids is to act as a safety valve, absorbing excess light energy, converting it to heat energy, and thus reducing the danger of photo-oxidation of chlorophyll a.

1.2.2   Carbon dioxide

During photosynthesis green plants use trapped light energy to convert CO_2 from the air to organic compounds and indeed the rate of photosynthesis is usually measured by estimating CO_2 incorporation or organic matter accumulation. Under certain conditions, CO_2 may become rate-limiting for photosynthesis.

Read Evans, pp. 89–90, CARBON DIOXIDE SUPPLY.

Note   Lucerne, or alfalfa (*Medicago sativa*) is a legume, a plant belonging to the pea and bean family.

QUESTION   There is plenty of CO_2 in the air; why then may CO_2 become rate-limiting for photosynthesis at high light intensities?

ANSWER   Because it is not so much CO_2 in the air that matters as CO_2 levels at the site of photosynthesis in the chloroplasts. To reach the chloroplasts, CO_2 must diffuse through the stomata,[2] through the air spaces between leaf cells, across the cell wall and through the cell cytoplasm. It is the rate of these diffusion processes that limits CO_2 supply, and the speed of diffusion depends on the steepness of the concentration gradient of CO_2 between outside air and internal chloroplasts.

QUESTION   Evans points out two ways of increasing this gradient. What are they?

ANSWER   Increasing external CO_2 concentrations or increasing air turbulence so that CO_2 levels are not locally reduced around leaves (see Fig. 6, a and b).

QUESTION   What is the third way, illustrated in Figure 6c, of maintaining a steep CO_2 gradient?

ANSWER   Lowering the CO_2 levels within the leaf by removing virtually all the CO_2 from the intercellular spaces.

warm climate strategy for photosynthesis

photo-oxidation

CO_2 gradient

12

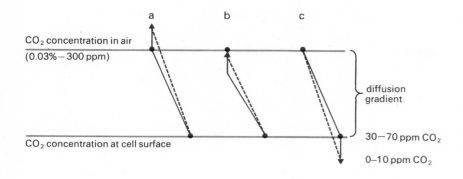

A measure of the ability of cells to remove CO_2 and lower the concentration in the leaf is provided by the CO_2 compensation point. This is the equilibrium concentration attained when CO_2 output due to respiration just balances uptake due to photosynthesis, so that, for an enclosed leaf, the CO_2 level in the air remains constant. The lower the compensation point the greater the ability of the plant to remove CO_2 from the air and to re-use the CO_2 released during respiration.

compensation point

TABLE 3

Species	CO_2 compensation point at 25 °C
	ppm*
Maize (*Zea mays*)	2·7
Sugarcane (*Saccharum officinarum*)	7·0
Wheat (*Triticum sativum*)	78·0
Tobacco (*Nicotiana tabaccum*)	48·0
Onion (*Allium cepa*)	90·0

* Parts per million.

QUESTION Which of the species in Table 3 will be least likely to show rate limitation of photosynthesis due to CO_2 levels when light intensity is high?

ANSWER The first two. These have low CO_2 compensation points and are able, therefore, to remove nearly all the CO_2 from the intercellular spaces, thus maintaining a steep diffusion gradient for CO_2 from the outside air to the cells.

QUESTION In the discussion so far about CO_2 limitation of photosynthesis, it has been assumed that CO_2 can enter the leaf from the atmosphere quite freely. Is this always true?

ANSWER. No. The stomatal pores on the leaf surface must be open for free entry of CO_2. The pores may close in response to certain environmental conditions such as a water deficit[2]. CO_2 may become limiting because of stomatal closure.

1.2.3 Supply of CO_2 for aquatic plants

Carbon dioxide reacts with water to give carbonic acid which in turn dissociates:

$$H_2O + CO_2 \rightleftharpoons H_2CO_3 \rightleftharpoons H^+ + HCO_3^- \rightleftharpoons H^+ + CO_3^{2-} \qquad (1)$$
$$\text{carbonic acid} \qquad \text{bicarbonate} \qquad \text{carbonate}$$

Since all reactions are readily reversible, an equilibrium is set up between the different forms, the proportions of each depending on water pH and on the amount of cations (positive ions) available to neutralize the bicarbonate and carbonate anions.

Figure 7 illustrates the variations of CO_2, HCO_3^-, and CO_3^{2-} concentrations in sea water with changes in pH.

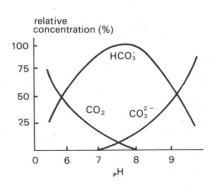

Figure 7 Effect of pH on concentrations of CO_2, bicarbonate and carbonate in sea water of 34 per cent salinity (Fogg, 1968).

ITQ 9 In which of the following types of water will free CO_2 concentration be highest?

(a) 'Soft' water (acid fresh water with low levels of cations).

(b) 'Hard' water (alkaline fresh water with high levels of cations).

Read the answer to ITQ 9.

All aquatic plants are able to take up and use in photosynthesis the free CO_2 and carbonic acid dissolved in water, but not all are able to take up bicarbonate and none appears able to take up and use carbonate. If taken up, both carbonic acid and bicarbonate are converted to CO_2 within the plant cells.

QUESTION Suggest three factors which will determine the supply of CO_2 for aquatic plants.

ANSWER 1 Type of water (pH and cation level).

2 Ability of plants to take up bicarbonate.

3 Rate of diffusion of CO_2 and/or bicarbonate from (a) the cell surface to the chloroplasts (the smaller the cells of algae and the closer to the surface the chloroplasts lie, the less likely is the rate of CO_2 diffusion to become limiting) and (b) in *still* water, from water to the cell surface (just as, in still air, the rate of diffusion of CO_2 into leaves may become limiting).

Among the plants which can take up and use bicarbonate directly are various pondweeds (*Elodea canadensis*, Canadian pondweed, and *Potamogeton lucens*, shining pondweed, for example), freshwater algae such as *Chara* and a large group of minute marine phytoplankton, the Coccolithophorids. Bicarbonate uptake in the pondweeds and probably in the Coccolithophorids is accompanied by excretion of OH^- ions from the cells, which causes a local rise in pH and precipitation of insoluble calcium carbonate. This is used by Coccolithophorids for the production of intricate external scales; about half of the world's chalk deposits originate from this source.

bicarbonate uptake

When aquatic plants grow and photosynthesize very rapidly under favourable conditions of light, temperature and nutrients, the removal of CO_2 from the water may be so rapid that CO_2 replenishment by diffusion from air to water fails to keep pace and consequently the equilibrium shifts to the left (see equation 1): carbonates dissociate to give bicarbonates and water pH rises. This can be a serious problem in nutrient-enriched eutrophic lakes where pH may rise to 10 or 11 (see Unit 2). When this happens, when plants themselves affect water pH, they also affect their own supply of CO_2.

1.3 Rate of photosynthesis and plant growth rate

Study comment This short Section discusses how the rate of photosynthesis may be limited by internal processes, such as transport of assimilate away from the site of synthesis, and how photosynthetic production is related to overall rates of plant growth. This last part of the Section can be read rapidly, since this topic is discussed in greater detail in Unit 2.

There is one more factor which may affect the rate of photosynthesis, an internal rather than an external (climatic) factor.

Read Evans, p. 88, THE EFFECT OF DEVELOPING STORAGE ORGANS.

source and sink relationships

QUESTION Why should removal of tomato fruits affect the rate of photosynthesis of tomato leaves?

ANSWER Because high rates of photosynthesis in leaves can only be maintained if the organic products are transported away to 'sink' organs, in this instance the tomato fruits.

Not surprisingly, the fast-growing tropical or subtropical grasses such as maize or sugarcane are extremely efficient at transporting sugars from their leaves but they appear to need high temperatures (30 °C or more) to do this. In experiments where the tropical grass *Digitaria* was subjected to night temperatures of 10 °C the starch content of isolated chloroplasts next morning was seven times that of plants kept at 30 °C overnight, and both plant growth rate and rate of photosynthesis during the day showed severe inhibition.

QUESTION Starch is an insoluble form of storage carbohydrate which can be broken down to give soluble sugars. Suggest two possible explanations for the slower removal of starch from chloroplasts when night temperatures are low.

ANSWER Firstly the enzymic breakdown of starch to sugar prior to export from the chloroplasts will be slower at the low temperature. Secondly, the sugars move in the phloem down a concentration gradient from 'source' to 'sink' (see reference[4]) and removal of sugars by the sink depends on their conversion to insoluble products, such as starch, or their utilization in respiration: both these processes depend on enzymic reactions which will be slower at the lower temperature.

temperature and transport

When considering whole leafy plants or populations of algal cells, rather than single leaves or cells, then clearly the total amount of energy trapped in photosynthesis will be related to the numbers of leaves or algal cells present. But growth of leaves and algae depend not only on photosynthetic rates but also on supplies of mineral nutrients and water. In hot dry deserts there is usually ample light and CO_2 for photosynthesis but insufficient water for rapid growth; in this environment, therefore, water is the major factor limiting growth and photosynthetic production in the primary producers. In tropical seas, on the other hand, increases in the phytoplankton population are often limited by the supply of mineral nutrients (especially phosphates and nitrates) and this is the major factor limiting total carbon fixation. This topic will be considered in greater detail in Unit 2.

Now you can attempt SAQ 3.

1.4   The mechanism of photosynthesis

Study comment This is a difficult Section for those with limited biochemical background, but for students who read S2–1 (*Biochemistry*) much of Sections 1.4.1 and 1.4.2a may be treated as revision. You are not expected to memorize the biochemical pathways shown but should be able to describe them briefly and know the major inputs and outputs. The important ideas to note are that:

1   'Light' reactions of photosynthesis are concerned with the conversion of light to chemical energy in the form of ATP and $NADPH_2$.

2   'Dark' reactions of photosynthesis utilize this trapped energy, chiefly for the conversion of CO_2 to complex organic compounds.

3   In green plants, the most important pathway for carbon fixation is the Calvin cycle, which occurs in all higher plants. In certain plants in tropical climates, an additional pathway, the Hatch–Slack pathway, is found.

4   In light, Calvin cycle plants may oxidize fixed carbon without releasing useful energy (photorespiration).

The equation for photosynthesis given in Section 1.2 is a greatly oversimplified version of the process and, in particular, conceals the fact that trapping of light energy is a quite distinct process from conversion of CO_2 to carbohydrates. This last is simply one way of using the trapped energy. A more general definition of photosynthesis makes no mention of either CO_2 or O_2: 'photosynthesis is a series of processes in which light energy is converted to chemical energy which can be used for biosynthesis'.

1.4.1   Trapping light energy

The light reactions of photosynthesis in green plants involve four basic events:

light reactions of photosynthesis

1   Chloroplast pigments absorb light energy, some of which causes electrons to shift to a higher orbital (a higher energy state).

2   Absorbed energy, in the form of excited electrons, is passed from pigment molecules to non-pigment molecules (electron acceptors).

3   As electrons are passed from one molecule to another some energy is tapped off and used to produce adenosine triphosphate (ATP) from adenosine diphosphate and inorganic phosphate

$$ADP + Ⓟ_i \longrightarrow ATP$$

and, in addition, stable organic molecules which can donate electrons or hydrogen atoms to other molecules ('reducing power') are produced.

Note   If you find this confusing, you can read an elementary account of cell energetics and ATP formation in reference[5], but we have included a more modern treatment of this subject in Appendix 1 (Black), p. 31. Read this if you want a better understanding of energetics and ATP.

4   Light-induced splitting of water molecules, yielding oxygen as a by-product, provides a source of electrons to replace those lost from the chloroplast pigments.

Thus light energy is converted to chemical energy in the form of ATP and reducing power which can be used to fix CO_2 or to drive any other reactions needing a supply of energy.

Considering this process in more detail, the primary event of light trapping is the absorption of packets of light energy (photons) by pigment molecules. The (energetically speaking) 'excited' electrons produced in this way may be transferred to neighbouring pigment molecules so that a chain-reaction is set up until, finally, electrons are transferred to a slightly modified form of chlorophyll a. These special pigment molecules, which are called *trapping centres*, transfer energy only to non-pigments, so they mark the real beginning of the reaction sequence.

trapping centres

This sequence is shown in outline in Figure 8, but if you wish to know more about it consult the books by Fogg (1968) or Hall and Rao (1972) in the list of recommended reading at the end of this Unit, p. 30.

The oxygen released in photosynthesis is the source of all oxygen in the Earth's atmosphere: we depend on plants not only to trap solar energy but also to provide a breathable atmosphere. Until about 1941 the origin of oxygen released during photosynthesis was not known for certain: some held that it derived from CO_2 and others that water was the source.

QUESTION   How could the origin of this oxygen be investigated?

ANSWER CO_2 or H_2O labelled with the heavy isotope, O^{18}, could be used (oxygen has *no* stable radioactive isotope). Plants or isolated chloroplasts could be supplied with either CO_2^{18} or H_2O^{18} in the light, and the oxygen released examined in a mass spectrometer to determine its molecular weight. Using this technique it was found that only H_2O^{18} released O_2^{18} so that oxygen must be released in photosynthesis by the splitting of water molecules.

1.4.2   Carbon fixation

The conversion of CO_2 into complex organic compounds is accomplished using the ATP and $NADPH_2$ generated in the photosynthetic light reactions. Carbon fixation is thus not *directly* dependent on light but only on the products of the 'light' reactions: there is a clear distinction between the light reactions which trap light energy and the dark reactions which utilize this energy.

dark reactions of photosynthesis

1.4.2a   The Calvin cycle

The first major pathway for carbon fixation was worked out between 1946 and 1953 by an American research group led by Melvin Calvin, after whom it was named the Calvin cycle. The main steps in the cycle are summarized in Figure 9. Calvin's experiments were done with cultures of unicellular green algae which were supplied, in the light, with radioactive $^{14}CO_2$ and then rapidly killed at different times so that the sequential appearance of the ^{14}C label in fixed compounds could be followed.

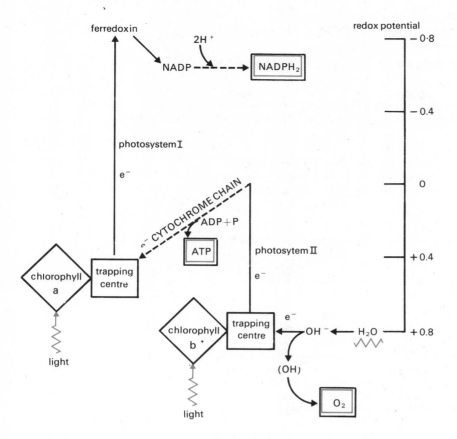

Figure 8 The light reactions of photosynthesis.

Conventions and explanations relating to Figure 8

1 The redox potential (scale on right) provides a measure of the ability of components to donate electrons: the more negative the potential the greater is the ability to donate electrons to substances of lower potential, i.e. the greater the reducing power of the component.

2 Electrons are represented by e^-, and hydrogen ions (protons) by H^+.

3 Ferredoxin is an iron-containing protein which accepts electrons very readily and which can, in turn, pass on electrons to the coenzyme NADP (nicotinamide adenine dinucleotide phosphate), a substance closely related to NAD, the coenzyme involved in respiration[6]. The NADP then combines with two protons (H^+), which derive from H_2O, and forms $NADPH_2$.

Note particularly There are *two* primary light reactions, one utilizing only chlorophyll a pigments (Photosystem I), and one utilizing mainly chlorophyll b which transfers electrons to a special form of chlorophyll a (Photosystem II). Each Photosystem has a different trapping centre, and chlorophyll b, an accessory pigment, may be replaced by other accessory pigments such as fucoxanthin or phycoerythrin in certain aquatic algae (see Section 1.1.2).

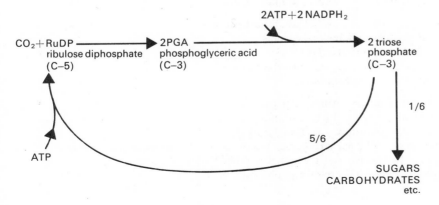

Figure 9 The Calvin cycle.

After studying Figure 9, work through the questions below.

QUESTION   In Calvin's experiments, what would be the first labelled compound to appear?

ANSWER   A phosphorylated organic acid with three carbon atoms per molecule, phosphoglyceric acid, PGA. The Calvin cycle is also referred to as the C–3 (3-carbon) cycle for this reason.

C–3 pathway

QUESTION   What is the primary acceptor of CO_2 (the first molecule to react with CO_2)?

ANSWER   A 5-carbon sugar phosphorylated at two positions, ribulose diphosphate, RuDP.

QUESTION   For one 'turn' of the Calvin cycle using $^{14}CO_2$ what proportion of the PGA formed would be radioactive?

ANSWER   50 per cent; since $^{14}CO_2$ reacts with a C–5 molecule to give 2 molecules of PGA, only one of the PGA molecules will carry the ^{14}C label.

QUESTION   Which steps in the cycle require an input of energy or reducing power?

ANSWER   (a)   The conversion of PGA to a 3-carbon phosphorylated sugar, triose phosphate, requires ATP and $NADPH_2$ derived from the light reactions of photosynthesis. This reaction actually proceeds in two steps: first a phosphate group (P) from ATP is added to PGA to give diphosphoglyceric acid which is a transitory unstable intermediate; this is then reduced by $NADPH_2$ and the second P removed to give triose phosphate. This is the major energy-requiring step in carbon fixation.
(b)   The regeneration of RuDP from triose phosphate (necessary to keep the cycle going) proceeds by a complex series of reactions and ATP is required for the final step in regeneration.

QUESTION   For one 'turn' of the cycle, how many molecules of a sugar such as glucose $(C_6H_{12}O_6)$ could be produced?

ANSWER   One-sixth of one molecule: from 2 molecules of triose phosphate (6 carbons), one-sixth (1 carbon) goes into the production of sugars and five-sixths for the regeneration of RuDP. Thus six turns of the cycle are needed to produce one molecule of glucose.

ITQ 10   Supposing the light above a well-illuminated culture of green algae were suddenly switched off: would you expect the levels of (a) PGA and (b) RuDP in the cells to fall, rise or remain constant?

Read the answer to ITQ 10.

Although sugars and carbohydrates are often described as the 'end-products' of photosynthesis, both PGA and triose phosphate occupy a central position as intermediates in the formation of a wide range of substances. Fats and amino acids can be synthesized directly from PGA for example, so the assumption that carbon fixation = carbohydrate production is not necessarily true. Although the reasons are not fully understood, there appears to be some correlation between the external conditions and the major end-products of photosynthesis:

end-products of photosynthesis

In high light and high CO_2 —— sugars and other carbohydrates are formed
in low light —— amino acids are major products
in high light and low CO_2 —— glycolic acid ($CH_2OHCOOH$) (a 2-carbon compound) and the amino acid glycine are major products.

When aquatic algae are growing in high light conditions, and particularly if growth is limited by low levels of mineral nutrients, the rate of photosynthesis may outstrip the plants' capacity to store or utilize the assimilated carbon. Under such conditions as much as 95 per cent of fixed carbon may be converted to glycolic acid and released from the cells into the water where it is probably used as a food source for bacteria (Watt, 1966). This release of photosynthetic

secretion of glycolic acid

product can be an important source of error when measuring primary production (discussed in Unit 2) and must be considered if algae are cultured as a food source.

1.4.2b Photorespiration

Production of glycolic acid may also be related to a special kind of respiration which takes place only in the light and in addition to the 'normal' respiration which takes place all the time in light or darkness. This *photorespiration* is particularly noticeable at high temperatures and in high light intensities and, under these conditions, net carbon fixation may be very low because CO_2 output due to respiration approaches or even exceeds CO_2 uptake in photosynthesis.

photorespiration

There is evidence that photorespiration is qualitatively different from normal respiration and Israel Zelitch (1967) has suggested that a different substrate is used, glycolic acid instead of the usual hexose sugars. Glycolic acid may be oxidized according to the equation

$$CH_2OH \cdot COOH + O_2 \rightarrow CHO \cdot COOH + H_2O_2 \rightarrow HCOOH + CO_2 + H_2O$$

glycolic acid   glyoxylic acid   formic acid

glycolate oxidation

The link between photorespiration and glycolate oxidation is still not fully understood but, for both processes, the important feature is that no useful energy is released (there is no ATP production) and, therefore, fixed carbon is effectively 'wasted' (Goldsworthy, 1970). Photorespiration, and glycolate oxidation, increase sharply with temperature and the effect of this on net carbon fixation in a tobacco leaf is shown in Table 4.

TABLE 4   Model of CO_2 budget for tobacco leaf in light at 25 °C and 35 °C.

	μmol CO_2 h^{-1} g fresh weight $^{-1}$	
	25 °C	35 °C
1 Gross CO_2 uptake	−100	−200
2 CO_2 output, dark respiration	+ 10	+ 20
3 CO_2 output, photorespiration	+ 15	+115
4 Net CO_2 uptake observed:	− 75	− 65
5 When photorespiration is inhibited*, net CO_2 uptake observed:	− 90	−180

* Photorespiration can be specifically inhibited by substances such as hydroxysulphonate.

Note   Negative values in Table 4 indicate CO_2 uptake and positive values CO_2 output.

QUESTION   What is the percentage loss of net carbon fixation due to photorespiration at (a) 25 °C and (b) 35 °C?

ANSWER   At 25 °C CO_2 loss due to photorespiration is 15 μmol and inhibition of net CO_2 fixation is $\frac{15}{90} \times 100 = 16 \cdot 7$ per cent.

At 35 °C the same calculation shows that inhibition is $\frac{115}{180} \times 100 = 69 \cdot 4$ per cent.

This figure for 35 °C represents a very large loss of fixed carbon; there is currently much interest in reducing rates of photorespiration in crop plants or breeding new varieties with intrinsically low rates. In certain tropical and subtropical grasses no photorespiration can be detected.

QUESTION   Suggest possible reasons for this.

ANSWER   It may be that they do not produce or oxidize glycolic acid in large quantities (although glycolic acid and glycolate oxidizing enzymes have been detected in these species); or perhaps photorespiration occurs but the plants then re-use efficiently the CO_2 released.

QUESTION Refer back to *Evans*, p. 87, Figure 21; suggest now an explanation for the different temperature optima for photosynthesis in the subtropical and the temperate grass.

ANSWER In ryegrass, but not in *Paspalum*, the rate of net photosynthesis will decline at higher temperatures owing to increased photorespiration.

It is in certain tropical and subtropical species such as *Paspalum* that the second pathway for carbon fixation occurs—*the C-4 or Hatch–Slack pathway.*

1.4.2c The Hatch–Slack pathway

This pathway was discovered comparatively recently, between 1966 and 1968, by two Australians, M. D. Hatch and C. R. Slack (Hatch and Slack, 1970) and there is still much controversy about the precise reaction sequence involved. An outline of the probable reaction sequence is given in Figure 10; the question mark indicates that there is considerable doubt about that reaction step.

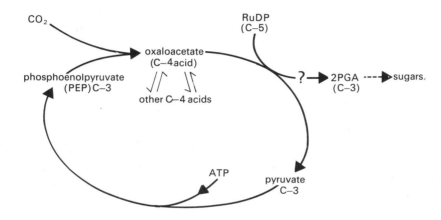

Figure 10 The Hatch–Slack or C-4 pathway for carbon fixation.

QUESTION How does the Hatch–Slack pathway differ from the Calvin cycle in respect of (a) the primary CO_2 acceptor and (b) the first formed product of the reaction sequence?

ANSWER (a) In the Hatch–Slack pathway the primary CO_2 acceptor is a 3-carbon compound, phosphoenolpyruvate (PEP) and not a 5-carbon compound (RuDP).
(b) The first formed product is a 4-carbon compound, oxaloacetic acid and not a 3-carbon compound (PGA), hence the alternative name for the pathway of C-4 path.

C-4 pathway

The enzyme PEP carboxylase, which catalyses the reaction of CO_2 and PEP, has a very high affinity for CO_2, much higher than the enzyme catalysing the reaction of RuDP and CO_2 in the Calvin cycle (ribulose diphosphate carboxylase). This could explain the remarkable ability of C-4 type plants to extract CO_2 from the surrounding air and their low CO_2 compensation points (see Section 1.3.2). Plants which possess the C-4 pathway also contain all the enzymes needed to carry out carbon fixation by the C-3 pathway, but the two processes appear to take place in different cells within the leaf. In leaves of C-4 type plants, the layer of cells surrounding the vascular bundle* (the bundle sheath) are bright green in colour, have numerous chloroplasts but contain only enzymes of the C-3 pathway. Enzymes to operate the C-4 pathway occur only in the mesophyll* cells spread throughout the leaf. (In C-3 type plants, the bundle sheath cells are colourless and devoid of chloroplasts.) You should remember that, unlike the Calvin cycle, the C-4 pathway is restricted to certain plants which occur in tropical climates.

affinity of enzymes for CO_2

bundle sheath cells

Now you could attempt SAQs 4–6.

---

* For details of plant anatomy see reference[7]. The vascular bundle or leaf vein is the conducting strand in which xylem and phloem are found. Mesophyll is the name given to the central parenchyma tissue in the leaf.

20

1.5 Plants with high or low photosynthetic capacity

Study comment Much of this Section is revision of the Unit so far. You should be able to use earlier information to distinguish the broad characteristics of high- and low-capacity primary producers.

Among the leafy terrestrial plants there are certain species, occurring in the tropics and subtropics, which are two to three times more efficient than others in the photosynthetic fixation of CO_2. Naturally, these 'super-plants' have attracted a lot of attention: they are ideal primary producers for agricultural ecosystems. But how do they do it? Why is it that crops such as rice, soya bean, peanuts, all tropical plants, are low and not high capacity producers? Among wild plants, what are the ecological consequences of being in the high- or low-capacity bracket? In this Unit there have been repeated references to special characteristics—physiological, biochemical and morphological—of 'certain plants in the tropics and subtropics': these are the high-capacity producers.

ITQ 11 Try to summarize the characteristics of high and low capacity producers by filling in the blanks in Table 5. References to where you may find the necessary information in the Unit are supplied in some cases, but note that item 6 is filled in since you have not been given the information.

After completing Table 5 and checking the answer to ITQ 11, answer the following ITQs:

ITQ 12 What two environmental conditions are necessary for the attainment of high rates of photosynthesis in high capacity species?

ITQ 13 It is not known why high-capacity species have low water requirements but, given that they do, would you expect to find them in arid regions, oases or deserts (especially after rain)? **Read the answers to ITQs 12 and 13.**

TABLE 5 Characteristics of high- and low-capacity primary producers (modified from Black (1970)).

	High-capacity producers	Low-capacity producers	Ref.
General type of plant			
Morphology 1 Leaf characters			1.4.2c
Physiology 2 Rate of photosynthesis in light			1.2.1 & *Evans* 85–8
3 Response to temperature			1.2.1 & *Evans* 85–8
4 CO_2 compensation point			1.2.2
5 Sugar transport out of leaves			1.3

6 Water requirement
    (grams water needed to
    produce 1 g dry matter)
	260–350	400–900	

Biochemistry 7 Carbon fixation			1.4.2 a & c
8 Photorespiration			1.4.2b

Now you can attempt SAQs 7 and 8.

Now read quickly right through Evans, noting the following points:

1 On pp. 82–3, THE BIOCHEMICAL EFFICIENCY OF PHOTOSYNTHESIS, the unit of wavelength for light used, Å (angström), is equivalent to 10^{-10}m or 10^{-1}nm. Evans also uses kilocalories as units of energy: throughout this Course we have used the International System of Units (SI) which recommends joules or kilojoules as energy units (1 joule = 4·2 calories, 1 kilojoule = 4·2 kilocalories).

2 References to Sybesma and Rabinowitch (e.g. p. 73) are to a paper by these authors in *Penguin Science Survey 1968*.

3 Losses due to respiration (pp. 90–1) will be discussed further in Unit 2.

Now you can attempt SAQs 9 and 10.

1.6 Bacterial photosynthesis and chemosynthesis

Study comment The next two Sections are concerned with variations in photosynthesis among procaryotes[8] and with bacterial chemosynthesis. Differences in methods of primary production between procaryotes and eucaryotes have important implications for energy flow and mineral cycling in ecosystems.

1.6.1 Bacterial photosynthesis

Photosynthetic bacteria are usually found in the surface layers of soil, the mud of shallow lakes and swamps and floating in water at depths of 4–12 m. It follows that they are usually overlaid or overshadowed by algae or higher green plants.

QUESTION How will this overshadowing affect the light available to photosynthetic bacteria?

ANSWER Most of the red and blue wavelengths will be absent due to selective absorption by chlorophyll pigments and/or absorption by water.

The problem is resolved in the bacteria by the possession of a different kind of photosynthetic pigment, *bacteriochlorophyll*, which absorbs light in the near infrared (wavelengths between 800–900 nm); this is light mostly not absorbed by other plants.

bacteriochlorophyll

As primary producers the photosynthetic bacteria are of minor importance, the amount of organic matter produced and the efficiency of production being very low compared with higher plants. But they are important in other ways one of which, nitrogen fixation, will be considered in Section 1.7. The following equations represent:

(A) A generalized scheme for bacterial photosynthesis, where X is unspecified.
$$2H_2X + CO_2 \longrightarrow (CH_2O) + H_2O + 2X$$

(B) A specific example of bacterial photosynthesis.
$$2H_2S + CO_2 \longrightarrow (CH_2O) + H_2O + 2S$$
hydrogen sulphide   sulphur
                                                                                            ↓
                                                                         may be converted
                                                                         to sulphate, SO_4^{2-}

oxidation of H_2S

QUESTION How does this process differ from that in green plants?

ANSWER There is no release of oxygen: the major electron donor is not water but some substance such as hydrogen sulphide.

This is the critical difference between photosynthetic bacteria and green plants: the former never release oxygen as a by-product of photosynthesis and are, in fact, *obligate anaerobes* able to photosynthesize only in the complete absence of oxygen. As well as hydrogen sulphide, molecular hydrogen (H_2) or simple organic compounds, such as malic acid, can serve as electron donors.

obligate anaerobes

22

Hydrogen sulphide is a highly toxic (and evil-smelling) substance and may be released in considerable quantities by other (heterotrophic) bacteria which decompose dead organic remains in anaerobic soils or the bottom mud of lakes. Figure 11 shows the chemical composition and the distribution of algae and photosynthetic bacteria in Lake Belovod, USSR, in summer.

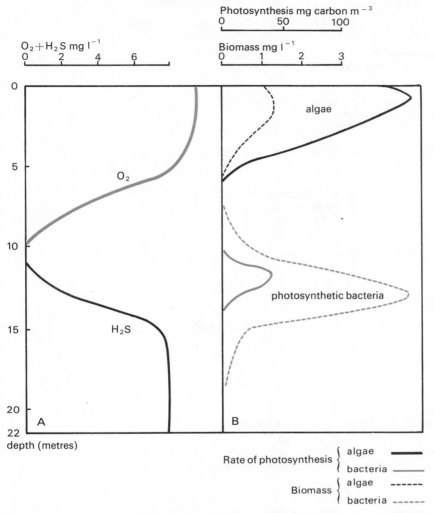

Rate of photosynthesis { algae ———— / bacteria ————

Biomass { algae - - - - - / bacteria - - - - -

Figure 11 Lake Belovod, USSR. (A) levels of oxygen and H_2S at different depths. (B) rates of photosynthesis and biomass of algae and photosynthetic bacteria at different depths.

ITQ 14 Apart from using up 'spare' light energy, do the photosynthetic bacteria have any obvious function in this ecosystem?

ITQ 15 Suggest ways in which this kind of ecosystem could be disrupted.

ITQ 16 A list of the activities of photosynthetic bacteria in Lake Belovod is given in (a)–(c). Indicate the probable rank order of their importance in maintaining ecosystem productivity.
(a) Fixation of CO_2.
(b) Oxidation of H_2S.
(c) Release of sulphate.

Read the answers to ITQs 14–16.

1.6.2 Chemosynthetic bacteria

All the primary producers considered so far use light as their source of energy and, indeed, 'ability to use light' is sometimes included in the definition of autotrophes. But there are bacteria which are classed as autotrophes but which do not require light for growth. They obtain energy by the oxidation of simple inorganic (and a few 1-carbon organic) compounds and can use it to fix CO_2 into organic compounds. None of the substances oxidized may be used by heterotrophes as a source of energy. Unlike the photosynthetic bacteria, such *chemosynthetic* or *chemoautotrophic* bacteria do require oxygen, or another oxidizing agent, for growth.

chemoautotrophes

Species of *Thiobacillus* are typical of the chemosynthetic bacteria. They oxidize sulphur compounds such as H_2S or sulphur itself, as for example:

$$S + 1\tfrac{1}{2}O_2 + H_2O \rightarrow H_2SO_4$$
sulphuric acid

Other chemosynthetic bacteria oxidize molecular hydrogen, methane (CH_4), ferrous iron salts (to ferric salts), and one particularly important group oxidizes nitrogen compounds: ammonium salts (NH_4^+) to nitrite (NO_2^-), and nitrites to nitrates (NO_3^-). These bacteria play a vital role in the cycling of nitrogen and are discussed in greater detail in Unit 4. All these substrates for chemosynthetic bacteria may be produced by heterotrophic bacteria as end-products of decomposition.

Refer back to Figure 11: Lake Belovod also contains chemosynthetic bacteria, mainly *Thiobacillus* species capable of oxidizing H_2S.

QUESTION   At what depth and at what time of day in summer would you expect to find maximum rates of chemosynthesis in the lake?

ANSWER   At about 10 m depth, where both oxygen and H_2S are present, with maximum activity occurring during the night when photosynthetic bacteria utilizing H_2S are inactive.

Sorokin (1966), working in the USSR, has shown that the chemosynthetic bacteria in the oxygenated zone of various lakes and in the Black Sea are an important source of food for grazing zooplankton. In fact, the combined activities of chemosynthetic and photosynthetic bacteria in lakes such as Lake Belovod (Figure 11) can produce almost as much organic matter as the phytoplankton, and such bacteria are readily taken in and digested by filter-feeding zooplankton such as the crustacean *Daphnia*.

Work through the following questions and then answer ITQ 17, which concerns the interrelationships of different trophic levels in freshwater lakes such as Lake Belovod.

QUESTION   What is the source of the substrates oxidized by chemotrophic bacteria in lakes?

ANSWER   They derive from the anaerobic bottom mud of the lakes and are end-products of heterotrophic bacterial decomposition.

QUESTION   Apart from dead aquatic organisms which sink to the lake bottom, what other sources of organic matter become available for the heterotrophic bacterial decomposers in the bottom mud?

ANSWER   Organic matter washed in, or blown in, from the land. This is called allochthonous material from the Greek *allos* = other and *khthōn* = land, and can be an important source of organic material for aquatic ecosystems.

QUESTION   In what ways do chemosynthetic bacteria 'conserve' energy in aquatic ecosystems with an anaerobic hypolimnion (lower layer)?

ANSWER   By utilizing the simple products of anaerobic decomposition as an energy source for carbon fixation. These products cannot be utilized as an energy source by any other organisms and would literally 'go to waste' and their energy be lost from the ecosystem but for the chemosynthetic activity. (In the same way, one could say that the photosynthetic bacteria prevent light energy not absorbed by the surface phytoplankton from going to waste.)

ITQ 17   Figure 12 is a model of a fresh water lake:
(a)   What are the energy inputs labelled 1, 2, and 3?
(b)   Name the organisms labelled 4–8 and give their trophic level.
(c)   What do organisms labelled 4 provide for other organisms?

Read the answer to ITQ 17.

Now you could attempt SAQ 11.

Thiobacillus

oxidation of S

oxidation of N compounds

allochthonous material

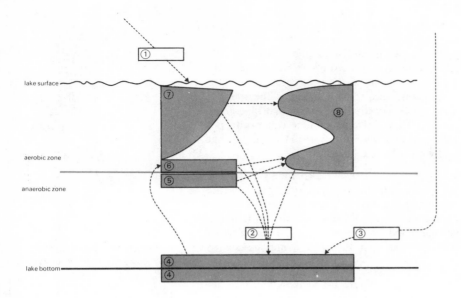

Figure 12 Model of a freshwater lake.

1.7 Other ways of using trapped light energy

Study comment Autotrophes can use trapped light energy for processes other than carbon fixation. The most important 'alternative use' is fixation of atmospheric nitrogen to form nitrates, performed by certain bacteria and blue-green algae. Some heterotrophic bacteria also fix nitrogen. The total fixed by all these organisms provides the most important source of nitrate to replenish and maintain the nitrogen cycle in ecosystems.

After studying both higher plants and bacteria it should be clear that autotrophy is very versatile: bacterial autotrophes can use light or simple chemicals to obtain energy; photoautotrophes (light-using) show variations in the electron donor used in light reactions (Section 1.6.1), and also variations in the utilization of trapped light energy. These alternative uses of trapped light energy are discussed in this Section. Carbon fixation is only one, the most important, way of using the ATP and reducing power generated in the light. Many plants, take up nitrates (NO_3^-) which, before utilization of the nitrogen by the plant, must be converted to nitrite (NO_2^-) and then to ammonia (NH_3). Some higher plants and algae reduce nitrites to ammonia using light-generated $NADPH_2$ in chloroplasts: thus when *Chlorella* (a green unicellular alga) is illuminated in the complete absence of CO_2 oxygen is released and nitrites reduced.

reduction of nitrites

Some photosynthetic bacteria and blue-green algae (which are procaryotes not eucaryotes[8]) can reduce atmospheric nitrogen gas to ammonia using reduced ferredoxin and ATP generated in the light; the ammonia is then further oxidized to nitrite and finally to nitrate. For this process of nitrogen fixation, an enzyme, *nitrogenase*, is needed and the reaction can be summarized:

N-fixation

nitrogenase

$$N_2 + 3H_2O \xrightarrow[\text{nitrogenase}]{\text{light}} 2NH_3 + 1\tfrac{1}{2}O_2$$

As a form of primary production, nitrogen fixation is considerably less efficient than carbon fixation. For every gram mole of carbon fixed in photosynthesis, 470 kJ are stored, whereas for every gram mole of nitrogen the amount is only 310 kJ. But the ecological significance of nitrogen fixation is enormous. In many environments available nitrogen is a major factor limiting plant growth and so, indirectly, primary production.* In rice paddies, for example, the presence of nitrogen-fixing blue-green algae is essential to maintain fertility and the possibility of culturing these algae on a large scale for use as 'living fertilizers' in the paddies is being explored by research workers in the Far East.

* Nutrient limitation of growth and primary production are discussed in more detail in Unit 2.

25

1.7.1 The nitrogen-fixing organisms

(a) *Blue-green algae* These organisms usually consist of simple chains of cells with special thick-walled cells called heterocysts spaced evenly along the chain (Fig. 13). Nitrogen fixation seems to occur only in the heterocysts. The algae are widely distributed in freshwater lakes, seas, the top layers of the soil and on the surfaces of leaves and stems. It has recently been shown that blue-green algae are remarkably sensitive to pH. They thrive in alkaline water with pH above 7 but show progressive inhibition of growth at lower pH values so that acid bogs and lakes contain virtually no blue-green algae.

(b) *Nitrogen fixing photosynthetic bacteria* These are also found in soil or freshwater habitats but, like all photosynthetic bacteria they are obligate anaerobes (Section 1.6.1). For both bacteria and blue-green algae the major factors limiting nitrogen fixation are light and temperature but, in addition, adequate supplies of ionic molybdenum and iron are necessary. These serve as enzyme activators and are needed to maintain nitrogenase and associated enzymes in a functional state.

(c) *Heterotrophic nitrogen-fixers (free-living)* These are bacteria which do not photosynthesize but use complex organic molecules as a source of energy. Although they are not primary producers, we will consider them in this Section in their role as nitrogen fixers. These organisms are again widely distributed in soils and water. One group, including *Azotobacter* and *Bjerinckia*, is unusual in its tolerance of acid conditions and is particularly common in nutrient-poor tropical soils. It also occurs on the leaf surfaces of plants in tropical rainforest and of grasses of the humid coastal plains. Jakoba Ruinen (1965) measured the amounts of sugar leached from such leaves and present in dew or rainwater on the leaf surface: there was enough to support a flourishing population of bacteria but exactly how much of the fixed nitrogen released by these bacteria is taken up by leaves or how much is washed off into the soil is still unknown. In any case, the nitrogen fixed represents an input into the ecosystem.

(d) *Heterotrophic nitrogen-fixers (symbiotic)* These organisms live within the tissues of higher plants in special nodules, which usually occur on the roots but in a few species are found on the leaves. The bacteria receive a supply of carbohydrates from the host plant which in turn is supplied with soluble nitrogen compounds released by the bacteria. Both partners benefit from the association which can be termed a *symbiosis*.* Most members of the legume family (Leguminosae) which includes such common crop plants as peas, beans, clover and lucerne, contain symbiotic bacteria in root nodules; it is a very ancient agricultural practice to plant legumes as part of a crop rotation between cereal crops. Legumes replenish soil nitrogen: nitrates may actually be secreted from the roots when fixation is particularly active and, in addition, the dead roots or whole plants ploughed back into the soil provide excellent nitrogen fertilizer.

From studies on agricultural land it appears that the amount of nitrogen fixed at a particular site depends mainly on temperature and (particularly) water supply: certainly in grassland, drought conditions reduce drastically the quantity of nitrogen fixed in legume root nodules.

A number of non-legume species, all woody trees or shrubs, contain nitrogen-fixing root nodule bacteria, mainly *Rhizobium* spp. In this country the commonest example is the alder, *Alnus glutinosa*, which grows in wet boggy areas and on river banks. In general, these species grow on soils notoriously poor in nitrogen (sand dunes, eroded slopes and pastures, acid bogs and mountain slopes) and their success here and as colonizers of newly cleared land is undoubtedly due in part to the nodule bacteria which act as a built-in source of fertilizer.

For all nitrogen-fixing organisms, whether photosynthetic or heterotrophic, free-living or symbiotic, fixation is inhibited when the levels of soluble nitrogen compounds in the surrounding soil or water are high. As you might expect, heavy applications of nitrogenous fertilizer inhibit nodulation in legumes and nitrogen fixation in the soil organisms.

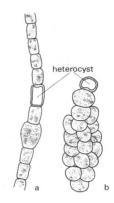

Figure 13 Blue-green algae: (a) *Anabaena*; (b) *Chlorogloea*.

N-fixation in tropical soils and on plant leaves

Soya bean roots, showing root nodules.

inhibition of N-fixation

---

* Symbiosis means literally 'living together' and in biological terms it implies a mutually advantageous association of organisms (e.g. algae and coral animals[9]). Symbiosis will be discussed further in Block C.

1.7.2 Detection of nitrogen fixation

Nitrogen fixation is considerably more difficult to demonstrate and measure than is carbon fixation.

QUESTION Suggest a reason for this.

ANSWER Carbon has a stable radioactive isotope, C^{14}, and the incorporation of $^{14}CO_2$ can be measured with relative ease and accuracy. Nitrogen has no stable radioactive isotope. There is a heavy isotope of nitrogen (molecular weight 15 compared to the normal 14) but incorporation into ammonia or organic nitrogen compounds can be demonstrated only with the use of a mass spectrometer which detects small differences in molecular weights. This is a much less sensitive and more difficult technique than the radioactive counting methods.

Early workers on nitrogen fixation used relatively insensitive and frequently unreliable methods: the ability of organisms to grow in nitrogen-free media, or apparent increases in total nitrogen content of isolated organisms or parts of plants, for example. The use of N^{15} was a considerable improvement on these early methods and is now the most reliable method of measurement, but with the disadvantages that it requires complicated and expensive equipment and considerable technical skill. An even more striking 'measurement breakthrough' occurred with the introduction of the acetylene reduction technique (Stewart *et al.*, 1967) which is simple, rapid and very sensitive. This depends on the ability of the enzyme nitrogenase to reduce not only nitrogen but also alternative substrates such as acetylene gas, which is relatively harmless if supplied to plants or bacteria. Acetylene is reduced to ethylene:

use of N^{15}

acetylene reduction technique

$$C_2H_2 \xrightarrow{\text{nitrogenase}} C_2H_4$$
$$\text{acetylene} \qquad \text{ethylene}$$

Ethylene can be measured with ease and high precision by gas chromatography.*

ITQ 18 A sample of water (3 litres) is withdrawn from a lake which is thought to contain nitrogen-fixing organisms. Given the equipment listed below, devise an experiment to test this hypothesis following the headings listed (1)–(4).

Equipment provided
Numerous 20 cm³ glass bottles with air-tight rubber caps (self-sealing if pierced with a needle).
Calibrated gas-tight syringes.
Supply of acetylene gas.
Gas chromatogram.

Experimental headings
1 Setting up samples with suitable controls.
2 Supplying acetylene.
3 Incubation.
4 Assay of ethylene.

Read the answer to ITQ 18.

1.7.3 How important is nitrogen fixation?

Nitrogen is an element which is recycled within ecosystems[10]. In the perfect (closed) nitrogen cycle, green plants take up mineral nitrogen (chiefly as nitrates) and convert it to organic nitrogen compounds. The plants may die or be eaten by animals, and dead organisms, together with waste and excretory products, are broken down by microbes which release the nitrogen as nitrates for further use. But all does not usually run so smoothly:

nitrogen cycling

(a) Nitrates can be lost from the soil, either washed out (leaching) or converted back to nitrogen gas by the action of denitrifying bacteria (see Unit 4).

losses of N

* This is a form of chromatography in which gaseous or volatilized compounds are carried along a special column at different rates; the separated compounds pass in turn through a flame, are ionized, and produce a change in the electrical conductivity of the flame which can be measured. The magnitude of the pulse depends on the quantity of the ionized compound.

(b)   Under some conditions (for example in acid bogs) the breakdown of dead organisms proceeds very slowly.

(c)   In the sea or in deep lakes, dead organisms may sink to the bottom before decomposition can occur and the return of nutrients to the surface layers (where photosynthesis takes place) may be very slow.

(d)   In agricultural ecosystems, where most of the above-ground parts of plants are harvested and removed from the ecosystem, the supply of dead organic material needed to keep the cycle going is inadequate and soils become depleted of nitrates.

There are basically four ways in which these deficiencies in the nitrogen cycle can be remedied, and Table 6 shows the relative contribution of each, estimated for the world as a whole during 1967–8.

sources of N

TABLE 6

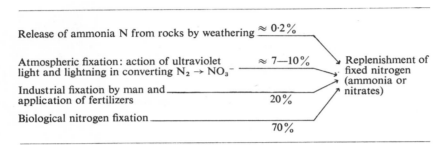

Release of ammonia N from rocks by weathering $\approx 0.2\%$

Atmospheric fixation: action of ultraviolet light and lightning in converting $N_2 \rightarrow NO_3^-$ ≈ 7—10%

Industrial fixation by man and application of fertilizers 20%

Biological nitrogen fixation 70%

Replenishment of fixed nitrogen (ammonia or nitrates)

Nitrogen fixation is clearly the most important way of replenishing the nitrogen supply within ecosystems. Table 7 shows the amounts of nitrogen fixed annually by various organisms.

TABLE 7   Nitrogen fixed as kg ha^{-1} year^{-1}.

Symbiotic bacteria	clover (a legume)	116
	average for legume crops	112–224
	non-legumes—*Alnus glutinosa*	224
Blue-green algae	in Indian paddy fields	34–90
	in arid Australian soils	3
Free-living soil bacteria	under wheat crop	43
	bare tropical soil	123

Note   1 hectare (ha) = 10^4 m^2 = 2.47 acre.

Now you could attempt SAQ 12.

1.8   Summary of the Unit

For most of the Earth, the major input of energy to ecosystems is solar energy which is trapped and converted to complex organic substances in photosynthesis (Section 1.0). Much solar energy is lost, due to absorption or reflection, during passage through the Earth's atmosphere and the spectral composition is also considerably altered due to selective absorption of ultraviolet and infrared wavelengths (Section 1.1.1). Spectral composition of light is further altered during passage through water. The chlorophyll pigments which are directly involved in photosynthesis absorb light in only a limited waveband, but aquatic algae possess an array of accessory pigments which absorb additional wavebands and pass on the absorbed energy to chlorophyll a (Section 1.1.2). During the course of a year an average of only 0.2 per cent of the light reaching the Earth's surface is converted to chemical energy in photosynthesis, and the theoretical maximum conversion is only 5 per cent (Table 1).

The efficiency with which leafy plants intercept solar radiation is related to the numbers, arrangement and structure of leaves; the leaf area index (*L*) provides some measure of interception efficiency (Section 1.1.3). But the amount of light is only one factor which may limit the rate of photosynthesis: the ability of plants to utilize light of high intensity (degree of light saturation) is important (Section 1.2.1) and similarly temperature, supply of CO_2 to the chloroplasts, and rate of growth and assimilate removal may all become limiting under certain conditions (Sections 1.2.1, 1.2.2, 1.3). Because of the equilibrium between CO_2, bicarbonate and carbonate ions in water, the supply of CO_2 for aquatic plants depends not only on the diffusion rate of CO_2 and on water turbulence but also on the pH and cation levels in water and on the ability of the plant to take up bicarbonate ions (Section 1.2.3). In certain tropical and subtropical land plants, special physiological characteristics contribute towards a remarkable ability to sustain high rates of photosynthesis: absence of light saturation and high temperature inhibition of photosynthesis, low CO_2 compensation point, and rapid rates of starch removal from chloroplasts.

The process of photosynthesis consists of two quite separate series of reactions: those related to the trapping of light energy and its conversion to ATP and $NADPH_2$ (the light reactions), and those concerned with the utilization of ATP and $NADPH_2$ in synthetic processes (the dark reactions). There are two primary light reactions involving absorption of light by photosynthetic pigments which then transfer 'excited' electrons to non-pigment molecules. The excitation energy of electrons is tapped off in a complex series of reactions and used in the formation of ATP. Electrons are finally transferred to NADPH which in combination with H^+ ions yields the strongly reducing $NADPH_2$ ('reducing power'). Replacement electrons for the photosynthetic pigments are provided by splitting of water molecules, and oxygen is released as a by-product of this reaction (Section 1.4.1).

The most important dark reactions are concerned with the conversion of CO_2 to organic compounds (Section 1.4.2) and two pathways of carbon fixation are described: the Calvin Cycle or C–3 pathway (Section 1.4.2a) and the Hatch–Slack or C–4 pathway (Section 1.4.2c). For most plant species only the Calvin Cycle operates and, under conditions of high light intensity, these species may produce glycolic acid as an end-product of fixation. Glycolic acid is thought to be the substrate for a special kind of respiration occurring only in the light (photo-respiration) and because its oxidation is not linked to the release of useful energy (ATP production) photorespiration must be regarded as a basically wasteful process (Section 1.4.2b). Plants possessing the C–4 pathway are all tropical or subtropical herbs; they do not show photorespiration. In fact, these are the species mentioned earlier as having special physiological adaptations and high photosynthetic capacity: the biochemical characteristics explain, at least partially, the physiological characteristics. The contrasting features of high- and low-capacity primary producers are summarized in Section 1.5.

Among the procaryotes (bacteria and blue-green algae) autotrophy is much more varied than in green plants (Sections 1.6 and 1.7), and this has important ecological implications. The photosynthetic bacteria, which are all obligate anaerobes, do not use water as an electron donor in photosynthesis but substances such as H_2S or H_2. The chemosynthetic bacteria (Section 1.6.2) do not use light as an energy source but obtain energy by oxidizing simple (mainly inorganic) compounds. These compounds may be released as end-products of heterotrophic bacterial decomposition and their utilization by chemosynthetic bacteria not only conserves energy within ecosystems but is also of great importance in the cycling of mineral elements.

Photoautotrophes can use trapped light energy in other ways than carbon fixation; nitrogen fixation is the alternative use of greatest ecological significance (Section 1.7). Nitrogen fixation can also be carried out by certain heterotrophic bacteria, some of which are free-living and others symbiotic (chiefly in root nodules). Methods of measuring nitrogen fixation and its importance for maintaining supplies of nitrate essential for the growth of higher plants are discussed at the end of the Unit (Sections 1.7.2 and 1.7.3).

Publications cited in text

Black, C. C. (1971) Ecological implications of dividing plants into groups with distinct photosynthetic production capacities, *Advances in Ecol. Res.*, **7**, 87–114.

Fogg, G. E. (1968) *Photosynthesis*, English Universities Press.

Gates, D. M. (1965) Radiant energy, its receipt and disposal, *Metero. Monogr.*, **6**, 1–26.

Goldsworthy, A. (1970) Photorespiration, *Bot. Rev.*, **36**, 321–40.

Hatch, M. D., and Slack, C. R. (1970) Photosynthetic CO_2 fixation pathways, *Ann. Rev. Plant Physiol.*, **21**, 141–62.

Ruinen, J. (1965) The phyllosphere. III Nitrogen fixation in the phyllosphere, *Plant and Soil*, **22**, 375–93.

Sorokin, J. (1966) On the trophic role of chemosynthesis and bacterial biosynthesis in water bodies, in Goldman, C. R. (ed.) *Primary Productivity in Aquatic Environments*, pp. 189–205, University of California Press.

Stewart, W. D. P., Fitzgerald, G. P., and Burris, R. H. (1967) *In situ* studies on N_2-fixation using the acetylene reduction technique, *Proc. Nat. Acad. Sci.*, **58**, 2071–8.

Watt, W. D. (1966) Release of dissolved organic material from cells of phytoplankton populations, *Proc. Roy. Soc. B*, **164**, 521–51.

Zelitch, I. (1967) Water and CO_2 transport in the photosynthetic process, in A. San Pietro *et al.* (ed.) *Harvesting the Sun*, pp. 231–48, Academic Press.

References to other Open University Courses

1   S100, Unit 15, Section 15.8.
2   S22–, Unit 3, Section 3.8.1.
3   S22–, Unit 3, Section 3.8.2.
4   S22–, Unit 3, Section 3.9.
5   S100, Unit 15, Section 15.4.
6   S100, Unit 15, Section 15.6.3.
7   S22–, Unit 2, Section 2.1.2.
8   S22–, Unit 1, Section 1.2.
9   S22–, TV programme 11.
10 S100, Unit 20, Section 20.1, Figure 3, and Unit 34, Section 34.2.1.

Recommended reading

Fogg, G. E. (1968) *Photosynthesis*, English Universities Press.

Hall, D. A., and Rao, K. K. (1972) *Photosynthesis* (Institute of Biology's Studies in Biology No. 37), Edward Arnold.

Björkman, O., and Berry, J. (1973) High efficiency photosynthesis, *Sci. Amer.*, **229**, 80–93.

Scientific American offprints:

Bassham, J. A. (1962) *The Path of Carbon in Photosynthesis*. (This covers only the Calvin Cycle.)

Levine, R. P. (1969) *The Mechanisms of Photosynthesis*.

Appendix 1 (Black) Cell energetics and ATP*

For a reversible reaction

$$A + B \rightleftharpoons C + D$$

the equilibrium position, when the ratio of reactants to products is constant, can be defined in terms of the *standard free energy change* of the reaction, $\Delta G^\ominus$**.

When the equilibrium is far to the right, the reaction has a large negative $\Delta G^\ominus$: free energy is released during the reaction.

When the equilibrium position is in the middle (equilibrium mixture contains equal amounts of A, B, C and D), $\Delta G^\ominus$ is zero.

When the equilibrium position is to the left, $\Delta G^\ominus$ is positive: free energy is used up during the reaction.

Free energy changes are additive, so that if a reaction proceeds in two steps (or can be represented in two steps) the $\Delta G^\ominus$ of the total reaction is the sum of the $\Delta G^\ominus$ values of the two partial reactions. If three compounds are in equilibrium:

$$A \rightleftharpoons B \rightleftharpoons C$$

and the $\Delta G^\ominus$ changes are as follows:

$$A \to B, \Delta G^\ominus = -20 \text{ kJ mol}^{-1}$$
$$B \to C, \Delta G^\ominus = +4 \text{ kJ mol}^{-1}$$

then the $\Delta G^\ominus$ of the reaction $A \to C$ is

$$(-20 + 4) = -16 \text{ kJ mol}^{-1}$$

Note that if the $\Delta G^\ominus$ for $A \to C$ is -16 kJ mol^{-1}, then the $\Delta G^\ominus$ for $C \to A$ is $+16$ kJ mol^{-1}: the reactions must be written the right way round before adding them up.

Most catabolic ('breaking down') reactions in the cell have large negative $\Delta G^\ominus$ values while anabolic ('building up' or synthetic) reactions have large positive $\Delta G^\ominus$ values when written in their simplest form. This may be misleading. For example, the equation for carbon fixation by the C–3 pathway can be written as:

$$CO_2 + H_2O + 2NADPH_2 + 3ATP \to (CH_2O) + O_2 + 2NADP + 3 ADP + 3\,\text{\textcircled{P}}_i - 52 \text{ kJ}$$
phosphate

This is an anabolic reaction involving the reduction of one molecule of CO_2 to the level of glucose, but there is a net release of free energy (negative $\Delta G^\ominus$). The puzzle is resolved by looking at the constituent parts of the reaction:

(i) $\quad CO_2 + H_2O \to (CH_2O) + O_2 \quad +480 \text{ kJ}$
(ii) $\quad 2NADPH_2 + O_2 \to 2NADP + 2H_2O \quad -440 \text{ kJ}$
(iii) $\quad 3ATP + 3H_2O \to 3ADP + 3\,\text{\textcircled{P}}_i \quad -92 \text{ kJ}$
$$\overline{ -52 \text{ kJ}}$$

The reduction of CO_2 is coupled to the oxidation of $NADPH_2$ and the hydrolysis of ATP, the last two reactions 'driving' the first. In the same way, the synthesis of ATP from ADP and $\text{\textcircled{P}}_i$ ($\Delta G^\ominus = +31$ kJ) can be coupled to reactions with large negative $\Delta G^\ominus$. This occurs in the light reactions of photosynthesis, when electrons, originally 'excited' by absorption of light by pigment molecules, are transferred from one cytochrome molecule to another along the 'cytochrome chain'. It occurs also during the oxidation reactions of respiration. So ATP can be regarded as the 'energy currency' of the cell: energy released during ATP hydrolysis can be used to drive anabolic reactions, and energy released during catabolic reactions can be used in the formation of ATP.

* Modified from S2–1 (*Biochemistry*), Unit 3, Section 3.2.

** The superscript $\ominus$ represents a G function measured under standard conditions of temperature, pressure and composition of solution; free energy changes can vary widely under different conditions.

Self-assessment questions

SAQ 1 (*Objective 2*) Compare extra-terrestrial sunlight with light at ground level—what are proportionately the greatest changes in spectral composition for conditions 1–3? In each case, state the chief causes for the loss or losses. Refer to Figure 1 (p. 6) for help in answering.

Light losses in:
A   ultraviolet
B   visible
C   near infrared (700–1000 nm)
D   far infrared (1000 nm or more)

Conditions
1   A clear, sunny day.
2   A completely overcast cloudy day.
3   A sunny day beneath a dense canopy of beech trees.

SAQ 2 (*Objective 3*) The plants A and B, from which leaf sections are shown (Fig. 14) were grown under different light intensities:

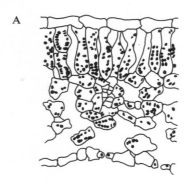

Figure 14 Transverse sections of leaves from separate plants of balsam, *Impatiens parviflora*.

(a)   Which plant was grown under the higher light intensity?
(b)   Which anatomical features of the leaf enable you to reach this conclusion?
(c)   The surface areas of the leaves shown in Figure 14 were 7 cm² and 19 cm²; state which leaf had which surface area and give reasons for your answer.

SAQ 3 (*Objective 4*) Which factor or combination of factors is most likely to limit the rate of photosynthesis for the following organisms under the conditions indicated:

1   Bluebells (*Endymion non-scripta*) growing in a dense oak wood on a windless sunny day in mid-June.
2   A green algal mutant, deficient in carotenoid pigments, exposed to full sunlight in well-aerated stirred water.
3   Maize (*Zea mays*) on a clear, sunny day with the leaves wilting and a leaf temperature of 30 °C.
4   Oak leaves growing on the uppermost branches of the tree on a clear windy summer day with leaf temperature 30 °C.
5   A pondweed (*Elodea canadensis*) submerged to 20 m in a tank of clear soft water with no water movement and full sunlight on the water surface.

SAQ 4 (*Objective 5*) If intact chloroplasts were extracted from a plant and incubated in the dark with CO_2, ATP and $NADPH_2$, would carbon fixation occur? Give reasons for your answer.

SAQ 5 (*Objective 5*) What is the importance for living organisms of the light-induced splitting (photolysis) of water?

SAQ 6 (*Objectives 5 and 7*) In a batch of tomato seedlings the following mutant forms were found:

1   Mutant deficient in the enzyme ribulose diphosphate carboxylase.
2   Mutant deficient in the enzyme glycolic acid oxidase.
3   Mutant deficient in chlorophyll a.

For each of the mutants 1–3 state, with reasons, whether you would expect net carbon fixation to be (a) higher or (b) lower than for non-mutant seedlings.

SAQ 7 (*Objective 7*) Give three physiological characteristics of 'high-capacity producers' which help to explain their superior photosynthetic capacity, and in each instance link the physiological characteristic to a biochemical mechanism.

SAQ 8 (*Objective 7*) The distribution of high and low capacity species was studied on the tropical island of Java (Hofstra *et al.*, 1972). Some of the data are in Tables 8 and 9 (opposite page).

From Table 8:

(a)   Which kinds of plants are totally confined to open habitats?

(b)   Do high- or low-capacity species predominate in open habitats?

(c)   Briefly describe the distribution of high- and low-capacity species in open and shaded habitats; suggest a possible reason for this distribution pattern.

From Table 9:

(d)   At which site do sedge species predominate over grass species? Are they mainly high- or low-capacity sedges?

(e)   Briefly describe and try to explain the relative distribution of high- and low-capacity sedges and grasses in relation to altitude.

SAQ 9 (*Objectives 3, 4, 6*) Describe a hypothetical 'ideal' crop plant from the point of view of production efficiency.

SAQ 10 (*Objectives 4, 6*) Which of the following plant characteristics relates most closely to photosynthetic efficiency during the course of the growing season?
(a)   Net assimilation rate.
(b)   Possession of the C–4 pathway.
(c)   Absence of photorespiration.
(d)   Leaf area index.
(e)   Possession of accessory pigments.

SAQ 11 (*Objective 8*)   (a)   How does photosynthesis in bacteria differ from that in green plants?

(b)   How do chemoautotrophes differ from heterotrophes?

SAQ 12 (*Objectives 8 and 10*) Figure 15 shows the nitrogen transformations in two areas of temperate grassland during one year. Area A contained only grass and received nitrogenous fertilizer; area B contained both grass and clover and received no fertilizer.

(a)   What process and which organisms convert atmospheric nitrogen directly to soil organic nitrogen?

(b)   Why does more soil organic N derive from the source given in (a) for area B compared with area A?

(c)   How is atmospheric N_2 converted to soil inorganic N?

(d)   What two processes result in loss of inorganic soil N from the fertilized area but not from the unfertilized area? (e)   Considering the input of N as fertilizer in area A and as atmospheric N_2 fixed by clover root nodule bacteria in area B, and comparing this input with the N content of the cut herbage (N output), which area gives the more efficient conversion of input N to output N? (f)   Supposing that at the end of the year, when the herbage was cut, the two areas were ploughed and sown with wheat. If no fertilizer were applied, in which area would you expect to find wheat growth limited by availability of N? Give reasons for your answer.

TABLE 8   The distribution pattern in sunny open habitats and shaded habitats of high- and low-capacity producers*

Site (lowland)	Species plot^{-1} (m^2)	High-capacity species (% of total)			Low-capacity species (% of total)		
		grasses	sedges	others	grasses	sedges	others
Open area	(1) 15	20	7	7	0	0	66
	(2) 17	35	6	6	0	0	53
	(3) 16	44	0	0	0	0	56
	(4) 11	37	0	0	0	0	63
Shaded area	(1) 13	8	0	0	8	0	84
	(2) 13	0	0	0	0	0	100
	(3) 10	0	0	0	20	0	80
	(4) 9	11	0	0	11	0	78

TABLE 9   Distribution of high and low capacity grasses and sedges at four open-habitat sites in Java.*

Site (all open)	Height above sea level (metres)	No. of species of grasses and sedges in 500 m^2 areas			
		High-capacity		Low-capacity	
		grasses	sedges	grasses	sedges
Seaside	1	11	4	0	0
Riverside	200	10	5	0	1
Plateau	2 000	2	1	4	2
Mountain top	3 000	0	0	1	6

* Work by J. J. Hofstra, S. Aksornkoae, S. Atmowiejojo, J. F. Banaag, Santosa, R. A. Sastrohoetomo, L. T. N. Thu (1972), published in *Annales Bogroriensis*, **5**, 143–57.

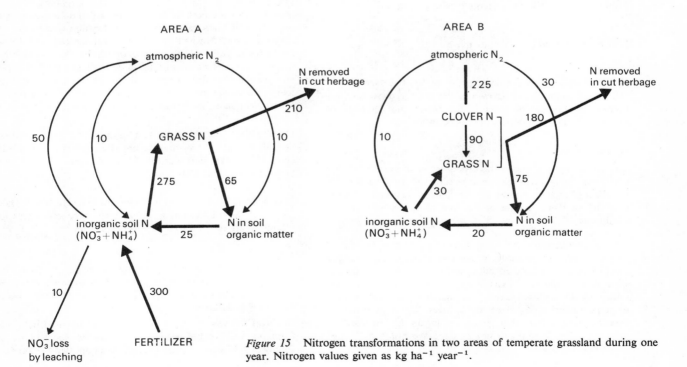

Figure 15   Nitrogen transformations in two areas of temperate grassland during one year. Nitrogen values given as kg ha^{-1} year^{-1}.

Pretest answers

1 Autotrophes are 'self-feeding'; they synthesize complex organic substances, using simple inorganic substances and a source of energy (usually light), and are independent of other organisms for food. Heterotrophes ('other-feeding') obtain energy and most of their mineral nutrients by breaking down complex organic substances made by other organisms.

(a) Heterotrophes, decomposers.
(b) Autotrophes, primary producers.
(c) Heterotrophes, consumers.
(d) Heterotrophes, decomposers.
(e) Autotrophes, primary producers.
(f) Heterotrophes, consumers.

2 Respiration: during respiration, a catabolic process, complex organic substrates are broken down and energy is released. Some of this energy is used to synthesize ATP for use by the organism, but the remainder is dissipated as heat.

3 Plants take up inorganic salts of nitrogen and phosphorus from the soil by way of their roots. The supply is maintained chiefly by cycling: all dead organic matter is broken down by decomposer organisms so that N and P in organic molecules are converted to nitrates and phosphates which can be taken up by plants. Small amounts of N and P may be released by weathering of rocks; nitrogen in the atmosphere may be converted to mineral nitrogen by lightning, by biological nitrogen fixation and by industrial processes controlled by man (fertilizer production).

4 (a) Ecological succession. (b) The climax.

5 Procaryotes; bacteria and blue-green algae.

6 (c) In all eucaryote cells photosynthesis occurs in specialized organelles, the chloroplasts.

7 (b) is the major route: small amounts may be supplied by (a) or (c) but little, if any, by (d). When stomata are closed then (a) and (c) become the major sources of CO_2.

Note If you answered five out of the seven questions correctly you do not need to revise but if fewer than five then you will probably find some preliminary revision useful. Revise from S100, Unit 15, Section 15.8, and Unit 20, Sections 20.1 and 20.5, and from S22-, Unit 11, Section 1.2 and Unit 3, Section 3.8.

8 (a) The epilimnion. (b) The hypolimnion. (c) The thermocline.

9 A, D, E, H, K (oligotrophic) B, C, F, G, J (eutrophic).

Note If you were unable to answer questions 8 and 9 revise from S2–3, Block 3, Section 8.3.

ITQ answers

ITQ 1 The solar flux at a given place will depend upon (a) time of day, which is governed by the axial rotation of the Earth; (b) season of the year, which is governed by the orbital movement of the earth; (c) latitude (the density of the solar flux is greatest at the equator and lowest at the poles). All three factors affect the solar flux at a given point because they affect the angle at which the Sun's rays reach the earth, or whether any light reaches that point at all. The farther this angle deviates from 90° the smaller is the energy reaching a unit area.

ITQ 2 10 per cent $\left(\dfrac{5}{50} \times 100 \right)$

ITQ 3 Because there are fewer plants per unit surface area to absorb the light. Plant growth is limited in these habitats because of shortage of water in the deserts and shortage of nutrients in the open oceans (discussed in Unit 2).

ITQ 4

(a) Advantages: it allows the experimenter to vary individual environmental factors (light, temperature, CO_2) and to examine the effect of each on photosynthesis. This is not possible 'in the field' where there is little or no control over environmental conditions.

(b) Disadvantages arise when measuring photosynthesis of leaves *in the field*: the rate of gas flow through the chamber must be very carefully controlled, so that the gas maintains the same composition as normal air despite oxygen uptake and CO_2 release by the enclosed leaves; the chamber may need cooling to prevent overheating of enclosed leaves. The basic problem, therefore, is to ensure that conditions inside the chamber are the same as those 'in the field' outside it (see *Evans*, p. 74, end of second paragraph).

ITQ 5 Net assimilation rate (average rate of net photosynthesis per unit leaf weight) and leaf area index (ratio of total leaf area to ground area occupied by the plant).

ITQ 6 At all light intensities below about 25 per cent full sunlight, i.e. where there is a linear increase in photosynthesis with increasing light intensity; there is no increase in photosynthesis for intensities greater than 25 per cent so that light intensity cannot be rate limiting.

ITQ 7 For plants 2 and 3 (sugarcane and sorghum), environment B: these are both tropical grasses which do not show light saturation of photosynthesis. Light saturation does occur for plants 1, 4 and 5, which are all temperate species and do not use light efficiently in hot sunny conditions but do so in environment A. Because days are long in A but short in B the total amount of energy fixed may be quite similar for the tropical and temperate species but the *rate* of fixation will be much greater for tropical plants in A than for temperate plants in B.

ITQ 8 Plants do not show light saturation of photosynthesis at high light intensities and do not show inhibition of photosynthesis at high temperatures. They also make more efficient use of the available CO_2.

ITQ 9 In (a): the low pH and low cation levels of soft water mean that the equilibrium position is well to the left in equation (1) and, therefore, levels of free CO_2 are high.

ITQ 10
(a) PGA levels would rise: all RuDP would combine with CO_2 to form PGA but conversion of PGA to triose phosphate would be blocked since the supply of ATP and $NADPH_2$ would be cut off in darkness.
(b) RuDP levels would fall: RuDP would be 'used up' in the formation of PGA but regeneration would be blocked once the supply of ATP derived from the light reactions had been cut off.

ITQ 11 Completed version of Table 5:

	High-capacity producers	Low-capacity producers
General type of plant	Herbaceous and mostly grasses or sedges.	Herbs, shrubs or trees from all plant families.
Morphology		
1 Leaf characters	Bundle sheath cells around vascular bundles packed with chloroplasts.	No chloroplasts in the bundle sheath cells.
Physiology		
2 Rate of photosynthesis	40–80 mg CO_2 dm^{-2} h^{-1} in full sunlight. No light saturation.	10–35 mg CO_2 dm^{-2} h^{-1} in full sunlight. Light saturation at 10–25% full sunlight.
3 Response to temperature	Growth and photosynthesis optimal at 30–$45\,°C$.	Growth and photosynthesis optimal at 10–$25\,°C$.
4 CO_2 compensation point	0–10 ppm CO_2	30–70 ppm CO_2
5 Sugar transport out of leaves	Rapid and efficient: 60–80 per cent in 2–4 h (at high temperatures).	Slower and less efficient: 20–60 per cent in 2–4h
6 Water requirements (grams water needed to produce 1 g dry matter)	260–350	400–900
Biochemistry		
7 Carbon fixation	Hatch–Slack (or C–4) and Calvin cycle (or C–3) paths.	Calvin cycle (C–3) pathway only.
8 Photorespiration	Not detected	Present

ITQ 12 High light intensity and high temperature: light and temperature optima are both high for photosynthesis in high-capacity species.

ITQ 13 No: a few species do occur in these habitats, but low night temperatures are characteristic of deserts and these are disadvantageous for high-capacity species since low temperature slows down the rate of starch removal from the chloroplasts and hence the rate of daytime photosynthesis.

ITQ 14 They effectively remove the toxic H_2S from the water and presumably release sulphate which can be used for plant growth.

ITQ 15 Any form of pollution (such as nutrient-rich run-off water from agricultural land) which increased the growth of algae could result in shading-out of the photosynthetic bacteria, with a resultant fall in the rate of H_2S removal. As more dead algae sank to the bottom the rate of H_2S release would rise. Similar shading-out could occur with the introduction of light colloidal material. Excessive disturbance of the water surface—by boats or storms—could increase the oxygen content of the water, increasing the depth of oxygenated water and forcing photosynthetic bacteria to greater depths (where light intensity is lower).

ITQ 16 On the evidence you have been given the probable rank order is (b), (c), (a): however, you will read in Section 1.6.2 that chemosynthetic bacteria also oxidize H_2S and the combined growth (and carbon fixation) of these two groups of bacteria can form an important energy input and food source for herbivorous zooplankton.

ITQ 17
(a) 1, light; 2, dead aquatic organisms and their waste products (going to the decomposers); 3, allochthonous material derived from the land (going to the decomposers). (b) 4, heterotrophic decomposer bacteria living in the anaerobic bottom mud; 5, photosynthetic bacteria living on the fringe of the anaerobic zone (photoautotrophes); 6, chemosynthetic bacteria (chemoautotrophes) which require aerobic conditions; 7, phytoplankton, which are photoautotrophes; 8, grazing zooplankton, which are heterotrophes and feed on phytoplankton and bacteria (note how the spatial distribution is related to the food source). (c) The heterotrophic bacteria (4) supply the photosynthetic bacteria (5) with H_2S or possibly other end-products which can serve as a source of electrons for the photosynthetic light reactions. They also provide a food source for consumers in the bottom mud.

ITQ 18
1 Place samples of (say) 10 cm^3 of lake water in the glass bottles and set up the following treatments with duplicate or triplicate bottles for each treatment:
(a) To be supplied with acetylene.
(b) No acetylene supplied (control 1).
(c) Acetylene supplied but water sample previously boiled or filtered to remove organisms (control 2).
2 Seal the bottles with air-tight rubber caps and from treatment (a) and (c) bottles remove some of the air (about one-fifth of the air volume is usually suitable) with a gas-tight syringe and replace with an equal volume of acetylene.
3 Shake the bottles well to suspend the organisms and incubate all bottles at the same temperature for the same length of time. A suitable time is usually 30 minutes but if, after this period, no ethylene can be detected, a longer incubation should be tried. The 'best' incubation period is a matter of trial and error, but periods longer than 5–6 hours are inadvisable because organisms may become dormant or die, owing (for example) to lack of oxygen or accumulation of waste products.
4 Withdraw gas samples from the bottles with a syringe, and either inject directly into the gas chromatogram for ethylene estimation or inject into an empty bottle and store for later analysis.

SAQ answers and comments

SAQ 1

1 Losses are proportionately greatest in the ultraviolet (A) and the infrared (D): losses in A are mainly due to absorption in the upper atmosphere, especially the ozone layer, and losses in B are mostly due to absorption by water vapour in the atmosphere (see *Evans*, p. 82).

2 A and C plus D: the very high losses in the infrared are due to absorption by water vapour in the clouds (see *Evans*, p. 82).

3 B and D: chloroplast pigments absorb visible light with a high degree of efficiency and water in the plant cells absorbs far infrared radiation.

SAQ 2

(a) Plant A.

(b) The greater thickness of the leaf and, in particular, the greater number of layers of palisade cells (the upper elongated cells). The thicker cuticle on the upper surface of A is also characteristic of 'sun' leaves.

(c) Leaf A, surface area 7 cm², leaf B surface area 19 cm²: remember that 'shade' leaves are thinner but have a greater surface area than 'sun' leaves.

SAQ 3

1 Light intensity will be the major limiting factor because of the oak tree canopy: that it is a sunny day is of no consequence to plants growing in deep shade, and CO_2 limitation in windless conditions is only likely to occur when light intensity is high.

2 Carotenoid pigments absorb 'excess' light and prevent damage to photosynthetic pigments by photo-oxidation; in the algal mutant, therefore, high light intensity will inhibit and be limiting for photosynthesis.

3 CO_2 supply will be limiting for photosynthesis; because the leaves are wilting stomatal pores will be closed.

4 Temperature is the most likely limiting factor. On such a day, light and CO_2 are unlikely to be limiting (air turbulence permits rapid diffusion of CO_2) but, as you know from *Evans*, leaf temperatures of 30 °C are likely to be inhibitory for photosynthesis.

5 In such deep water, light is the most probable limiting factor. Water absorbs light selectively and pondweeds possess none of the algal accessory pigments. In perfectly still water the rate of supply of CO_2 will also be very slow, but is not likely to be limiting here.

SAQ 4

Yes it would. Light *per se* is not required for the dark reactions of photosynthesis (carbon fixation here) but only the products of the light reactions, ATP and $NADPH_2$, are essential.

SAQ 5

Firstly, it provides a source of electrons (and H^+) for the light reactions of photosynthesis; secondly, the oxygen released is required by all organisms that have aerobic respiration.

SAQ 6

1 Lower: tomato plants have C-3 type carbon fixation and this enzyme, which catalyses the reaction of CO_2 and RuDP, is essential for the efficient operation of the Calvin Cycle.

2 Higher: this enzyme catalyses the oxidation of glycolic acid in photorespiration. Since photorespiration reduces net carbon fixation any inhibition of photorespiration increases the latter.

3 Lower: chlorophyll a is the most important of the photosynthetic pigments on which the light reactions (and therefore indirectly the dark reactions and carbon fixation) depend.

SAQ 7

1 Lack of light saturation in high capacity producers, which relates partly to the absence of photorespiration and partly to their low CO_2 compensation point: this in turn is probably dependent on the high CO_2 affinity of PEP carboxylase in the C-4 pathway.

2 Absence of high-temperature inhibition of photosynthesis: this relates chiefly to the absence of photorespiration, which increases markedly at high temperatures.

3 The low CO_2 compensation point and therefore the ability to use all available CO_2, other conditions being favourable. The biochemical explanation of this is given in (1) above.

SAQ 8

(a) High-capacity sedges and high-capacity 'other species'; grasses, both high- and low-capacity types and low-capacity 'other species', do occur in shaded areas.

(b) In all four open habitats the percentage of low-capacity species exceeds that of high-capacity species.

(c) The high-capacity species occur chiefly in open areas and they are mostly grasses or sedges. In shaded areas, there are very few high-capacity species and these are all grasses. A possible explanation for this distribution pattern is that high-capacity species photosynthesize rapidly only with high light and temperature: in open areas, where such conditions occur, high-capacity species will grow faster and dominate the low capacity species, but in shade areas there will be no such advantage and, presumably, low-capacity species grow better than high-capacity species under low light conditions.

(d) On mountain tops, all species are low-capacity plants and, of the seven species present, six are sedges.

(e) At low altitudes, all grasses and sedges of open habitats are high-capacity types, but with increasing altitude a progressively greater proportion of grasses and sedges are low-capacity species until above 2000 m all are low-capacity types. The most likely explanation for this distribution pattern is the decrease in average temperature with increasing altitude. High temperatures are necessary for rapid photosynthesis and efficient removal of assimilate in high-capacity species and these species may be unable to compete with low-capacity species when average temperatures are too low.

SAQ 9

The first paragraph of the CONCLUSION in *Evans* (p. 91) summarizes most of the main points; in addition, an absence of photorespiration, lack of high temperature inhibition and an upright leaf angle to permit high planting densities would all contribute to efficient production. For tropical crops, possession of the C-4 pathway would also be advantageous but it is not at all certain that C-4 plants would make efficient crop plants in temperate climates.

SAQ 10

(d) The leaf area index. Figure 17 in *Evans* (p. 80) shows the close relationship between L and photosynthetic efficiency. NAR varies during the growing season, declining towards the end, for example, but this is not so important in determining efficiency as is L. (b), (c) and (e) do contribute to photosynthetic efficiency but they do not vary during the growing season. Leaf area is the really critical factor.

SAQ 11

(a) Photosynthetic bacteria do not use water as an electron donor for the light reaction of photosynthesis, but instead use substances such as H_2S, H_2 or organic compounds. All green plants use water in photosynthesis and release oxygen by photolytic splitting of water. Photosynthetic bacteria do not release oxygen and are all obligate anaerobes. They have a different photosynthetic pigment (bacteriochlorophyll) from higher plants.

(b) Chemoautotrophes obtain energy through the oxidation of simple substances which are mainly inorganic compounds, and they are able to use this energy to fix CO_2. Heterotrophes also obtain energy through substrate oxidation but the substrates are complex organic compounds and are never inorganic. Heterotrophes cannot fix CO_2 directly and obtain carbon for growth from their 'food' substrates.

SAQ 12

(a)   The free-living nitrogen-fixing organisms (both autotrophes and heterotrophes) in the soil. Nitrogen input from this source is 10 in area A and 30 in area B (right-hand arrow).

(b)   Probably because nitrogen fixation is inhibited by high levels of inorganic nitrogen in the soil, as occur in the fertilized area A.

(c)   By the action of ultraviolet light and lightning, which cause oxidation of atmospheric N_2.

(d)   Leaching (washing through the soil and loss in drainage water) causes losses, particularly of the very soluble nitrates. Ammonium losses are less severe because the NH_4^+ ions tend to adsorb to soil colloids. Denitrification (left-hand arrow in A), i.e. conversion of nitrates to N_2 by the action of denitrifying bacteria, causes further losses (see references[6, 10]) and there is more detailed discussion in Unit 4. Losses from these sources do not occur in B because the levels of inorganic soil N are much lower.

(e)   Area B. Conversion efficiency is $\dfrac{\text{output N}}{\text{input N}} \times 100$ per cent,

which for area B gives $\dfrac{180}{225} \times 100 = 80$ per cent

and for area A, $\dfrac{210}{300} \times 100 = 70$ per cent.

Because of the losses described in (d) it is actually less efficient to apply artificial fertilizer than to utilize 'natural' fertilizers such as clover.

(f)   In area A: first, the clover roots plus their nitrogen fixing root nodules would be left in the soil in area B and provide a rich source of N for the wheat crop after decomposition had occurred. Secondly, there is more soil organic N (apart from clover roots) in area B than in area A, and this is the main source of inorganic N for the wheat crop during the following season. In area A, inputs of N to soil organic matter are $65 + 10 = 75$, and outputs $= 25$, leaving 50 kg ha^{-1} of soil organic N. For area B, inputs $= 30 + 75 = 105$, outputs $= 20$, leaving a balance of 85.

Acknowledgments

Grateful acknowledgement is made to the following sources for material used in this Unit.

FIGURES

Figure 1: D. M. Gates and Meteorological Monographs and E. P. Odum; *Figure 7:* Societas Physiologiae Plantarum Scandinavica and the author for E. Paasche, *Physiological Plant Supplement III*, 1964; *Figure 11:* Originally published by the University of California Press in C. R. Goldman (ed.), *Primary Productivity in Aquatic Environments* 1966, reprinted by permission of the Regents of the University of California.

TABLES

Table 1: W. B. Saunders Co. and the author for E. P. Odum, *Fundamentals of Ecology* 1971; *Table 4:* Academic Press Inc. and the author for I. Zelitch 'Water transport and CO_2 transport in the photosynthetic process' in San Pietro *et al.* (ed.), *Harvesting the Sun*; *Tables 8 and 9:* Dr J. J. Hofstra, University of Groningen.

Unit 2

Primary production in ecosystems

Contents

Table A1

List of scientific terms, concepts and principles in Unit 2

Introduced in a previous Unit	Unit No.	Developed in this Unit	Page No.
ecosystem trophic level	*Intro. A* *Intro. A*	energy flow equations for primary producers:	
		$A = P + R$	7
		$P = T + C + D$	7
		biomass	8
		$P : B$ ratio	9
		Phenology	13
		consumption by herbivores	18
		limiting factors for primary production	21
		eutrophication	29
		methods of measuring rates of primary production in terrestrial and aquatic ecosystems:	
		harvest methods	32
		dimensional analysis	32
		gas exchange methods	33
		energy subsidy for agricultural ecosystems	42

Table A2

Prerequisites from Science Foundation and Second Level Courses

Course	Unit No.	Section No.
S100*	20	20.1
		20.2.1
		20.2.2
		20.5
		20.6.3
S22–**	2	2.4
		2.5.1
	3	3.7
		3.10.1
		3.10.2
		3.11
		3.12
	7	7.2
		7.2.1
	IS†	
S2–3‡	Block 3	Part 2

* The Open University (1971) S100 *Science: A Foundation Course*, The Open University Press

** The Open University (1972) S22– *Comparative Physiology*, The Open University Press.

† The Open University (1972) S22– *Invertebrate Survey*. Supplementary material for the S22– Course.

‡ The Open University (1972) S2–3 *Environment*, The Open University Press.

Study guide

The methods of trapping and utilizing energy among primary producers are considered in Unit 1; Unit 2 takes a much broader look at primary production in different ecosystems. The simple equations which are used to build up energy balance sheets for primary producers are considered in Section 2.0: there is total energy trapped (gross production), energy expenditure for maintenance (respiration) and energy storage as growth of new plant tissues (net production). These equations provide the basic theoretical framework for energy flow studies: they indicate what needs to be measured.

Section 2.1 discusses the relationship between biomass and primary production, accumulation of biomass being simply one way of storing energy before it passes to other trophic levels (decomposers or herbivores). You may find it useful at this stage to read Appendix 1 (Black) which lists the world vegetation types, so that the meaning of terms such as savannah, tundra or tropical forest is clear to you. Sections 2.2–2.4 consider specific components of the production equations beginning with respiration (R) and net production (P). The balance between R and P varies widely not only between ecosystems but also between different leaves on a single plant depending on the microclimate of light and temperature (Section 2.2.2).

The energy which is not used in respiration is available to plants for the formation of new tissues (net production); Section 2.3 discusses the kinds of tissue formed at different phases in the life cycle, the contribution to permanent woody biomass, and the balance between producing organs (sources) and the growth of non-producing organs (sinks). Over long periods of time (a year or more) the new tissues either die and pass to decomposers, form a permanent addition to the plant biomass, or are consumed by herbivores or parasites. In Section 2.4 the consumption of net primary production by herbivores is considered in different ecosystems and also the effect of consumption on subsequent primary production.

One of the crucial questions for production ecologists is what factors limit primary production in different ecosystems. This is considered in Section 2.5. The factors discussed are those which affect a plant's capacity to grow and produce (e.g. temperature, water and nutrients); factors which directly influence the rate of photosynthesis (light and CO_2 supply for example) have been discussed already in Unit 1. Consideration of limiting factors is extended in Section 2.6 where primary production in aquatic ecosystems is examined in detail.

Section 2.7 describes and assesses the methods used for measuring primary production. In connection with this, you will find it useful to read about problems of sampling in *ABE*. The first part (Section 2.7.1) relates to terrestrial ecosystems and includes reading a set paper (see below) which describes the measurement of energy flow in a forest ecosystem studied for many years by scientists at the Brookhaven National Laboratory in the USA. It is essential that you study this paper in conjunction with the comments and questions in the Unit text. Methods used in the study of aquatic ecosystems are outlined in Section 2.7.2 and details of methods are given in Appendix 2. You should be able to answer the ITQs and SAQs associated with this Section and you will probably find Appendix 2 essential for this. Section 2.7.2 and Appendix 2 may be read either before or after Section 2.8 which considers the results of studies on forest productivity. Skim through Section 2.8 if short of time, but do not omit it.

To conclude the Unit we look at primary productivity on a global scale, attempting to draw comparisons between different ecosystems and discussing the problems involved in making valid comparisons. The 'energy subsidy' in advanced agricultural ecosystems is introduced here and you should study this Section carefully.

Before starting on the Unit text, you should do PTQs 8 and 9 of the Pretest at the beginning of Unit 1 to find out whether revision of earlier Courses will be helpful before reading this Unit.

The set paper for Unit 2 is: Woodwell, G. M., and Botkin, D. B. (1970). Metabolism of terrestrial ecosystems by gas exchange techniques: the Brookhaven approach, in Reichle, D. E. (ed.) *Analysis of Temperate Forest Ecosystems*, pp. 73–85, Springer. This will be referred to as *W & B* throughout the text.

Objectives

After studying this Unit you should be able to:

1 Define correctly, or distinguish between true and false statements concerning each of the terms and concepts listed in Table A1.

2 Given appropriate information:
(a) Solve the equations
$$A = P + R$$
$$P = T + C + D$$

(b) Calculate the ratio of $P : B$ and use it to characterize types of organisms or ecosystems.
(c) Correlate data about the distribution of P between organs or the pattern of P over time with type of organism or ecosystem and its maturity relative to climax vegetation.
(Tested in SAQs 2, 3 and 12 and ITQs.)

3 Distinguish between biomass and primary productivity of ecosystems. (Tested in SAQs 1 and 15.)

4 Correlate climatic changes with changes in net primary production and respiration.
(Tested in SAQ 10 and ITQs.)

5 Given appropriate information, assess the effects of consumption by herbivores on primary productivity.
(Tested in SAQ 4 and ITQs.)

6 Given information about climate and physical surroundings, assess the factors limiting primary production in different terrestrial and aquatic ecosystems and, given information about limiting factors, deduce or predict the amount and pattern of primary production in given ecosystems.
(Tested in SAQs 5, 6, 7, 8, 9 and 10.)

7 Describe simple methods of measuring primary production in terrestrial and aquatic ecosystems and use information about such methods to:
(a) evaluate critically experimental studies;
(b) design experimental studies to measure given parameters for specified ecosystems;
(c) assess the reliability and validity of given methods for given situations.
(Tested in SAQs 11, 12, 13 and 14.)

8 Study and evaluate published papers or data about primary production and assess the validity of conclusions reached.
(Tested in questions associated with W & B.)

9 Use information about ecosystems (including climate and the kinds of primary producers they contain) and information about A, P, R and B, or some combination of these, to assess the productivity of an ecosystem, as defined by specified criteria, and to make comparisons between ecosystems.
(Tested in SAQ 15 and ITQs.)

10 Given suitable data, assess the position of agricultural ecosystems in relation to unmanaged ecosystems and apply the principles developed in this Unit to make hypotheses about ways of increasing primary production in managed ecosystems.
(Tested in SAQ 16.)

6

2.0 Introduction

Study comment To understand energy flow through primary producers it is necessary to specify the various inputs and outputs and to describe the relationship between them. This is done by means of simple equations, which are described here and which form the basis for studies of primary production.

In Unit 1, the basic processes of primary production, the trapping of light energy and the fixation of carbon and nitrogen, were described. The amount of solar energy utilized by autotrophs depends on a complex set of factors, some relating to the external environment (light intensity, levels of CO_2 and temperature, for example) and others to the structure of the plant community or to the structure and physiology of individual plants. But a simple analysis of photosynthetic rates does not give a full description of primary production in ecosystems. Consider the 'economic model' in Figure 1.

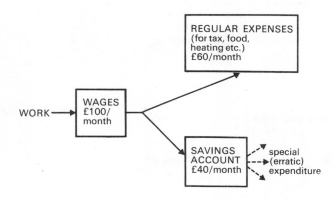

Figure 1 An 'economic model' for primary production.

If photosynthesis is equivalent to 'work', then the total amount of light energy fixed can be equated with wages: this is gross production (A).

Out of the wages of an individual a regular amount goes for essential expenses to maintain a healthy trouble-free existence: green plants expend energy in a similar way for maintenance through the process of respiration (R).

Money left after expenses is placed in a saving account and this is equivalent to the net production (P) of primary producers.

Then   Gross earnings = essential expenditure + savings   *energy flow equation*

and $A = R + P$

This is the basic equation for production studies. For primary producers, it is necessary to know what proportion of A is used up in respiration, what is P and what happens to it.

Erratic expenditure eats into the savings account; the energy of net production is converted into new plant tissues and tissues may be consumed by animals or die and enter the decomposer cycle. For net production, therefore, another equation is needed:

$$P = T + C + D$$ *equation for net production*

considering a time period t_1 to t_2

T is the accumulation of new tissues (increase in biomass).

C is consumption by herbivores.

D is loss due to death of organs or individuals.

It is T which measures the amount of material available for harvest by man.

But it has been shown that substantial amounts of soluble compounds, such as sugars, may be leached from aerial organs by rain or secreted into the surrounding soil or water. Material lost in this way (S) may be of the order of 1 t ha^{-1} year^{-1}. To allow for this, the last equation is modified: $P = T + C + D + S$.

There are very few measurements of S, and this can be a source of error in estimates of net primary production.

In this Unit, factors which affect or limit the amount of primary production are examined and the methods used to study primary production are considered in some detail. This last is essential for critical assessment of experimental studies when the basis and validity of the methods used must be understood.

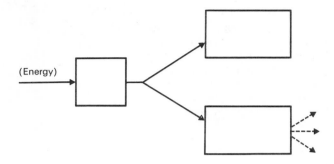

Figure 2 An energy flow model for primary production.

ITQ 1   Fill in the symbols A, R, P, T, C and D in Figure 2, which is a model of primary production based on Figure 1. State the source of energy.

Read the answer to ITQ 1 (p. 53).

QUESTION   Apart from the energy input in Figure 2 what other input not shown in the Figure is required by primary producers to maintain production?

ANSWER   An input of chemical elements, carbon, oxygen, nitrogen, phosphorus, etc. is required for building up new tissues.

2.1   Biomass and productivity

Study comment   The biomass of primary producers and their productivity are not identical and need to be clearly distinguished. Long-term accumulation of biomass is one way in which energy may be stored within ecosystems but production per unit biomass may decline with increasing biomass. Reasons for the decline are discussed and another way of storing energy, the accumulation of partly decomposed organic matter, is described briefly.

Biomass is the amount of living material in a given area and can be expressed in units of dry weight or of energy per unit area. For woody plants, most of the 'wood' consists of xylem tissue which is, of course, dead, but as long as a branch or trunk has the capacity to produce leaves or plays an essential role in supporting the plant it is considered to be part of the plant biomass. Unfortunately, some research workers include dead branches still attached to the plant as part of the biomass: in this Unit we do not do this, but you should be aware of this source of confusion. Productivity is a rate term and is the amount of energy (or dry weight) fixed or accumulated by unit biomass or (more usually) in unit area per unit of time. A high biomass does not necessarily indicate a high rate of production (gross or net); it indicates only that a certain proportion of net production has accumulated over an undisclosed time as living tissue ('plant capital'). Look at Table 1, where biomass (B) and net primary production are compared for two ecosystems.

biomass

productivity

QUESTION   The ratio of net production to biomass is 6·22 for the algae and 0·044 for the tropical plantation. Suggest reasons for this difference.

ANSWER   The planktonic algae have a high productivity, a high ratio of $P : B$ because (a) all the living tissue is productive tissue (there are no 'non-productive' roots or stems) and (b) these small algae have short life cycles so that energy input may be high but energy output due to death and decomposition is also high and there is little or no accumulation of biomass. Energy flows through this system very rapidly. For the

8

TABLE 1 Biomass and net primary production in two contrasting ecosystems

	Average biomass g m^{-2}	Net production dry kg m^{-2} year^{-1}
Algae* in sewage pond	0·9	5·6
Tropical plantation (trees)	85·0	3·7

* These are mainly small, floating (planktonic) algae with a very simple structure and short life span.[1] (The superscript number refers to another Open University Science Course considered to be a prerequisite to this Course; see p. 44.)

trees in the plantation, however, much of the biomass is non-productive woody supporting tissue and, during their long life span, a considerable amount of energy is stored in this form: energy is trapped within the system and flows through much more slowly than for the sewage pond.

When comparing plants of the same type, e.g. different kinds of algae, the $P : B$ ratio is often used as an index of photosynthetic efficiency. When comparing plants of different form and structure the ratio is more indicative of the proportion of non-photosynthetic tissue in the plants.

P:B ratio

Look at Table 2.

TABLE 2 Data for oak forests. (Values as kg dry wt m^{-2}.)

		\multicolumn{4}{c}{Oak forests}
		1	2	3	4
Total biomass (B)		7·0	15·0	29·7	35·3
Percentage composition of biomass	leaves	5·0	2·3	1·2	1·0
	woody stems	62·0	74·7	80·5	84·4
	roots	33·0	23·0	18·3	14·5
Net annual production (P)		0·74	1·46	1·70	1·58
Ratio $P : B$		0·106	0·097	0·057	0·045

QUESTION Suggest an explanation for the declining ratio of $P : B$ in the oak forests 1 to 4.

ANSWER The proportion of leaves (the photosynthetic tissue) falls as total biomass increases. Thus net production does not keep pace with increasing biomass and the $P : B$ ratio declines.

QUESTION In Table 2, forest 4 has a higher biomass but a lower net production that forest 3. Suggest an explanation for this.

ANSWER Although much of the woody tissue consists of dead xylem cells, there are always living cells (e.g. cambium, phloem, xylem parenchyma) associated with the woody parts. The maintenance costs of these living cells, i.e. the energy losses due to respiration, rise as B rises. Up to a point the respiratory 'cost' of the woody tissue is more than compensated by greater numbers of leaves on the growing trees; thus P increases in forests 1–3. But, above a certain biomass, R increases faster than A so that, since $A = P + R$, P actually falls. The critical biomass of the oak forests in Table 2 must be somewhere between 29·7 and 35·3 kg m^{-2}.

It follows that maximum plant biomass is not always correlated with maximum rates of net production. The increasing respiratory load is one reason for this but, in addition, there is evidence that old plants (with high biomass) show a decline in photosynthetic efficiency: the rate of photosynthesis per unit leaf area actually declines while leaf respiration remains constant.

decline in *P:B* for forests

For aquatic ecosystems based on free-floating phytoplankton producers there is often an even more dramatic decline in productivity with increasing biomass (see Table 3). The decline applies to gross as well as net production and, unlike trees, there is no evidence that increased respiration 'costs' are responsible for the decreasing net production.

TABLE 3   Data for phytoplankton with similar species composition in two different months

	May	June
Gross production (A) (mg carbon m^{-3} day^{-1})	43·75	99·23
Biomass (B) (mg fresh wt m^{-3})	156	1250
Ratio $A : B$	0·28	0·08

The reasons for the decline in gross production per unit biomass are still not fully understood but three factors might be involved:

decline in $P{:}B$ for algae

(i)   The supply of nutrients essential for photosynthesis, particularly CO_2, may become rate limiting at high algal densities.

(ii)   Algae may secrete substances into the water which may inhibit photosynthesis when in sufficiently high concentrations (e.g. when cells are crowded).

(iii)   At very high cell densities, serious self-shading can occur so that utilization of the available light is inefficient. This contrasts sharply with terrestrial ecosystems where individual plants and plant communities are both 'structured', the precise arrangement of leaves ensuring maximum light interception with minimum self-shading (Unit 1, Section 1.1.3). Planktonic communities have no 'structure' at all.

Even in ecosystems where there is no long-term accumulation of biomass, organic matter which is separate from the plant body may accumulate. Partly decomposed phytoplankton may accumulate in the bottom sediments and litter from terrestrial plants may accumulate as peat. The amount and rate of this accumulation depends on the efficiency of decomposer organisms. When conditions are unfavourable for decomposers and decomposition does not keep pace with litter deposition then organic matter accumulates. The energy content of these ecosystems increases just as it does in a growing forest and some mineral nutrients are permanently removed from the nutrient cycles. The amounts of nutrients are usually small because the bulk of undecomposed material consists of structural carbohydrates (made up largely of carbon, hydrogen and oxygen): most of the essential mineral elements (nitrogen and phosphorus, for example) are released by decomposer action.

accumulation of dead organic matter

Now you could attempt SAQs 1 and 2 (p. 51).

2.2   Respiration and net production

Study comment   This Section is concerned with the quantitative importance of respiration in production studies. For primary producers, the proportion of A used up in respiration is related to the type of plant, ecosystem maturity (for forests) and climate. The ways in which leaf microclimate affects P and R during the course of a day are described.

2.2.1   Respiration 'costs' in different ecosystems

In Section 2.0, respiration was equated with the 'expense budget' of the wage earner (plant). Look at Table 4 which shows how the balance between production and respiration varies for different ecosystems.

QUESTION   What is the average energy loss due to respiration for all primary producers?

ANSWER   Using the average figures for the Earth it is 50 per cent $\left(\dfrac{600}{1200} \times 100\right)$.

TABLE 4 Annual primary production and respiration in $10^4 J\, m^{-2}\, year^{-1}$

	Alfalfa* fields (USA)	Maize (per 100 days)** (USA)	Young pine forest (England)	Medium aged oak–pine forest (New York)	Mature tropical rainforest (Puerto Rico)	Average for the Earth
Gross primary production (A)	10 210	3400 (12 420)**	5100	4970	23 140	1200
Respiration (R)	3850	790 (2900)**	1960	2730	17 820	600
Net primary production (P)	6360	2610 (9520)**	3140	2240	5320	600

* Alfalfa is a member of the legume family, which includes peas and beans.

** Maize production is measured during the growing season of 100 days. The figures in brackets are derived from extrapolation from 100 days to a whole year: if maize could be grown continually throughout the year (as alfalfa can) these values would be obtained.

Note In Table 4, the low average values for the whole Earth are due to the very low levels of primary production in the open oceans which occupy two-thirds of the Earth's surface.

QUESTION Suggest why the value of R, as a percentage of A, is lower for maize than for alfalfa (recall the characteristics of high- and low-capacity primary producers given in Unit 1).

ANSWER Maize is a high-capacity primary producer where the C–4 pathway for carbon fixation operates and where photorespiration is negligible (see Unit 1, Section 1.5.3); alfalfa is a low-capacity C–3 plant where 'wasteful' photorespiration may occur.

The terms 'young', 'medium-aged' and 'mature' applied to the three forest ecosystems in Table 4 refer to their status relative to stable climax vegetation[2] (see also *Introduction to Block A*, p. 5). Unless some major climatic change occurs, climax vegetation maintains approximately constant biomass and the rate of production of new tissue is balanced by the rate of tissue loss. It is clear from Table 4 that the proportion of A used in respiration increases as forests mature.

climax

QUESTION Suggest two reasons for this.

ANSWER The mature forest has a higher biomass and a higher proportion of non-photosynthetic tissue to maintain than the immature forest; in addition, very old trees in the mature forest may have a lower rate of photosynthesis than younger trees (refer back to Section 2.2, where this is discussed).

In the wet tropics, gross production of the forests is outstandingly high, chiefly because conditions for growth and photosynthesis are favourable throughout the year, not just in summer as in temperate regions. But high temperatures in the tropics result in high respiration rates (see Section 2.2.2) and, consequently, net production is not particularly high. Foresters working in tropical areas have found that net wood production for lowland sites does not usually exceed $16\, t\, ha^{-1}\, year^{-1}$, and is usually only about 10. At higher altitudes, however, net production of $20\, t\, ha^{-1}\, year^{-1}$ is common and a few species achieve 40. Although differences in soil fertility (nutrient supply) could explain some of this difference, the lower temperature at higher altitudes (and therefore the lower rate of respiration relative to photosynthesis) is probably a major contributing factor.

tropical rainforests

2.2.2 Microclimate, respiration and net production

In terrestrial ecosystems, measurements of respiration and net production are made on single leaves, groups of leaves or whole plants (details of methods used will be described in Section 2.7). But for each leaf the conditions of light, temperature and wind—the microclimate—may vary substantially in natural conditions, so the problem arises as to how this microclimatic variation affects

microclimate

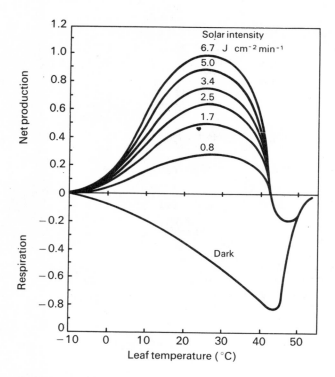

Figure 3 The rates of net production (at various light intensities) and respiration in darkness as related to leaf temperature for a temperate climate plant (Gates, 1968).

rates of R and P. Look at Figure 3, which shows how R and P (at various light intensities) vary with temperature for a typical leaf growing in a temperate climate.

QUESTION What are the temperatures for maximum net production and respiration in this plant?

ANSWER About 25 °C for P and 43 °C for R.

QUESTION At which temperatures does R exceed gross production?

ANSWER At temperatures above 42·5 °C P falls below zero, showing that R exceeds A (since $A = R + P$).

Now look at Figure 4, which relates to horizontal leaves at right angles to the

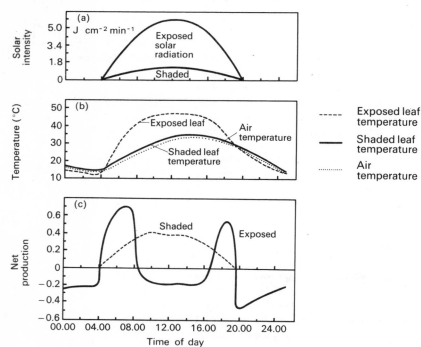

Figure 4 Daily variation in micro-climate and net production for a horizontal exposed leaf and a horizontal shaded leaf: (a) incident solar radiation, (b) air and leaf temperature, (c) relative net production (Gates, 1968).

incident light and at about 50° latitude. The weather is clear and sunny with little wind.

The pattern of carbon gain and loss is strikingly different for the exposed and shaded leaves. This can be explained by reference to Figure 3 and Figure 4 a and b.

ITQ 2 Why is net production for the exposed leaf greatest in the early morning and late evening?

ITQ 3 Why is net production for the exposed leaf negative (so that leaf dry weight falls rather than increases) during the middle part of the day?

ITQ 4 Throughout this experiment leaves were maintained at right angles to the incident light: would you expect exposed leaves, left undisturbed on the tree, to show the same pattern of net production? (Refer to Unit 1, Section 1.1.3.)

ITQ 5 Can the net production curve for the shaded leaf be adequately explained in terms of the temperature and light conditions?

Now read the answers to ITQs 2 to 5 (p. 53).

The microclimate of individual leaves clearly affects net production of the whole plant. But plants show remarkable adaptability to climate, on a micro-scale and on a macro-scale. When *Impatiens parviflora* (busy-lizzie, balsam) was grown in controlled environment chambers, a rise in temperature of 2·5 °C (from 17·5 to 20 °C) caused a reduction in the rate of photosynthesis per unit leaf *weight* of 10 per cent but net production remained almost constant owing to an increase in leaf *area* (Evans, 1972). Furthermore, the temperature for maximum net photosynthesis varies with climate, being around 25–30 °C in temperate regions but only 15 °C for alpine or arctic plants.

adaptation to climate

2.3 Net production and seasonal climate

Study comment Plants use the energy not required for maintenance (respiration) to produce new tissues (net production). The kind of tissues formed and their energy content varies during the life cycle of a plant. Knowledge of this variation, in relation to climate, is important in production studies and also affects herbivorous consumers (Section 2.3.1). There are practical implications too: foresters need to know at which time of year and in which part of the life cycle most of the woody tissue of trees is laid down (Section 2.3.2) while for crop plants, where growth of specific edible organs is of primary importance to man, it is useful to know which parts of the plant supply assimilated energy to these organs (Section 2.3.3). If short of time, concentrate on Section 2.3.1 and read rapidly through the last two Sections.

2.3.1 Life cycles of plants: phenology

At different times of year and different stages of their life cycle, plants utilize the energy of net production to produce different kinds of tissue: wheat produces leaves in spring, flowers in early summer and fruits in late summer. The study of life cycles in relation to time of year is called *phenology*, and it is often essential to understand this before starting to measure primary production in ecosystems.

phenology

QUESTION Suggest three plant communities which do not show regular seasonal growth patterns.

ANSWER (a) Plants in the humid tropics, where day length and climate are both relatively constant throughout the year (note, however, that many tropical areas have regular wet and dry seasons and flowering, fruiting and leaf production may be related to this: see Appendix 1); (b) plants in desert areas, where rapid growth and flowering usually occur only after erratic rainstorms; (c) ephemeral plants in temperate areas (often these are weeds) which grow and flower throughout the year.

(a)

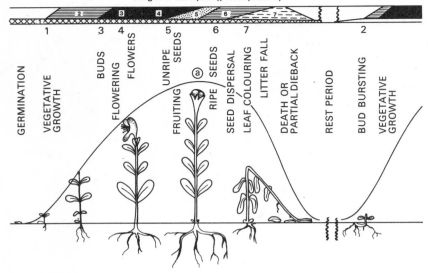

Figure 5a Life cycle of a typical annual species and accumulation of biomass (dry matter) (Lieth, 1970).

(b)

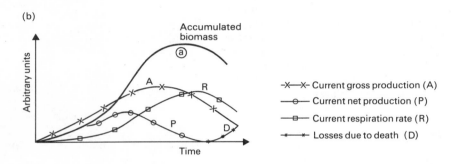

-×—×- Current gross production (A)
—○— Current net production (P)
—□— Current respiration rate (R)
—*—*— Losses due to death (D)

Figure 5b Typical growth and production curves for a herbaceous annual plant.

Look at Figure 5, which shows the phenology of a herbaceous annual plant.

In studies of herbaceous plants or plant communities it is essential to know the time of maximum biomass in the life cycle (see point (a) in Figs. 5a and 5b) when measuring net production by a harvest method (discussed in Section 2.7.1a). This time often coincides with flowering or when seeds are ripening.

time of maximum *B*

In forest ecosystems, the phenology of herbaceous plants (ground flora) and woody species are usually quite different. Consider a typical English wood: most members of the ground flora start producing new leaves in early spring and flower before the trees come into full leaf, often dying back to ground level by midsummer.

ground flora

QUESTION Suggest a reason for this.

ANSWER Although temperatures are lower and day length is shorter in spring, there is still much more light available for growth than in midsummer when the tree canopy is fully developed.

Thus, in this kind of woodland, primary production studies on the ground flora would need to be done much earlier in the season than similar studies on trees.

Another factor which relates to plant phenology is the variable energy content* of different organs and variations for particular organs during their life span. This is due to changes in the compounds synthesized (lignin, starch, protein, etc.) in different organs at different times of year and is illustrated in Table 5 for alder (see also Fig. 6).

energy content

* 'Energy content' is measured by combusting plant tissue in a bomb calorimeter and measuring the amount of heat evolved.

TABLE 5 Energy content of components of the alder, *Alnus glutinosa*. (Data from M. K. Hughes, 1973.)

Component	Date	kJ g^{-1} dry wt
Bole (trunk)	March	19·00
Branches	March	20·95
Bud scales	May	25·52
Flowers, seeds, fruits	Aug.–Nov.	22·94
Forest floor litter leaves	October	19·59
	December	19·21
	February	20·51
	May	19·57
Canopy leaves	May	21·88
	June	20·94
	August	20·72
	October	20·40
Falling leaves, green	August	20·42
	October	20·26
	November	19·74
Falling leaves, brown	September	20·61
	October	21·15
	November	21·49

Figure 6 Alder, *Alnus glutinosa*.

This kind of variation should be taken into account in production studies when converting increases in dry weight into increases in energy contents during the life cycle; quite often it is ignored and may be a serious source of error. Such variation also affects the nutritional value of plants for herbivores.

QUESTION For a leaf-eating animal feeding on alder, which leaves are likely to be most nutritious, and at what time of year?

ANSWER Probably the spring canopy leaves: May canopy leaves have the highest energy content. However, energy content is not the sole criterion of nutritional value; protein content and 'digestibility' are also important and there is further discussion of this in Unit 3.

In fact, the majority of leaf-eating animals, particularly insect larvae, do feed on spring leaves. This is partly because energy content and protein levels are high (a characteristic common to all young herbage) and partly because many trees synthesize toxic tannin compounds which accumulate in leaves in late spring and summer and render leaves indigestible. For these kinds of reasons the life cycles and reproductive cycles of herbivorous animals are often closely in phase with the growth and development of their food plants.

phenology of plants and herbivores

2.3.2 Net production in woody perennials

Plant organs, such as leaves, small roots, flowers or fruits, often show great variations in their life span depending on the species of plant and the climate. Leaves of temperate grasses have a life span of around six weeks; leaves of trees have a life span which ranges from about six months for temperate deciduous species to one to three years for temperate evergreens and one to nine years or more for tropical evergreens. On their death, these temporary organs are shed, form litter (see Unit 4) and enter the decomposer cycle.

life span of organs

In addition to producing 'temporary' organs, woody perennials direct a major part of net production into woody tissues which form a 'permanent' addition to the plant biomass. In trees, the woody biomass increases each year and this increase is often referred to as the *annual increment*: it is the difference between total net production and litter production (litter does include woody organs such as branches and twigs) plus losses due to grazing (*C*). During the life of

annual increment

15

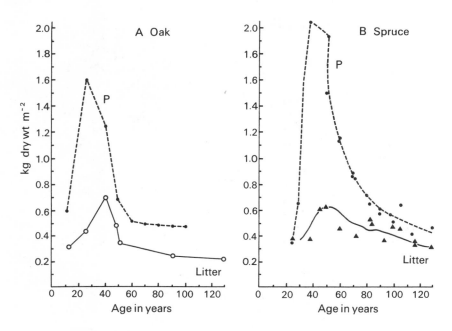

Figure 7 Annual net primary production and litter fall in relation to forest age.

a tree there are changes in annual net production and in the annual increment (see Fig. 7).

QUESTION Assuming that consumption by herbivores is negligible, how can estimates of the annual increment be obtained from the information in Figure 7?

ANSWER As the difference between the litter and net production curves.

QUESTION At what age is the annual increment greatest for (a) an oak forest; (b) a spruce forest?

ANSWER (a) About 25 years; (b) about 40 years: trees accumulate woody biomass most rapidly (have the largest annual increments) when they are relatively young—below 50 or 60 years old in most instances.

A 'good' tree for the forester is one where a high proportion of net production is diverted into trunk growth—the wood which is of greatest economic importance. The age at which trees are cropped is largely determined by the time at which the annual increment falls to a low value and little further increase in trunk girth occurs.

2.3.3 Storage and movements of assimilates

In leafy plants, the products of photosynthesis (assimilate) are usually transported out of the producing organs (the sources) by way of the phloem and stored or used in other organs (the sinks)[3].

The growth of roots and underground storage organs is supported by assimilate transported from green aerial organs; the growth of young unexpanded leaves and stems is supported by assimilate from older expanded leaves or from storage organs and seeds. Knowledge of the source supplying a particular sink is very useful if the sink organs are to be harvested by man. When breeding new plant varieties, for example, breeders can then select plants with extra large and durable source organs in order to increase crop yields. Recent work on barley (Walpole and Morgan, 1972) has shown that the main source of assimilate for developing barley grains are the flag leaf (the uppermost leaf on the shoot) and green tissue in the ear itself. The grains in a barley ear grow at different rates and may have very different final weights, but when the flag leaf was supplied with $^{14}CO_2$ radioactive assimilate was found to be evenly distributed between the grains in an ear (Fig. 8a). This was true at all times of testing during growth of the grains.

effects of sources on sinks

growth of barley grains

16

(a)

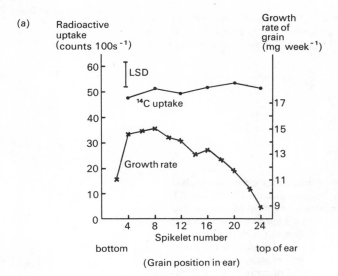

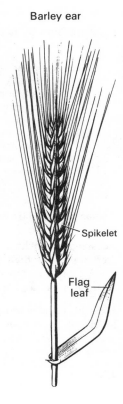

Barley ear

QUESTION From these results, what is the most likely explanation for the variations in rate of grain growth?

ANSWER Some source, other than the flag leaf, must supply assimilate to grains in such a way that the amount varies from grain to grain: this source is presumably the green tissue in the ear.

The problem remained as to *which* tissue in the ear contributes assimilate to the grain. It was observed that rate of grain growth showed a striking correlation with length of the awn in that spikelet (see Fig. 8b) and it was suggested that (a) the awn of a particular spikelet supplies assimilate only to the grain in that spikelet, and (b) that awns are major sources for grains, so that the longer the awn the bigger the grain.

QUESTION How would you test this hypothesis?

ANSWER The method used by Walpole and Morgan was to supply a single awn (on the plant) with $^{14}CO_2$. Then, after 3·5 hours, the ear was removed, dried, divided up into grains and the amount of radioactivity in each grain measured.

The following results were obtained:

Distribution of ^{14}C after application to the awn of spikelet 10 (expressed as percentage of total ^{14}C in the ear).

	T_1	T_2
Retention by spikelet 10	94·2	99·0
Moved up the ear	5·00	0·3
Moved down the ear	0·8	0·1

$T_1 = 7$ days after pollination.
$T_2 = 21$ days after pollination.

QUESTION Do these results support hypothesis (a)?

ANSWER Yes; nearly all the assimilate from a spikelet's awn goes to the grain in that spikelet.

QUESTION Do these results support hypothesis (b)?

ANSWER It is not possible to say without further information. The *absolute* amount of assimilate supplied by the awn is not given. If this were only a small proportion of the total assimilate entering the grain then awn size is unlikely to be a major factor controlling grain size. Awn length might correlate with the size of another part of the spikelet, a part which contributes much assimilate to the grain and is the real regulator of grain size.

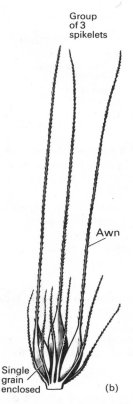

Group of 3 spikelets

Awn

Single grain enclosed

(b)

Figure 8b Barley ear and spikelets.

Source organs affect the growth of sink organs but the converse may also be true: the presence of sinks can affect rates of photosynthesis and growth of source organs. Refer back to Unit 1, Section 1.4, if you have forgotten the reasons for this.

Now you could attempt SAQ 3 (p. 51).

2.4 Consumption by herbivores

Study comment The energy of net primary production may either accumulate in the plant (T), pass to decomposers (D) or be consumed by herbivores (C). C is normally large in aquatic ecosystems or grasslands and must be measured to obtain a true picture of energy flow (Section 2.4.1). This is not always easy because herbivores not only consume tissue but may also affect the future potential of plants for growth and production and may affect rates of mineral cycling. Some of these complex interactions between herbivores and primary producers are considered in Section 2.4.1 and there is further detailed discussion about herbivores in Unit 3.

2.4.1 Consumption in different ecosystems

Ecosystems can be broadly grouped into two classes: those where herbivore consumption is high (strong grazing chain) and those where it is low (weak grazing chain). There are, inevitably, 'intermediate' ecosystems which fall between these two classes.

Look at Table 6 which shows the proportion of net production consumed by herbivores in various ecosystems: ecosystems 1 and 4 fall into the first class, ecosystem 3 into the second class and ecosystem 2 is an intermediate type.

TABLE 6

Ecosystem	Net primary production 10^4J m^{-2}yr^{-1}	Herbivore consumption 10^4J m^{-2}yr^{-1}	% of P	Type of herbivore
1 River (Silver Spring, Florida)	3696	1409	38·1	Small crustaceans
2 Acid bog lake (Cedar Bog Lake, Minnesota)	368	62	16·8	Small crustaceans
3 Beech forest (Germany)	170*	6·0	3·5	Leaf-eating insects
4 Grasslands (temperate European)	956	257	25·8	Sheep** (1 acre^{-1})

* Annual leaf production only (approximately 25 per cent of total net production).

** Consumption by herbivorous insects not measured.

QUESTION What happens to net primary production in ecosystems where herbivore consumption is low?

ANSWER It forms a permanent addition to the plant biomass or passes into the decomposer cycle.

QUESTION What other broad general feature distinguishes ecosystems in these two classes?

ANSWER Standing biomass is relatively low in the first group (aquatic ecosystems, grassland) and high in the second (forests).

The effect of grazing on production cannot be judged adequately by simply measuring the amount of plant material consumed. Herbivores, particularly insects, are often highly selective in the plants they eat, the organs eaten and the time of year eaten. There are insects which feed exclusively by chewing leaves, or buds and small twigs, or roots, or fruits; others bore into the bark or wood; aphids and scale insects suck the sap of leaves, soft twigs or roots. Herbivores feeding chiefly on young shoot tips or buds may have drastic effects on plant growth and production even if they consume only a small proportion of the plant dry weight. Similarly the boring and sap-sucking insects may cause deformed growth, disrupt the conducting tissues or transmit viral and fungal diseases. Figures quoted for 'losses due to pests' often do not mean that the pests actually consumed that amount of tissue: much loss is due to a reduced productive capacity of the plants.

selective consumption

2.4.2 How does grazing affect primary producers?

When grazers remove photosynthetic tissue you might expect an inevitable reduction in gross and net primary production. In the long term this is not always true, except when there is consistently heavy grazing. Consider a field grazed by cows: grazing tends to prevent grasses reaching the flowering and fruiting stage which, as you should recall from Section 2.3.1, heralds the onset of senescence and decline in gross production. Grasses have meristems at the nodes of the stem, and their leaves grow by cell division and expansion at the leaf base. Thus they are able to grow and produce new leaves even when the stem apex has been removed, and so grazing by cows maintains grasses in the early rapidly growing vegetative phase. Furthermore, the dung and urine produced by the cows serve as a fertilizer from which mineral nutrients are released by decomposer action much faster than from dead plant remains. So the nutrients cycle more rapidly in a grazed field than in ungrazed grassland and this helps to sustain high levels of primary production. Provided that grazing is light or is restricted to certain times of year (preferably when grasses are growing rapidly), grazing by cows can increase grass production in pastures.

grazing by cows

The effects of defoliating insects on forest trees are much more difficult to assess and the most recent information on this subject has come from IBP projects. There is some data about the production losses caused by insect pests to woody plants and there are numerous surmises, but little data, about consequent changes in the ecosystem and how these affect the plants and the pests. Most defoliation is caused by larvae, not by adult insects, and part of the problem in evaluating effects is the enormous fluctuation in larval numbers from year to year. This problem of population dynamics (considered in Block B) means that no general statements can be made about consumption by herbivorous insects since consumption may fluctuate by several hundred per cent in successive years.

defoliating insects

Consider a spring defoliator such as the gipsy moth, *Lymantria dispar*, whose caterpillars feed on deciduous trees, chiefly eating young oak leaves from the tree crown. If caterpillar numbers are low there is very little loss of spring leaves: holes in leaves allow more light to penetrate to lower leaves (where photosynthesis is light limited) and there is essentially no loss of net production by the oak trees.

gipsy moth larvae

When caterpillar numbers are greater and partial defoliation occurs, then a number of factors must be considered:

(a)   Most of the new woody tissue is laid down in spring and energy for this derives from the spring leaves: loss of spring leaves, either through direct consumption or through death and shedding of partly eaten leaves, results in a loss of wood production.

(b)   New leaves may grow in summer and partly replace those lost in spring. These leaves fall later in autumn than spring leaves but they do not contribute energy for wood production; instead, energy is diverted from wood to leaf production.

(c)   The faeces (frass) of the caterpillars and dead larvae fall to the ground and contribute to the woodland litter; frass accounts for more than 50 per cent of the food consumed. As you can see from Table 7, the nutrient content of frass, caterpillars, and tree leaves differ considerably.

nutrients in frass and litter

TABLE 7 Nutrient analyses of oak leaves, gipsy moth caterpillars and their frass.

| | Average concentrations % dry wt | | | | |
	N	P	K	Ca	Mg
Canopy leaves of oak	2·59	0·05	1·04	1·15	0·13
Frass	3·26	0·20	3·21	1·87	0·76
Larvae	9·62	1·53	2·98	0·39	0·27

Because frass and larvae have higher nutrient concentrations than plant litter and, like cow dung, are broken down more rapidly by decomposer organisms than is leaf litter, the nutrient cycles may be speeded up. When plant growth is nutrient limited (see Section 2.5.1) production (probably in the next growing season) will be enhanced. This applies, of course, only if the frass and larvae form a sufficiently high proportion of the total forest litter and if larval consumption does not reduce total litter (and its nutrients) substantially: many larvae are eaten by predators and some pupate and later emerge as adult moths. Table 8 shows the total forest litter and the proportion of frass and dead larvae when gipsy moth infestation is moderate and severe.

TABLE 8 Litter production and its nutrient content in two oak forests with and without gipsy moth infestation

| | Dry weight of litter and nutrients g m⁻² year⁻¹ | | | |
| | Forest A | | Forest B | |
Litter type	Litter	Total nutrients*	Litter	Total nutrients*
Uninfested areas				
Fallen leaves	433·0	22·95	328·0	17·00
Infested areas				
(a) debris of partly eaten leaves	21·4	1·11	34·2	1·75
(b) remains of spring leaves	364·0	19·31	212·0	10·96
(c) regenerated (summer) leaves	4·0	0·19	18·0	0·92
Total leaf fall	389·4	20·61	264·20	13·63
(d) frass	23·0	2·14	35·0	3·25
(e) dead insects	1·0	0·15	1·7	0·25
Total litter	413·4	22·9	300·9	17·13

* Total nutrients = the sum of N, P, K, Ca, Mg.

QUESTION From the data in Table 8, which forest is moderately infested and which is severely infested with gipsy moth larvae?

ANSWER In the infested areas litter components (a), (c), (d) and (e) are all substantially higher in forest B than in forest A: thus B is severely infested and A moderately so.

QUESTION How does caterpillar infestation affect total litter production?

ANSWER Comparing the infested and uninfested areas, total litter is slightly reduced in both forests: in A by $100 - \left(\frac{4134}{4330} \times 100 \right) = 4·5$ per cent and in B by 8·3 per cent. Insect debris comprises 5·8 per cent of total litter in infested A and 12·1 per cent in infested B.

QUESTION How does caterpillar infestation affect nutrient content of the litter?

ANSWER Perhaps surprisingly, total nutrient levels in litter are almost identical for infested and uninfested areas but, because there is less *total* litter in the former, nutrient concentration in the litter is higher for the infested forests. In forest A, nutrient concentration is 5·53 per cent in the infested and 5·30 per cent in the uninfested areas: in forest B, the figures are 5·60 per cent and 5·18 per cent respectively. The more severe the infestation the richer in nutrients is the litter.

Returning to the factors which must be taken into account when assessing defoliator effects on forest production:

(d)   Caterpillars release CO_2 through respiration, and frass deposition can also stimulate micro-organisms and therefore increase CO_2 release from the litter. It has been suggested (Rafes, 1970) that higher CO_2 levels could increase photosynthesis of the light-saturated sun leaves; at present there is no evidence to support this hypothesis.

(e)   Defoliation allows more light to penetrate to shrubs and ground flora and increased primary production by these plants might partially compensate for losses of tree production.

QUESTION   Taking into account all the factors (a) to (e) what will be the effects of gipsy moth caterpillar consumption on primary production in oak forest?

ANSWER   Because there is a loss of spring leaves (a), which is not compensated for by regrowth in summer (b), there will be a fall in net production in oak and, in particular, a fall in wood production. Because of (c), (d) and (e) there may be increased growth and production of some producers in the current and/or the following season. On balance, then, the total net production of the ecosystem may be little changed but the pattern of production, notably the proportion of wood produced, will be altered.

Now you can attempt SAQ 4 (p. 51).

2.5   What factors limit primary production?

Study comment   To understand how ecosystems function it is crucial to know the factors which limit production for different trophic levels. Primary productivity is related to (a) the rate of photosynthesis per unit of tissue (factors limiting this were considered in Unit 1) and (b) the total amount of photosynthetic tissue and the rate of plant growth. In this Section factors affecting (b) are discussed, chiefly in relation to terrestrial ecosystems.

This is one of the most important and controversial areas of production ecology and a great deal of research effort has been devoted to studying this in different ecosystems. To increase food supplies for man we need to pinpoint factors limiting crop production; to protect or conserve the environment we need to know the factors controlling production in 'natural' (or at least unmanaged) ecosystems. Also, pollution of lakes with sewage, industrial effluent and nutrient-rich run-off water from agricultural land can increase algal growth and production leading to unsightly algal 'blooms' and deterioration of water quality for human use. The precise factors causing the increased growth must be determined before large amounts of public money are spent in 'doing something about it'

Factors which may limit primary production can be divided broadly into two groups: (a) those which directly affect the rate of photosynthesis per unit of photosynthetic tissue and (b) those which affect total plant growth and therefore the formation of new photosynthetic tissue. For a field of beans the problem boils down to deciding whether it is the unit leaf rate (of photosynthesis) or the leaf area index (leaf area per unit ground area; Unit 1, Section 1.1.3) which is the more important in determining primary production. Factors in group (a) were discussed in Unit 1.

types of factor affecting primary production

QUESTION   List at least three factors which could limit net photosynthesis per unit leaf area.

ANSWER   Light intensity (whether too high or too low); light duration (day length).
CO_2 supply to the chloroplasts.
Rate of removal of photosynthetic products from the site of production.
Temperature (whether too high or too low).
Inefficient use of the available space causing excessive self-shading.

21

In practice, the distinction between factors of types (a) and (b) is not always clear. Temperature, for example, affects both growth rate and photosynthesis; light may affect the form and direction of growth (shoots grow towards light) and the timing of flowering and senescence. It is difficult to disentangle morphogenetic effects of light from direct effects on photosynthesis, so light will be excluded from group (b) factors in this discussion but will be considered in relation to aquatic ecosystems in Section 2.6.

2.5.1 Factors limiting growth and primary production

Temperature, water and nutrients are the three major factors which may limit primary production and terrestrial plant growth. Each will be considered in this Section, and in Section 2.6 the whole complex of factors limiting primary production in aquatic ecosystems will be discussed.

(a) *Temperature* This affects photosynthesis directly (see Section 2.5) but it also affects all the other metabolic processes in plants; you have already seen how differential effects of temperature on photosynthesis and respiration can affect net production greatly (Section 2.4.2). Extremes of high and low temperature may affect water supply indirectly; in the arctic tundra, for example (see Appendix 1), only for two or three months in the summer does the frozen ground thaw out sufficiently for plants to grow. During this brief growing season, conditions for growth and photosynthesis are often very favourable; annual figures for primary production, however, are very low.

temperature and metabolism

and water supply

(b) *Water* Land plants lose water chiefly through the stomatal pores on the leaf surface.[3] Because these pores are also the path of entry for CO_2 there is perpetual conflict between the need to conserve water and the need to obtain CO_2 for photosynthesis. Where annual rainfall is below about 40 cm year^{-1}, net primary production is linearly related to rainfall (Fig. 9), provided that rainfall is evenly distributed throughout the year. The scatter of points in Figure 9 results partly from uneven rainfall distribution and partly from seasonal extremes of temperature, i.e. very hot summers or very cold winters.

water and stomata

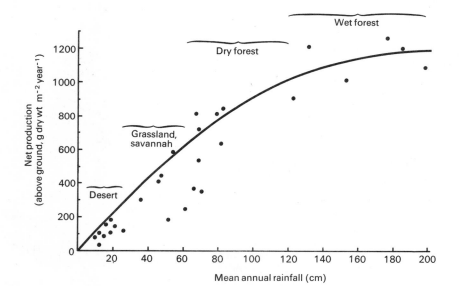

Figure 9 Relation of net annual primary production to rainfall for mature ecosystems.

QUESTION The net production curve in Figure 9 flattens off at high rainfall values; suggest a reason for this.

ANSWER Other factors become limiting for primary production (probably mineral nutrients).

Natural plant communities, as opposed to those planted by man, are highly adapted to make full use of available water. In Block C, the specialized morphology and physiology of desert plants will be described (Unit 10).

22

It should be emphasized that Figure 9 relates only to stable communities (climax). With unstable communities (successional), rates of primary production can be much higher than in the climax state (for further discussion, see Unit 5).

(c) *Nutrients* With the partial exception of mineral nitrogen, the availability of nutrients to primary producers depends mainly on microbial decomposition of organic material (see Unit 4): weathering of rocks and nutrients dissolved in rainwater provide meagre secondary sources.

nutrient availability

QUESTION How is mineral nitrogen replenished?

ANSWER By cycling via the decomposers and by nitrogen fixation (see Unit 1, Section 1.7.3).

In agricultural ecosystems, where most of the plant biomass is harvested and the natural cycling of nutrients is disrupted, fertilizers have been supplied to maintain fertility.

QUESTION Artificial fertilizers usually contain high levels of nitrate and phosphate: does this mean that these nutrients are limiting in unmanaged grasslands?

ANSWER Not necessarily: natural grassland may have adequate supplies of these nutrients through normal decay and decomposition of plant remains plus nitrogen fixation and cycling via animals. As explained in Unit 1, Section 1.7.1, nitrate application tends to suppress nitrogen fixation.

Nevertheless, phosphorus (P), as phosphates, and nitrogen (N), as nitrates or ammonium salts, are the mineral elements most commonly limiting plant growth, followed by potassium (K^+), calcium (Ca^{2+}), sulphur (S) and magnesium (Mg^{2+}), in that order. Which, if any, of these nutrients is in limiting supply depends on the nature of the soil and its 'holding capacity' for nutrients; on the efficiency of decomposition and recycling and on the inputs of nutrients from outside the ecosystem.

essential mineral elements

Levels of phosphorus in soil or water are usually very low, but whether or not P actually limits growth depends on two factors: (a) the rate at which P is released by decomposer organisms—the turnover rate, and (b) the amount of excess P stored in plants. Many plants appear to take up 'luxury' amounts of phosphorus at the start of a growing season and utilize the excess later in the season when soil or water phosphate is in short supply. The only practical way to determine whether or not a particular nutrient is limiting is to supply it to a sample plot and compare net production of fertilized and control plots at the end of the growing season. Table 9 shows the results of such an experiment.

phosphorus

TABLE 9 Response of Corsican pine (a coniferous evergreen) to applications of nitrogenous fertilizer, ammonium sulphate, $(NH_4)SO_4$, in a 35-year old plantation.

Annual application of N kg ha^{-1}	Growth response after two seasons of fertilization	
	Increase in trunk area m^2 ha^{-1}	Relative response (treated/control)
0 (Control)	0·03	1·00
84	0·10	3·33
168	0·11	3·67
336	0.13	4·33
504	0·14	4·67

Additional information for Table 9

Nitrogen content (kg ha^{-1}) of:

Corsican pine	257
Ground vegetation	8
Litter and heterotrophes on the forest floor	322
Soil to 107 cm depth	1365

Figure 10 Corsican pine.

23

QUESTION   Does the supply of nitrogen limit wood production?

ANSWER   *Probably* it does because production is increased by application of nitrogenous fertilizer. However, it is possible, but unlikely, that SO_4^{2-} is the limiting nutrient ion and, to clarify this, additional data are needed about the application of various sulphate and nitrogenous salts to dissociate the effects of S and N.

QUESTION   The soil and the litter layer together contain more than six times as much nitrogen as the living plants. Assuming that nitrogen is the limiting element, how can you explain the nitrogen limitation of growth?

ANSWER   Most of the nitrogen in the litter and in the soil is immobilized in organic material and is not available for uptake by the trees. It is the rate of release of this organic N by decomposer organisms that determines the supply of inorganic N for primary producers.

QUESTION   The growth response of the Corsican pines is not directly proportional to the amount of N supplied. Suggest possible reasons for this.

ANSWER   Perhaps nitrogen is not the limiting factor with applications above 84 kg ha^{-1}. When one nutrient is present in large excess the supply of another nutrient which is growth-limiting may be slightly increased, possibly due to enhanced microbial activity in the soil. So a small response to nutrient addition does not always imply growth limitation by that nutrient. Alternatively, the ability of the soil to retain the applied fertilizer may be involved. Ammonium sulphate is a soluble salt which can be leached from the soil, and possibly most fertilizer in excess of 84 kg ha^{-1} is lost in this way.

A notable feature of forest ecosystems is the high proportion of total nutrients that are permanently 'locked up' in the plant biomass. However, when comparing forests in different parts of the world, the ratio of nutrients in the plant biomass to those in undecomposed litter and micro-organisms and in soluble form in the soil varies considerably. Table 10 shows these ratios for three forest ecosystems. Note the variation between different forests.

nutrients in forests

TABLE 10   Mineral nutrient distribution in three forest ecosystems (total of all major nutrient elements)

Nutrients kg ha^{-1}	Pine forest	Ratio*	Beech forest	Ratio*	Tropical rainforest	Ratio*
in biomass	1112	100	4196	100	11 081	100
in annual litter	40	3·6	352	8·4	1 540	13·9
in soil**	649	58·4	1000	23·8	178	1·6

* Ratio = nutrients present in specified part: nutrients in plant biomass.

** Includes nutrients free in soil and present in partially decomposed litter.

The most striking feature here is the very low proportion of total nutrients present in the soil of tropical forests, despite the enormous litter fall.

rainforest

QUESTION   Suggest an explanation for this.

ANSWER   Decomposition of litter and uptake of nutrients are both extremely rapid.

Because of the high rainfall, often in the form of torrential downpours in tropical forests, soluble nutrients in the soil are rapidly leached away. The tight cycles of rapid decomposition/rapid uptake must be maintained if this loss from the ecosystem is to be avoided (see also Unit 4). Once tropical forest is cleared, nutrients are rapidly leached from the soil and nutrient supply becomes the chief factor limiting primary production.* This is the basis of the 'shifting cultivation' type of agriculture found in tropical regions: small areas of forest are cleared and the felled vegetation is burnt to release nutrients. Crops are grown and harvested but yields decrease progressively as leaching and nutrient

shifting agriculture

* See TV programme, 'Tropical Forest'.

limitation becomes severe, until, finally, the plot is abandoned and left to regenerate forest vegetation and build up nutrient levels again. This regeneration process takes at least 12 years and is successful only if the plot is relatively small so that litter from the surrounding forest becomes available.

The nutrients mentioned so far are all needed in fairly large amounts by growing plants, but there are other elements, the micro-nutrients or trace elements, equally essential but required only in very small quantities. Shortage of micro-nutrients does occasionally limit primary production; Odum (1969) cites an example in Southern Florida where, in an area with adequate rainfall and apparently rich soil, crop production was abnormally low. Here the trace elements copper and cobalt were found to be in limiting supply. Equally, high levels of trace elements can limit primary production through toxic effects. The 'copper soils' of Zambia provide a striking example of this, where large tracts of copper-rich soil have very sparse and poorly productive vegetation. Small-scale examples are to be seen on mineral spoil heaps at mines throughout Britain.

trace elements

Now you can attempt SAQs 5, 6 and 7 (p. 51).

2.6 Primary production in aquatic ecosystems

Study comment Limiting factors and patterns of primary production in a range of marine (Section 2.6.1) and freshwater (Section 2.6.2) ecosystems are considered and eutrophication in nutrient-enriched lakes is discussed briefly (Section 2.6.1). After reading this Section, you should understand better the complex web of factors which may control primary productivity even in apparently 'simple' ecosystems.

Nutrient supply is usually considered to be the major factor limiting primary production in aquatic ecosystems, but you should realize that in all these systems photosynthesis is only possible where light penetrates (the euphotic zone). The depth of this zone varies from less than 1 m to more than 100 m, and within this zone the rate of gross primary production is roughly proportional to depth (but see Unit 1, Section 1.2.1, regarding light inhibition close to the surface). When comparing different aquatic ecosystems there is no simple relationship between primary productivity and depth of the euphotic zone and, except in very murky turbid waters, light in summer is rarely the major factor limiting primary production. In temperate and polar regions, low light and low temperature during the winter months do limit the growth and primary production of phytoplankton (see Section 2.6.1).

euphotic zone

2.6.1 Marine ecosystems

Primary production in the open ocean of three climatic areas will be considered first (in (a) and (b)) with a brief discussion of coastal waters and estuaries in section (c).

(a) Temperate seas

For temperate seas, and indeed for all large bodies of water, three factors are of major importance in determining ecosystem productivity:

1 The primary producers, phytoplankton, necessarily occupy only the surface layers where light penetrates (see above).

2 Bacterial decomposition and release of nutrients occurs mainly in the deeper water which is usually outside the euphotic zone.

3 Large bodies of water are heated by absorbing solar radiation. Water is a poor conductor of heat and warm water is lighter than cold, so you might expect that a temperature gradient decreasing from surface to bottom would develop in summer. But it does not.

QUESTION   What happens?

stratification

ANSWER   The water stratifies and a thermocline forms. An upper layer of water (the epilimnion), which corresponds roughly with the euphotic zone, warms up; then below this there is a region of rapid temperature fall (the thermocline) and under this a body of almost uniformly cold water, the hypolimnion. (If you were unable to answer this question, look at reference [4].)

Once a thermocline is established there is virtually no circulation of water between the cold hypolimnion and warm epilimnion and consequently little circulation of nutrients between the decomposers and the primary producers. As phytoplankton organisms die and sink below the thermocline, nutrients are lost from the euphotic zone; the only nutrient inputs for primary producers come from the slow diffusion of nutrients across the thermocline, from the excretion by zooplankton and other animals feeding in the epilimnion, and from the limited decomposition which occurs in surface waters. In summer, therefore, nutrients in the epilimnion can become limiting for growth and production of phytoplankton in temperate seas and this may be one reason for the decline in phytoplankton numbers (see Fig. 11).

nutrient limitation in summer

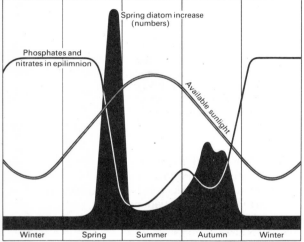

Figure 11   Seasonal changes in nutrients, light and diatoms in temperate seas.

Another factor which may contribute to the decline of phytoplankton in summer is grazing by herbivorous zooplankton. The marine copepod *Calanus* (a small crustacean which feeds on diatoms) increases sharply in numbers following the spring diatom increase (see Fig. 11). But often it is very difficult to determine whether the rise of grazers or the fall of nutrients is the primary cause of phytoplankton decline. Some research workers have concluded that grazing is of major importance in controlling phytoplankton production, but other workers hold that nutrient limitation is of more widespread importance in temperate seas. Part of the problem is selective grazing by zooplankton: usually algae of a certain size are preferred and grazing of one type of alga may permit increased growth of other non-grazed algae. Algae may also be infected by fungal parasites, though very little is known about the effects of this on marine primary production.

grazing in summer

With the onset of autumn, surface waters cool, there are storms and the thermocline breaks down allowing continuous circulation of water between surface and bottom and replenishment of nutrients in the surface waters. Now look again at Figure 11, noting in particular the strong seasonal fluctuations in the numbers and production of phytoplankton which are characteristic of temperate seas.

QUESTION   Using the data in Figure 11, and some common sense, suggest three factors contributing to the spring diatom increase.

ANSWER   1 Nutrient levels (P and N) are high in the surface water.

2   Available light is increasing.

3   Temperature is increasing.

In addition, numbers of grazing herbivores are usually low in spring.

To summarize the situation for primary producers of temperate seas: productivity is limited by low light and low temperature during the winter and by low nutrient levels and/or grazing by herbivores during the summer when the thermocline is established. The secondary peak of phytoplankton in autumn (see Fig. 11) is related to an increase in nutrients (often due to storms disturbing the thermocline), to decreased grazing and to water temperature: temperate seas are warmest during August and September.

(b) Polar and tropical seas

In *polar* seas the surface water never warms up sufficiently to permit thermocline formation.

polar seas

QUESTION   What factors are likely to limit primary production?

ANSWER   Light and temperature: because of free mixing of the water, nutrients are unlikely to be in limiting supply unless growth is extremely rapid.

Primary production is limited to a brief summer season when sufficient light is available and the water is slightly warmer. In the *tropics*, however, light and temperature are favourable the whole year round but there is also a permanent thermocline. This thermocline results in severe nutrient limitation (particularly of phosphorus) in the epilimnion and, in fact, primary production in open tropical seas is very low. The exceptions to this are in upwelling areas and coral reefs.

tropical seas

Upwelling occurs when winds and currents cause cold, nutrient-rich water in the hypolimnion to move up to the surface and this results in a huge increase in primary (and consequently secondary) production: some of the world's most important fisheries occur in these areas (e.g. off the coasts of Southern California and Peru).

upwelling areas

On coral reefs, all the communities of primary producers, decomposers and consumers live within the epilimnion, so dead organisms do not sink below the thermocline and their nutrients are always available for decomposition and recycling. There is very efficient recycling and retention of phosphorus in the reef ecosystem and, in addition, considerable nitrogen fixation occurs, probably by blue-green algae attached to the reef.

coral reefs

(c) Coastal waters and estuaries

So far in this Section only open seas have been considered, but gross primary production may be two to twenty times higher in coastal waters and estuaries.

TABLE 11   Comparison of primary production in marine ecosystems.

Ecosystem	Estimated annual net production	
	g dry wt m^{-2}	10^4 J m^{-2}
Temperate sea	170	320
Tropical sea	40–120	75–226
Tropical sea (upwelling area)	200–750	377–1413
Offshore coastal water	200–600	377–1130
Estuaries	500–4000	942–7500

The most important primary producers of inshore coastal waters and estuaries are attached algae and higher plants (macrophytes), which thrive on mud-banks and salt marsh. Nutrient levels are high because of good mixing of water layers and nutrient input from rivers. But water turbidity is also high because of detritus and silt carried down by rivers, and this restricts light penetration and limits planktonic primary production. There is further discussion of an estuarine salt marsh ecosystem in Unit 5.

macrophytes

Now you could attempt SAQs 8 and 9 (p. 51).

2.6.2   Freshwater ecosystems

(a)   Lakes

See TV programme, 'Esthwaite and the Blelham Tubes'

Lakes of temperate and tropical regions which are sufficiently deep to permit water stratification and establishment of a thermocline show similar patterns of primary production to the corresponding marine ecosystems. Nutrients are important in limiting primary production but there is much more variation as to amounts and pattern of primary production and types of limiting nutrients among lakes than is found in marine situations. Try to think of three reasons why this should be so, and then read on.

variation among lakes

Firstly, lakes are not always sufficiently deep to permit establishment of a thermocline.

Secondly, in clear shallow lakes, especially those with a gently sloping shore, the benthic flora of attached algae and higher plants contribute substantially to primary production. In general the smaller the lake the greater the contribution of benthic plants, unless the shore slopes very steeply.

QUESTION   Which marine ecosystems are similar in this respect?

ANSWER   Shallow coastal waters, estuaries and coral reefs (where there are numerous attached algae).

Thirdly, the chemical composition of lake-water (its pH and nutrient content) varies widely depending on the nature of the surrounding land, the underlying rock and the composition of inflowing water. The composition of sea-water is, by contrast, extremely uniform. Some lakes are more saline than the sea although the salts are different (sulphates and carbonates rather than chlorides); other lakes are almost distilled water.

ITQ 6

(a)   Which nutrient is commonly limiting to phytoplankton production in lakes but not in marine ecosystems? (If you are unable to answer this, look at reference[5].)

(b)   Is this nutrient equally limiting to all species of phytoplankton?

Read the answer to ITQ 6 (p. 53).

Perhaps because of the great variation between lakes, there is less agreement about the impact of herbivore grazing on primary production in these ecosystems than there is for the sea. From research in the Lake District, Lund (1965) concluded that diatom production is regulated largely by light, temperature and nutrients, but he also noted that 'in small bodies of water it is not uncommon to find mass destruction of vast algal populations by grazing'.

grazing by herbivores (in lakes)

Recall from Section 2.1, Table 3, that gross production of algae per unit biomass may decline as biomass increases. Recent experiments using *pure cultures* of small green algae in the *laboratory* have shown that low levels of grazing by herbivores (which, of course, reduce algal biomass) can increase algal production rates (measured in terms of oxygen output), while heavy grazing, as you might expect, reduces the rates (Cooper, 1973). But lakes may contain a wide range of different algal species with different densities: can we assume, therefore, that these results will apply to all algae in 'natural' situations?

The answer seems to be no. Consider the following evidence:

Porter (1973) enclosed samples of *natural* lake water in large polythene bags and suspended these in the lake. There were three kinds of bags: (a) normal, containing the wild population of phytoplankton and herbivorous zooplankton (mainly filter feeding Crustacea); (b) filtered, to remove zooplankton but not algae; (c) enriched with additional zooplankton so that the grazer population was about eight times that in the 'normal' bags (a).

After four days the numbers and kinds of algae in the bags were recorded and it was found that:

(i)   Numbers of some algae, notably certain large unicellular species and filamentous types (> 40 μm), were *unaffected* by filtering or enrichment: gut analyses of the grazers showed that these algal species were not consumed (type 1 algae).

(ii)   Populations of some algae, notably large diatoms, flagellates and small algae (2–30 μm) were strongly *suppressed* by enrichment (c) and *increased* by filtering (b): gut analyses showed that these species were readily consumed by grazers (type 2 algae).

(iii)   Numbers of large green algae which were enclosed in a gelatinous sheath were *higher* after enrichment and lower after filtering: these algae were found in herbivore guts but were not digested: they passed out unharmed in the faeces. In some way this passage through the gut stimulated their subsequent growth (type 3 algae).

The net effect of adding grazers on the total phytoplankton population was suppression.

> **ITQ 7**   What do you conclude is the probable effect of grazing on primary producers and on the pattern of primary production from spring to autumn in lakes similar to that studied by Porter?
>
> *Read the answer to ITQ 7 (p. 53).*

Lakes have been classified on the basis of levels, and rates of recycling, of inorganic nutrients in the water and coincident rates of primary production. Two large and contrasted groups of lakes are the eutrophic type, rich in nutrients, highly productive and deoxygenated in the hypolimnion when stratified, and the oligotrophic type, nutrient poor, with low levels of primary production and always highly oxygenated throughout. (These terms were introduced in an earlier Course.[5])

It is important to appreciate the dynamic nature of lake ecosystems; lakes are rarely static systems, they evolve and change from one type to another as sediments accumulate or as the nutrient levels of inflow water change. These natural changes are usually very slow, but human interference can produce rapid changes, chiefly through the introduction of sewage and other nutrient-rich effluents. In relatively few years an oligotrophic lake may become highly eutrophic. This enrichment or eutrophication of lakes is a growing problem.

Problems of eutrophication

Dense populations (or blooms) of algae in eutrophic lakes may photosynthesize and remove CO_2 at so high a rate that bicarbonate levels rise (Unit 1, Section 1.3) and water pH increases to 9 or more. The high pH of eutrophic lakes is often associated with increased growth of blue-green algae at the expense of other phytoplankton species. These algae not only form particularly dense blooms but are also unacceptable as food to many herbivores and contain gas vacuoles in the cells which increase buoyancy and cause the algae to form surface scums. Recent research on blue-green algae has shown:

(a)   that growth is usually inhibited if the water pH is below 8;

(b)   that CO_2 supply for photosynthesis does not limit growth at high pH (either because the blue-green algae can extract the low levels of free CO_2 present or can take up and use bicarbonate directly), but CO_2 does limit growth of green algae under these conditions.

In addition, some blue-green algae can fix atmospheric nitrogen (see Unit 1, Section 1.6) so that, if excess phosphorus is available and N becomes limiting, they have a strong competitive advantage over green algae.

> **ITQ 8**   Using the information given above, suggest a way, or ways, of reducing growth of blue-green and promoting growth of green algae in eutrophic lakes.
>
> *Read the answer to ITQ 8 (p. 54).*

Type 1 alga

Mallomonas caudata
(a chrysophyte)

Type 2 algae

Cryptomonas anomala
(a flagellate)

Asterionella formosa
(a diatom)

Type 3 alga

Gelatinous sheath — Algal cell

Sphaerocystis
(a gelatinous green alga)

Figure 12   Examples of the three types of algae found in Porter's grazing experiment.

increase in pH

blue-green algae

There has been much public debate about the nutrient factors responsible for algal blooms in eutrophic lakes, i.e. which nutrients limit growth. It is now generally agreed that increased levels of phosphorus, or sometimes nitrogen, are responsible for this. However, many research workers have found that when algae are sampled from eutrophic lakes and supplied with additional nutrients, the only nutrient which stimulates algal production is CO_2: they claim, therefore, that carbon enrichment is the major cause of eutrophication.

limiting nutrients

QUESTION   Is this a valid deduction?

ANSWER   No. CO_2 may indeed limit algal production once a lake has *become* eutrophic and phosphorus and nitrogen levels are high, but this does not mean that increased CO_2 *caused* eutrophication in the first place.

Now you can attempt SAQ 10.

(b)   Rivers and streams

The most striking differences between lakes and streams or rivers is obvious: rate of water flow. This has a profound effect on primary producers and their patterns of primary production.

QUESTION   What kinds of primary producers will be of greatest importance in rivers and streams?

ANSWER   In smaller rivers and streams, chiefly attached macrophytes and attached algae. In larger rivers, phytoplankton (mainly diatoms) are increasingly plentiful especially when water velocity is low as in backwaters.

In Table 12 the primary productivity of the fairly slow-flowing and deep River Thames near Reading is compared with a shallow fast-flowing stream in a chalk area, to illustrate this point.

TABLE 12

| | Annual net primary production 10^4 J m^{-2} | |
	River Thames (near Reading)	Chalk stream
Phytoplankton	1837	not measurable—very low
Benthic algae	29	not measurable
Macrophytes	10–18	2763

Rivers do not develop thermoclines, and nutrient levels depend on stream inflows and on run-off and seepage from the land.

QUESTION   Which factors do you consider most likely to affect primary production in rivers and streams?

ANSWER   Temperature, day length and water clarity (which affects light penetration and which can be very low where much detritus and silt is transported in the water). However, nutrient-rich inflows, such as sewage effluent, may enhance primary production, so that nutrients can be limiting factors.

limiting factors in rivers and streams

A river ecosystem will be considered as a whole in Unit 5, but it is relevant to point out here that for many rivers and streams primary production is of secondary importance as a source of energy for the ecosystem: allochthonous organic matter (originating from the land: from litter and soil, for example) is much more important, and detritus feeders and decomposer organisms are the starting points for many food chains.

2.7   Methods of measuring primary production

Study comment Earlier Sections have considered what must be measured when studying energy flow through primary producers; this Section considers how the measurements are made. The object is to give you a basis for critical appraisal of experimental results and some insight into problems of experimentation. Section 2.7.1 considers sampling problems and should be read in conjunction with relevant sections from *ABE*. Measurements in terrestrial ecosystems are discussed in Section 2.7.2 and you are required also to read the set paper by Woodwell and Botkin (*W & B*). Read this paper carefully together with the questions and comments in the Unit text. In Section 2.7.3 the methods used for aquatic ecosystems are outlined; the details are given in Appendix 2, which you may read now or later. Omit Section 2.7.3 and Appendix 2 if short of time.

The experimental study of primary production requires a great deal of laborious measurement, and the validity of the results is absolutely dependent upon reliable and accurate methods of doing this. Production ecologists have become increasingly aware of the inaccuracies in much of the earlier work and results should always be assessed in the light of the methods used and the assumptions made in obtaining them.

2.7.1   Sampling

This Section should be read in conjunction with Sections on sampling in *ABE* (Part 2, Section 2.0, and Part 4).

Suppose that a study of primary productivity is planned for an area of grassland. It is impossible to carry out detailed measurements of the whole area so a number of representative sample areas must be selected. (Refer to *ABE* and read up how to decide upon a suitable number of sample areas, a suitable sample size and whether to adopt a random or systematic sample design.) A knowledge of statistics would be useful at this stage but the final decisions must depend to a large extent on subjective estimates of the general nature and uniformity of the total area under study.

sampling design

Few sample areas may be required in a flat area of managed grassland containing few species, but in a hilly area, with patches of bog and rocky outcrops and a wide variety of plant species, there may be great problems in finding 'representative' sample areas, and many samples may be required.

It is clearly necessary to have some knowledge of the species composition and structure of the ecosystem under study. Probably the most difficult ecosystem of all from a sampling point of view is the tropical rainforest.

QUESTION   Why should this be so?

___

ANSWER   There is high species diversity and a complex structure* so 'representative' samples of a reasonable size are very hard to find.

Having selected sample areas there is a further problem concerning the timing and frequency at which observations should be made. Rates of primary production vary greatly at different times of the year and some knowledge of the phenology of the component species is essential before deciding upon sampling frequency (see Section 2.3.1).

times of sampling

2.7.2   Methods of measurement in terrestrial ecosystems

The techniques adopted depend very much on which components of the equation:

Gross production = Net production + Respiration

$$(A = P + R)$$

are to be measured. Some techniques measure only net production, while others allow measurement of respiration also so that the equation can be completely solved.

---

* Details of tropical forests can be seen in the TV programme 'Tropical forest'.

There are basically two kinds of techniques used in the measurement of primary production: (a) harvest methods, which measure only net production, and (b) gas exchange methods, which can be used to measure both net production and respiration.

(a) Harvest methods

In principle, these methods are extremely simple. The biomass of a sample is measured at some suitable time, t_0, which is usually at the beginning of a growth season. This is done by removing all plant material, drying and weighing it and, if desired, combusting the dried material in a bomb calorimeter to determine the energy content. When a suitable time has elapsed (ideally when the biomass of primary producers is maximal) at time t_1, the whole process is repeated on a second sample area which is strictly comparable with the first. Then the increase in biomass (T) during this time t_0–t_1, represents the net primary production.

In practice, there are many problems and sources of error associated with this method. Below is a list of four 'problem areas':

1 Herbivore consumption.
2 Death and shedding of plant organs.
3 Measurement of root biomass.
4 Wood production in perennials.

You should recall from Section 2.0 that $P = T + C + D$.

1 If there is consumption by herbivores (C) during the experimental period, then obviously the harvest method will give too low an estimate of net production. For grassland ecosystems a possible way round this is enclosure of sample plots in grazer-proof netting, but further problems can arise through changes in species composition since some species normally suppressed by grazing may become dominant (there is further discussion of this in Block C). Note that small herbivores may not be excluded by netting. Another solution, and usually the only one possible in forests and aquatic ecosystems, is a separate study of consumption by herbivores (see Unit 3).

problems of harvest methods

2 As plants grow there may be continuous death and/or shedding of organs (D) and this can lead to serious underestimation of P by the harvest method. Measuring the amount of litter shed by aerial parts helps to reduce the error, but there is no such easy solution to measuring death of underground parts, as dead and living roots are usually inextricably mixed. The dry weight of dead organs, whether roots or shoots, may decrease rapidly because of leaching and decomposition by microbial organisms.

3 Measurement of root biomass is extremely difficult, firstly because it is almost impossible to separate roots completely from soil and, secondly, because for large plants it is impossible to remove entire root systems. In tropical rainforests, up to 90 per cent of the roots are in the top 5–20 cm of the soil, so it is possible, but laborious, to dig up a whole sample area and remove most of the roots. Some research workers take cores of soil of known volume, separate roots and soil as gently and thoroughly as possible by washing, and calculate the root biomass for the whole sample area from this. Others use transparent chambers and actually measure the amount of root growth close to the chamber wall, estimating total growth from this.

4 It is usually neither practical nor economically advisable to chop down whole areas of forest to measure the production of woody tissues. One way round this has been to estimate the increase from simple measurements of changes in girth and length of branches and trunks, a technique referred to as *dimensional analysis*. Usually, selected branches are measured and estimates made of the total number of branches with particular growth rates; however, because of the inherent variability both within and between trees, the results require rigorous statistical analysis to assess their reliability. Figure 13 shows how measurement of tree girths at 1.3 m above ground provides a fairly reliable indicator of the total weight of woody tissue in the tree. This kind of 'short cut', using only one or two measurements to estimate total biomass, is widely used, sometimes without sufficient regard for the variations between different species and between different soil types: if used indiscriminately it can be very inaccurate. You will find further references to dimensional analysis in *W & B*.

dimensional analysis

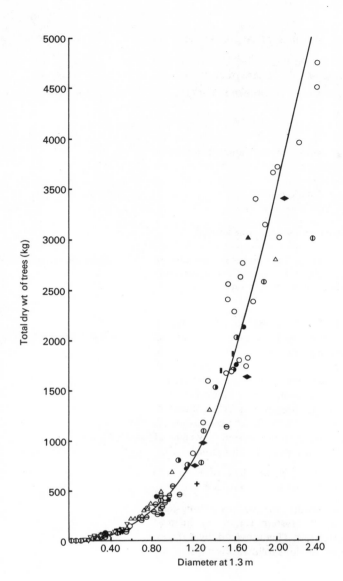

Figure 13 The relationship between above-ground woody biomass and trunk diameter at 1·3 m. Results are for seven species of deciduous trees in six forest ecosystems.

Species	Forest ecosystem
	1 2 3 4 5 6
Quercus robur (Oak)	⊖ ○ ◑ ⏀ ●
Fagus sylvatica (Beech)	△ ▲
Carpinus betulus (Hornbeam)	▽
Tilia platyphyllos (Lime)	✕
Betula pendula (Birch)	+
Fraxinus excelsior (Ash)	▮
Prunus avium (Bird cherry)	◆ ◆
Acer campestre (Field maple)	◣

(b) *Gas exchange methods*

Respiration (R) can be regarded in simple terms as the reverse of photosynthesis (PS):

$$6CO_2 + 6H_2O \underset{R}{\overset{PS}{\rightleftharpoons}} C_6H_{12}O_6 + 6O_2$$

and, in the light, the rate of PS usually exceeds the rate of R. Gas exchange techniques depend upon measurements of net CO_2 uptake (or O_2 release) in the light, and CO_2 release (or O_2 uptake) in the dark.

QUESTION Does the rate of CO_2 uptake in the light measure net production or gross production?

ANSWER Net production (P): in the light CO_2 is being released due to respiration and it is the difference between total uptake and total release that is measured.

QUESTION Does the rate of $^{14}CO_2$ uptake and incorporation in the light provide a measure of A or P?

use of $^{14}CO_2$

ANSWER It depends on the length of the experiment. In a short-term experiment (minutes rather than hours) A would be measured because total in-going CO_2 can be distinguished by means of the radioactive label. In long-term experiments, however, some of the assimilated $^{14}CO_2$ would be released due to respiration, so a value closer to P would be obtained. This introduces a basic uncertainty into the method and frequently the parameter measured is intermediate between gross and net production.

33

When ^{14}C-labelled carbon is not used then measures of A are obtained by summing

rate of CO_2 uptake in light + rate of CO_2 release in dark

(or rate of O_2 release in light) (or rate of O_2 uptake in dark)

P + R

QUESTION   What assumption is made regarding the rate of respiration in the above method?

_____

ANSWER   That the rate is constant during light and darkness.

QUESTION   Is this always a valid assumption? Give reasons for your answer.

_____

ANSWER   No. If, for example, photorespiration is occurring then respiration rates in the light may be much higher than in darkness (see Unit 1, Section 1.4.2b); temperature may be much lower in the dark and this will decrease respiration rates.

respiration in light and dark

For terrestrial ecosystems the measurement of CO_2 rather than O_2 is nearly always preferred, one reason being that a convenient instrument, the infrared gas analyser (or IRGA) can be used to measure CO_2 levels either in the field (with a portable generator) or in the laboratory. For this, air of known and, as far as possible, constant CO_2 level is pumped over plant organs enclosed in a transparent chamber and the CO_2 level of the outgoing air is monitored with the IRGA. Knowing the rate of air flow and the difference in CO_2 content of the ingoing and outgoing air, the rate of photosynthesis (or if the chamber is kept dark, the rate of respiration) can be calculated and expressed as weight of CO_2 per unit area or unit dry weight of enclosed tissue per unit time.

infrared gas analyser

TURN TO Woodwell, G. M., and Botkin, D. B. (1972) Metabolism of terrestrial ecosystems by gas exchange techniques: the Brookhaven approach.

The paper discusses methods used and some results obtained in a long-term study of primary production in a temperate forest ecosystem. It is one of the most detailed studies of forest production ever carried out. This is essentially a review paper of the authors' own work with descriptive sections followed by a discussion section.

Before starting to read the paper note:

1   The authors use different symbols from those used in this Unit.

	Symbol in Unit	*Symbol in W & B*
Gross primary production	A	GP
Net primary production	P	NPP
Respiration	R	Rs (with Rs_A referring to autotrophe respiration, Rs_H to heterotrophe respiration and Rs_E to total ecosystem respiration).

2   Before reading a section in *W & B* read the comments on it in this Unit; after reading a section try to answer the numbered questions with the prefix *W & B*. These will test your understanding of the paper and indicate how to read a paper critically and extract information from it.

THE INTRODUCTORY PARAGRAPHS (p. 73 in *W & B*). Read this rapidly to 'set the scene'.

THE PRODUCTION EQUATIONS (p. 73). Read this, noting that much is revision but also that Woodwell and Botkin introduce a modified equation which takes into account the consumption by heterotrophes (animals and microbes). The authors measure the respiration of heterotrophes and assume that this can be equated with 'consumption' in the ecosystem and subtracted from net primary production to give net *ecosystem* production for a temperate forest.

net ecosystem production

After reading, answer W & B 1 and 2.

W & B 1 Since the authors equate Rs_H with consumption, what do they assume about the productivity of consumers and decomposers?

A 1 That the populations are static and that there is no net heterotrophe production; thus $A_{heterotrophes} = Rs_H$. Some would argue that this is a necessary simplification but remember that it *is* a major assumption for which no supporting evidence is given.

W & B 2 Write an equation to show the relationship between NPP and NEP as the terms are used in the paper.

A 2 $NEP = NPP - Rs_H$.

METHODS FOR MEASUREMENT OF THE METABOLISM OF ECOSYSTEMS (p. 74). This summarizes much of the material discussed in Section 2.7.2 of the Unit. *Note* (a) In the list of techniques, Item 2b (flux and aerodynamic techniques) is new to you: there are comments on this before *W & B 6*, which is related to the next section of the paper. (b) The heat load mentioned at the foot of p. 76 refers to the problem of overheating of plants enclosed in chambers when the rate of air flow is low.

summary of methods

Now answer W & B 3, 4 and 5.

W & B 3 Why do fluctuations in the CO_2 levels in the air cause problems when using an infrared gas analyser to measure CO_2 output by plants?

A 3 CO_2 changes due to plant metabolism are small (p. 76, end of first paragraph) and very difficult to detect if there are large erratic background fluctuations: it is a problem of background 'noise'.

W & B 4 Why are leaf and air temperatures measured so carefully (p. 78, first paragraph) in the small chambers?

A 4 Because rates of respiration and photosynthesis vary with temperature (see Section 2.2.2); if enclosed leaves heated up too much this could be a serious source of error. The opaque reflecting paint used on stem chambers (where there is respiration but no photosynthesis) reflects light and helps to prevent undue temperature rise in the chambers.

W & B 5 In the enclosures of forest floor, $0.25 \times 0.25 \times 1$ m^3, described in paragraph 3, p. 78, which organisms will contribute to (a) CO_2 uptake, (b) CO_2 output?

A 5 (a) Small shrubs and herbs less than 1 m tall in the ground vegetation.
(b) As for (a), plus microbial decomposers, soil animals and plant roots.

TOTAL RESPIRATION OF THE BROOKHAVEN FOREST: TEMPERATURE INVERSIONS— A SIMPLIFIED FLUX TECHNIQUE (p. 78). Read the following comment before reading *W & B*.

Comment The temperature inversion method (a flux technique) depends on the fact that, on some nights, air temperature is lowest near the ground (unlike the usual daytime situation). Since the cooler air is denser, the air column remains vertically stable for several hours: CO_2 released by respiration accumulates, accumulation at any height being approximately proportional to respiration rate at that height. The 'fetch' referred to in the first paragraph means the area over which the stable air column is maintained and 'cold air drainage' occurs when cold air at ground level flows into valleys. The technique is not very accurate and can be used only under certain climatic conditions and in flat areas, but it is one of the few methods which gives information about total respiration of the ecosystem.

temperature inversion method

Now answer W & B 6 and 7.

W & B 6 From Figure 3, p. 79, which part of the forest ecosystem has the highest rate of respiration?

A 6 The soil and ground layer (lowest of the four curves): this is almost certainly due to a large CO_2 output from soil heterotrophes, a point which the authors do not make clear.

W & B 7 At the foot of p. 78, Woodwell and Botkin suggest that the Brookhaven forest respires a total of 2104 g of dry matter per year (estimated by the CO_2 inversion method). List the steps by which the authors reached this figure and state the assumptions made and the possible sources of error at each stage. (If short of time, look at the steps in *A 7* and work out the assumptions for yourself.)

A 7 Steps	*Assumptions and sources of error*
1 Measure CO_2 accumulation at different heights: use the slope of the rate curve (Fig. 3) as an index of rate of Rs.	1(a) That Rs at night = Rs during the day. (b) That no CO_2 is absorbed at night (dark fixation)
2 Knowing Rs at different heights calculate Rs_E for the whole forest as $g \, CO_2 \, m^{-2} \, day^{-1}$.	2 That Rs is uniform over the whole forest.
3 Plot Rs_E against mean temperature (Fig. 4) and draw lines of best fit (linear regression curves).	3 Temperature (T) is measured during the night-time inversion: in the day T will be higher and fluctuate more—no allowance is made for this.
4 From Figure 4 obtain an expression relating Rs_E to temperature during winter and summer (°K = °Kelvin, = °C + 273).	4 The regression line (especially for summer) is not a very good fit: considerable error here.
5 Knowing the average monthly temperature, calculate average Rs_E for each month and plot these values against time (months). Measuring the area under this curve (integrating) gives the total amount of CO_2 respired over one year.	5(a) The authors do not say if average temperature is for night, day or the whole 24 hours. (b) This step involves a lot of averaging—each contributes to the final error.
6 Convert CO_2 released into dry weight respired.	6 It is assumed that 1 g of CO_2 is released when 0·614 g of carbohydrate is respired: if other types of material are respired (quite possible) this will not be true.

RESPIRATION BY SMALL CHAMBER TECHNIQUE (p. 80). Read this and answer *W & B 8*.

W & B 8 In order to extrapolate data on tree respiration obtained with the small chamber technique to the whole forest, what additional information is required and how did the authors obtain this?

A 8 The information needed is the area of leaves and twigs in the small chambers and the total areas of these organs for different species in the forest. These areas were estimated by dimensional analysis (see Section 2.7.2a).

RESPIRATION OF STEMS: ANNUAL CURVE (p. 80) and RESPIRATION OF STEMS: RESPIRATION/TEMPERATURE METHOD (p. 81). Read these sections and note:

(a)   'Integrating under a curve' means measuring the total area under the curve.

(b)   Absolute temperature is the same as degrees Kelvin (see *A 7*, step 4).

(c)   In Figure 6, numbers on the graph are month/date and different symbols indicate sets of observations at the dates shown.

Now answer W & B 9.

W & B 9 When estimating the average respiration of stems by the respiration/temperature method, what is the one important assumption on which the validity of the method depends?

A 9 That the relationship between respiration rate and temperature is constant irrespective of variations in other climatic conditions, e.g. water supply, humidity or light intensity.

RESPIRATION OF SOIL, SHRUBS AND GROUND COVER (p. 82) and TOTAL RESPIRATION OF THE ECOSYSTEM BY SMALL CHAMBER TECHNIQUES (p. 82). Read these sections and then answer *W & B 10*.

W & B 10 The authors make no attempt to estimate respiration of green leaves and twigs and say that there 'is no practical way of monitoring respiration during photosynthesis': explain why.

A 10 Respiration of photosynthetic organs can be monitored only in the dark. The authors must regard respiration rates in the dark as non-equivalent to rates in the light and, as you know from reading about photorespiration (Unit 1, Section 1.4.2b), this is probably so.

You have now read about all the methods used by Woodwell and Botkin to measure respiration in the forest. Note that no attempt has been made to measure separately the respiration of animals and microbes above ground: like many botanists the authors regard this as negligible, but many zoologists would disagree!

NET PHOTOSYNTHESIS (p. 82). Read this section and note that, having measured respiration, the next step is to measure net primary production so that the production equation can be completely solved.

Now answer W & B 11 and 12.

W & B 11 In Figure 7, why are the CO_2 values for net photosynthesis negative?

A 11 CO_2 is being taken up, not released as in respiration, so $C_2 - C_1$ is negative.

W & B 12 How accurate is the figure of 3453 g dry wt m^{-2} $year^{-1}$ as a measure of NPP? Specify sources of error.

A 12 Not very accurate: maximum rates of photosynthesis are assumed for the three tree species and, as is shown in Figure 7 and as you know already from Section 2.2.2, there is great variation between maximum and minimum rates, depending upon light intensity, temperature and leaf position. The authors conclude that gas exchange techniques using small chambers are not very satisfactory for measuring net primary production and estimates from dimensional analysis are to be preferred.

DISCUSSION (p. 83). Read the following comments first.

Comments (a) The radiation method for measuring Rs_H (mentioned in the first paragraph) depends on the differential sensitivity of plant roots and decomposer organisms to radiation damage from a radioactive source. The plant roots are more sensitive than the decomposer organisms, so by measuring Rs after different amounts of irradiation a point is reached at which most roots are dead and most decomposer organisms still alive; then $Rs = Rs_H$ (more or less). It is an indirect, and not very accurate, way of measuring heterotrophe respiration in the soil.
(b) In paragraph 2 there is an error in the calculation of NEP from $GP - (Rs_A + Rs_H)$: in fact $(Rs_A + Rs_H) = (1520 + 621) = 2141$ (and not 2127 as stated). Thus NEP becomes $2715 - 2141 = 574$.

Now answer W & B 13 and 14.

radiation method for Rs_H

37

W & B 13 In the authors' opinion, what is the most important use of gas exchange techniques in the study of forest productivity?

A 13 As a tool for measuring respiration of both autotrophes and ground living heterotrophes. The flux technique appears to be a simpler way of measuring Rs_E but is less accurate, and the authors use the estimates from gas exchange methods in their calculations (paragraphs 1 and 2): note that for respiration of bark and branches the average of values obtained by the annual curve (950) and the respiration/temperature methods (1242) is taken (=1096).

W & B 14 From data in the paper fill in the values in the Table below for the oak-pine forest at Long Island.

	g dry wt m^{-2} *or* g dry wt m^{-2} year^{-1}
Total biomass of primary producers (B)	
Gross primary production (GP)	
Net primary production (NPP) (by dimensional analysis)	
Autotrophe respiration (Rs$_A$)	
Heterotrophe respiration (Rs$_H$) (in soil and litter)	
Net ecosystem production (NEP)	

A 14 B, 10 192 g dry wt m^{-2}. All other values are in g dry wt m^{-2} year^{-1}: GP, 2715: NPP, 1195: Rs$_A$, 1520: Rs$_H$, in soil and litter only, 621: NEP, 574 (note earlier comment about calculating this).

Having read the paper you will probably appreciate how difficult it is to measure primary or 'ecosystem' production. Every method involves assumptions, estimates and errors, and there are no easy solutions to the problems: in large-scale studies of complex ecosystems this is inevitable. The simple conclusions about energy flow in an immature deciduous forest are that:

Of gross primary production, 56 per cent is used in plant respiration; 46 per cent is left as net primary production; of NPP, approximately (very much so) 52 per cent passes to the soil heterotrophes and is respired away; the remaining 48 per cent is the net accumulation of energy (in woody biomass and organic material in the soil) for the whole ecosystem.

summary of findings

The really dubious part of these conclusions (obtained only after many years' work) is the amount of energy passing to heterotrophes in the soil and above ground. Probably this is best approached through direct studies of the consumers and decomposers and such studies are described in Units 3 and 4.

Now you can attempt SAQs 11 and 12 (pp. 51–2).

2.7.3 Measurement of primary production in aquatic ecosystems

See TV programme, 'Esthwaite and the Blelham Tubes'

QUESTION From your reading of earlier Sections in this Unit, state what are the three main types of primary producers found in aquatic ecosystems.

ANSWER Phytoplankton, attached higher plants (macrophytes) and attached algae (described as benthic if they are on the bottom or epiphytic if attached to other larger plants). Floating higher plants are occasionally found in freshwater—duckweeds, *Lemna*, or the water fern, *Azolla*, for example.

types of aquatic producers

For aquatic ecosystems as a whole, phytoplankton is the most important group of primary producers and only the methods of measuring primary production which relate to this group will be discussed here.

(a) *Harvest methods*

When using harvest techniques for the measurement of net primary production in phytoplankton three complicating factors must be considered:

(i)   The life span of phytoplankton is short (a few days to a few weeks).

problems when harvesting phytoplankton

(ii) Depending on the amount of turbulence, variable numbers of living and dead phytoplankton sediment out of the euphotic zone and organisms may also be carried horizontally by water currents.

(iii) A variable amount of phytoplankton may be grazed by zooplankton or attacked by parasites.

QUESTION   Taking these factors into consideration, under what conditions could measurements of biomass increase for phytoplankton be reasonably attempted?

ANSWER   When horizontal movement of water was negligible and when losses due to sedimentation and grazing were negligible (or known).

QUESTION   How frequently should phytoplankton be sampled in such a study?

sampling frequency

ANSWER   At very short intervals, certainly not exceeding one week. (Large fluctuations in phytoplankton numbers can occur within the space of a day.)

If determinations of biomass increase are feasible for measuring net primary production, then the next problems are to decide on ways of sampling the population and actually measuring its biomass. Methods are listed below and details are given in Appendix 2 (White).

Sampling   (i) plankton net samples (net dragged through water); (ii) enclosure (fill a water bottle at a known depth).

Biomass estimation   (i) measure the chlorophyll a concentration; (ii) measure the dry weight of samples; (iii) count the cells of each species and, knowing average cell volumes, calculate total algal cell volume.

(b) *Gas exchange methods*

These provide an alternative to harvest techniques but, if results are to be expressed in terms of gas evolved or taken up per unit of tissue, then biomass estimations are still necessary. The principles of these methods are as described for terrestrial ecosystems (see Section 2.7.2b and *W & B*) but the practice is very different. Two sample bottles are used for each measurement, one transparent (so that photosynthesis can occur) and one blackened (so that only respiration occurs). Oxygen release and uptake in the bottles can be used to estimate P and R. The IRGA, however, cannot be used to measure CO_2 uptake and release in aqueous media, and incorporation of $^{14}CO_2$ (introduced as radioactive bicarbonate) is always used instead. This last method was pioneered by a Danish ecologist, Professor E. Steemann Nielsen, and has been of great value in aquatic production studies. A more detailed account of these methods is given in Appendix 2, which you should read now.

use of 'light' and 'dark' bottles

use of $^{14}CO_2$

Now you could attempt SAQs 13 and 14 (p. 53).

2.8   Primary production studies in forest ecosystems

Study comment   Section 2.7 described a wide range of methods used in the study of primary production. In this Section, some results obtained in studies of forest ecosystems are examined, together with methods used, so that results can be assessed and general conclusions drawn where possible.

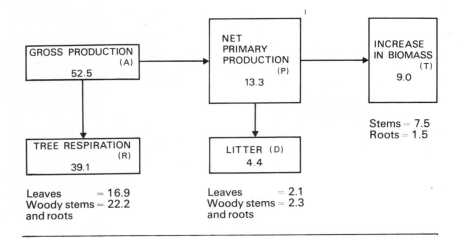

Figure 14 Primary production in a mature tropical rainforest. (Values as t ha^{-1} year^{-1}.)

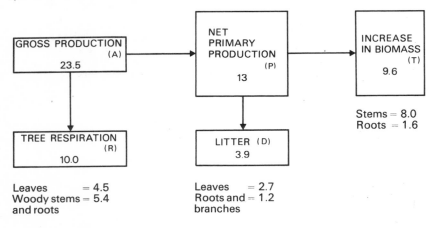

Figure 15 Primary production in an immature beech forest. (Values as t ha^{-1} year^{-1}.)

The first study relates to a mature tropical forest in the Ivory Coast: it was done by two Danish ecologists, Müller and Nielsen in the early 1960s (Fig. 14). For the second study, an immature beech forest in Denmark was studied (Fig. 15). Similar methods were used for both studies, and a description of these given below. A detailed assessment of the Ivory Coast study together with much other relevant information is given in Evans (1972) *The Quantitative Analysis of Plant Growth* (see recommended reading, p. 45).

Ivory Coast study of rainforest

Danish study of beechwoods

For the tropical forest study:

(a)   Two sample plots 30 m^2 and 40 m^2 were used and observations were made over five years.

sampling

(b)   Respiration rates were measured by gas-exchange techniques (CO_2 output) after removing pieces of trunk, branches, and leaves from the top and lower branches; measurements were made on the three commonest tree species.

respiration

(c)   Litter production was not measured directly: the authors estimated the life spans of various plant organs and calculated the annual rate of loss. Litter collection in other tropical forests gives annual values of 10–11 t ha^{-1}, so the litter estimate by Müller and Nielsen is probably considerably too low.

litter

(d)   The net increase in biomass, T, was measured by a combination of harvest techniques and dimensional analysis. All above-ground parts of trees were measured (average numbers and sizes of leaves and branches and trunk size) and comparable trees outside the sample plots were felled and their parts measured and weighed. This allowed the weight of measured trees in the sample area to be calculated. Trees were measured again two and five years later and the increase in biomass calculated. Roots were assumed to be one-sixth of the total tree biomass.

annual increment

Using this information about the tropical forest study, answer the following questions:

QUESTION   How were P and A estimated?

ANSWER P by adding T and estimated litter fall; A by adding P and tree respiration.

QUESTION   Suggest two things which were not measured in this study but which could affect the value of P and A?

ANSWER   (i)   Neither P nor R for the ground flora, which is probably sparse, or for the climbers and epiphytes (plants growing on the trees—orchids, for example), which could have been very numerous, were measured.

(ii)   No measurement of herbivore consumption in the tree layer was made, but this is likely to be a very small proportion of P (see values for temperate forests in Section 2.4).

QUESTION   Do you think that the estimates of P and A are likely to be underestimates or overestimates?

ANSWER   Given that litter fall was probably underestimated and that there were two unmeasured quantities (R and P for ground flora and climbers, see above), they are likely to be underestimates.

QUESTION   Mature tropical forests do not show marked increases in overall size (biomass). How do you explain the finding that T in the Ivory Coast forest, which is classed as mature, was 9 t ha^{-1} year^{-1}?

ANSWER   This could be described as a sampling problem. The forest *as a whole* may not increase in biomass but there will be a constant flux with large trees dying and other trees growing up to replace them. For the forest as a whole, tree death and litter production plus herbivore consumption probably equal P. In the sample areas studied here, either no large trees died and/or trees were growing to replace trees that had died earlier.

Use the information about both the tropical forest and the beech forest to answer the following questions.

QUESTION   The percentage ratio of R to A is 74·5 for the tropical forest and 42·1 for the beech forest. Suggest possible reasons for this difference.

ANSWER   The beech forest is described as 'immature' and, from your earlier reading of the Unit (Section 2.2.1), you know that because of their lower biomass immature forest ecosystems have a lower ratio of R to A than mature ones. Probably the main reason is that tropical forest is continually leafy with high average temperatures throughout the year and, consequently, high rates of respiration (Section 2.2.2). The beech forest is leafy for only half the year and average temperatures are considerebly lower: during the non-productive winter period the low temperatures ensure low respiration costs for woody stems and roots.

The following data were obtained for a nearly mature European beech forest using harvest methods (values are expressed as t ha^{-1} year^{-1}):

study of a mature beech forest

$P = 13$, litter $= 9$ (leaves $= 4·9$, roots and stems $= 4·1$), annual increment $T = 4$.

QUESTION   From the data given here and earlier for the immature beech forest (Fig. 15). briefly describe the changes in pattern of primary production as the beech forest matures.

ANSWER   The proportion of P retained annually as plant biomass (T) decreases and the proportion lost as litter (to the decomposer cycle) increases. Roots and stems contribute proportionately more to litter in the mature beech forest than in the immature forest, where leaf litter is more important.

An excellent review of primary production in forests is given by Ovington (1962).

Now you can attempt SAQ 15 (p. 53).

2.9 Comparisons of primary productivity in different ecosystems

Study comment In this Section, the aim is to look at the overall pattern of world primary production and to make comparisons between ecosystems. Note particularly the status of agricultural ecosystems in the general scheme.

It should be clear by now that measurements of primary production are subject to numerous errors and are best regarded as 'informed estimates' rather than absolute values. Accepting these limitations, it is still useful to compare levels of primary production in different ecosystems, in order to gain some insight into the overall pattern of world productivity: how natural and man-managed ecosystems compare; which are the most productive ecosystems; which contribute most to world production (this depends on both area and rates of production per unit area).

reasons for comparisons

The problem arises, however, of how best to express rates of primary production so as to make meaningful comparisons between ecosystems. The ratio of gross to net production ($A:P$) varies widely, depending not only on the kind of ecosystem (low in aquatic ecosystems but high in forest ecosystems) but also on the age and relative maturity of the ecosystems. Comparisons of both A and P are made but, because man has interests in agriculture and forestry and is more concerned to pick out and study the rapidly growing ecosystems, where P is highest, comparisons of net primary production are more common. In comparisons between forests, the annual increment is likely to be preferred because this provides a measure of the rate of increase in woody biomass. Clearly, there is no single figure or rate which will give all the necessary information. Table 13 shows net primary production, average biomass and the $P:B$ ratio for various ecosystems, with the contribution each makes to world net primary production.

Note that values for net primary production and biomass in Table 13 are *average* values: the maximum and minimum values may differ by several hundred per cent. In open oceans for example, P ranges from 3·8–756 and B from 0–0·005.

ITQ 9 Of all the ecosystems listed in Table 13 which is the most 'productive'?

ITQ 10 Ecosystems fall roughly into four natural groups on the basis of their $P:B$ ratio. Given that agricultural ecosystems are one group, work out from Table 13 what the other three groups are and comment briefly on their significance (i.e. what the $P:B$ ratio indicates about the producers in these ecosystems).

Now read the answers to ITQs 9 and 10 (p. 54).

Two other points emerge from Table 13 regarding the pattern of primary production. Firstly, the marine ecosystems, although occupying two-thirds of the Earth's surface, contribute only one-third to world net primary production; this can be related chiefly to the low production rates of open oceans, where nutrient limitation is severe. Secondly, the forest ecosystems contribute a high proportion (44 per cent) of world production and have very high rates of production per unit area. It follows that widespread deforestation will reduce the energy trapped in the biosphere and the numbers of heterotrophes which can be supported. As human requirements for living space and agricultural land expand, global considerations of this kind may become increasingly important.

relative contributions of marine and forest ecosystems

Odum (1969) has stressed that there are really two distinct kinds of agricultural ecosystem: the subsistence agriculture practised in 'underdeveloped' regions and the fuel-subsidized agriculture practised in 'developed' regions. Net primary production of the former is approximately one-quarter that of the latter. This disparity is partly because better higher-yielding crop varieties are used in developed countries but, far more than this, it relates to the level of energy subsidy by man. To increase crop production in fuel-subsidized agriculture, herbicides and pesticides are used in large quantities to suppress weeds and pests; there is heavy application of artificial fertilizer to remove nutrient limitations to plant growth; there may be elaborate drainage or irrigation systems, or other soil treatments designed to provide the best environment for crop roots. All these procedures require an expenditure of energy—in manufacturing processes, tractor fuel, etc., and high crop production is achieved chiefly because energy is used to create the best conditions for plant growth.

subsistence agriculture

fuel-subsidized agriculture

energy subsidy

Now you could attempt SAQ 16 (p. 53).

TABLE 13   (Modified from Whittaker and Woodwell, 1971)

Ecosystem	Area 10⁶ km²	Average net primary production 10 J m⁻² yr⁻¹	World net primary production 10¹⁹ J yr⁻¹	Average biomass kg dry wt m⁻²	Ratio P : B
Land and freshwater					
Extreme desert, rock and ice	24	6	0·14	0·02	300
Desert scrub	18	132	2·4	0·7	189
Tundra and alpine	8	265	2·1	0·6	442
Lake and stream	2	945	1·9	0·02	47 250
Temperate grassland	9	945	8·5	1·5	630
Woods and shrub	7	1134	7·9	6·0	189
Agricultural land	14	1229	17·2	1·0	1 229
Tropical savannah	15	1323	19·8	4·0	331
Northern conifer forest	12	1512	18·1	20·0	76
Temperate deciduous forest	18	2475	44·6	30·0	92
Tropical forest	20	3780	75·6	45·0	84
Swamp and marsh	2	3780	7·6	12·0	315
Total or average (land and freshwater)	149	1380	205·6	12·5	110
Marine					
Open ocean	332	242	80·3	0·003	80 667
Continental shelf	27	662	17·9	0·01	6 620
Attached algae and estuaries	2	3780	7·6	1·00	3 780
Total or average (marine)	361	293	105·8	0.009	32 556
Total for Earth	510	605	311	3·6	168

2.10   Summary of Unit

Of the total light energy trapped by primary producers (gross production) a certain proportion is utilized for routine maintenance (in respiration) and the surplus (net production) is available for the formation of new tissues (Section 2.0). If living plant material (biomass) is sampled at two times between which there are no losses except by respiration then, from the simple equation

$$A = P + R$$

P by definition must equal the change in biomass, T, of the two samples. Usually, however, there are additional losses due to consumption by herbivores (C) and death of plant tissues (D) so that

$$P = T + C + D$$

Standing biomass of primary producers and net or gross productivity are not necessarily directly related and, in ecosystems such as forests where over a period of years there is a large accumulation of biomass, annual net production is greatest in the immature or successional stages, declining when the stable climax with maximum biomass is reached (Section 2.1). This decline is related partly to the increased proportion of A used up in respiration (Section 2.2.1). For aquatic ecosystems where there is no long-term accumulation of phytoplankton biomass, there may be a fall in gross production per unit biomass with increasing population density (Section 2.1) and, in both aquatic and terrestrial ecosystems where decomposition is slower than litter production, partly decomposed organic matter may accumulate.

Respiration, as a percentage of gross production, varies widely between ecosystems and between different organs on individual plants (Section 2.2). There are several reasons: differences in the ratio of photosynthetic to non-photosynthetic tissues, degree of self-shading within the community and within individuals and, in particular, temperature, since the optimum temperature for respiration is higher than that for photosynthesis (Section 2.2.2).

Ecosystems can be broadly divided into two groups depending on the 'fate' of net production. On the one hand are those typified by forests where biomass accumulation is high, herbivore consumption low and much energy passes directly (as litter) to the decomposer organisms. On the other hand are ecosystems, typically aquatic, where biomass accumulation is low, herbivore consumption high and the decomposer cycle is supplied equally by producers and consumers together with allochthonous material from outside the system. The accumulation of biomass can be related to the life cycles of plants and to the seasonal climate and, for both short-lived herbaceous species and woody perennials, maximum rates of net production are associated with particular stages of the life cycle (Sections 2.3.1 and 2.3.2). In addition, the growth rate of particular organs may be precisely related to net production rates (supply of assimilates) of other organs (Section 2.3.3). Herbivore consumption is not only a 'fate' of net production but may also have direct effects on the production capacity of plants. By reducing numbers of phytoplankton, herbivores in aquatic ecosystems maintain a low standing biomass and, therefore, a high rate of production per unit algal biomass (Section 2.1, Table 3); by damaging growing points and young tissues in higher plants, herbivores may greatly reduce the growth and productive capacity (Section 2.4.1). The effects of grazing on primary production are often complex and this is illustrated with reference to cows grazing grassland and insect larvae defoliating forest trees (Section 2.4.2).

Of the factors limiting primary production, those affecting directly the rate of photosynthesis were considered in Unit 1; in this Unit, it is chiefly the factors affecting total plant growth and thus, indirectly, the rates of primary production that are considered (Section 2.5). Limitations due to temperature, water and nutrient supply are considered in general terms (Section 2.5.1, a, b and c) and limiting factors in various aquatic ecosystems are then considered in detail (Section 2.6). The importance of nutrient supply and the effects of water stratification in different situations are compared while, for lakes, the problems of eutrophication are discussed (Section 2.6.2a).

Studies of primary production in forest ecosystems are assessed in relation to the experimental methods used (Section 2.8). These methods are described (Section 2.7) and particular problems and sources of error discussed in each instance. For forest ecosystems, the gas exchange techniques emerge as useful methods for measuring respiration of non-photosynthetic tissues (*W & B*); there is no satisfactory way of measuring R for photosynthetic organs in the light, and harvest methods or dimensional analysis provide the most reliable way of estimating net production.

For aquatic ecosystems, gas exchange techniques, including incorporation of $^{14}CO_2$, are also widely used for measuring phytoplankton production but the problem of heterotrophe respiration here is still a major source of error for which there is no easy solution.

The contributions of various ecosystems to world primary production are finally considered (Section 2.9) and the status of managed or agricultural ecosystems assessed. It is difficult (you might conclude it is impossible) to make meaningful comparisons of primary production between widely different types of ecosystems.

References to other Open University Courses

1   S100, Unit 18, Appendix 2.

2   S100, Unit 20, Section 20.5.

3   S22–, Unit 3, Section 3.7.

4   S22–, Unit 3, Sections 3.5 and 3.8.1.

5   S2–3, Block 3, Section 8.3, and chapter 2 of its set book, Macan, T. T., and Worthington, E. B. (1972) *Life in Lakes and Rivers*, Fontana New Naturalist.

Publications cited in text

Cooper, D. C. (1973) Enhancement of net primary productivity by herbivore grazing in aquatic laboratory microcosms, *Limnol. Oceanogr.*, **18**, 31–7.

Duvigneaud, P. (1971) Concepts sur la productivité primaire des écosystèmes forestiers, in Duvigneaud, P. (ed.), *Productivity of Forest Ecosystems*, pp. 111–40, Unesco, Paris.

Evans, G. C. (1972) *The Quantitative Analysis of Plant Growth*, Chapter 28, Blackwell Scientific Publications.

Franklin, R. T. (1970) Insect influences on the forest canopy, in Reichle, D. E. (ed.), *Analysis of Temperate Forest Ecosystems*, pp. 86–99, Springer.

Gates, D. (1968) Towards understanding ecosystems, *Adv. in Ecol. Res.*, **7**, 1–35.

Hughes, M. K. (1973) Seasonal calorific values from a deciduous forest in England, *Ecology*, **52**, 924–6.

Lieth, H. (1970) Phenology in productivity studies, in Reichle, D. E. (ed.), *Analysis of Temperate Forest Ecosystems*, pp. 29–46, Springer.

Lund, J. W. G. (1965) The ecology of freshwater phytoplankton, *Biol. Rev.*, **40**, 231–93.

Möller, C. M., Müller, D., and Nielsen, J. (1954) Graphic presentation of dry matter production of European beech, *Forstl. Forsøkso. Danm.*, **11**, 327–35.

Müller, D., and Nielsen, J. (1965) Production brute, pertes par respiration et production nette dans la forêt ombrophile tropicale, *Forstl. Forsøkso. Danm.*, **29**, 69–160.

Odum, E. P. (1969) *Fundamentals of Ecology*, Chapter 3, W. B. Saunders.

Ovington, J. D. (1962) Quantitative ecology and the woodland ecosystem concept, *Adv. in Ecol. Res.*, **1**, 103–92.

Porter, K. G. (1973) Selective grazing and differential digestion of algae by zooplankton, *Nature (Lond.)*, **244**, 179–80.

Rafes, P. M. (1971) Pests and the damage which they cause to forests, in Duvigneaud, P. (ed.), *Productivity of forest ecosystems*, pp. 357–67, Unesco, Paris.

Walpole, P. P., and Morgan, D. G. (1972) Physiology of grain filling in barley, *Nature (Lond.)*, **240**, 416–17.

Westlake, D. F. (1966) Some basic data for investigations of the productivity of aquatic macrophytes, in Goldman, C. R. (ed.), *Primary Production in Aquatic Environments*, pp. 229–48, University of California Press.

Whittaker, R. H., and Woodwell, G. M. (1971) Measurement of net primary production of forests, in Duvigneaud, P. (ed.), *Productivity of Forest Ecosystems*, pp. 159–75, Unesco, Paris.

Recommended reading

Evans, G. C. (1972) *The Quantitative Analysis of Plant Growth*, Blackwell Scientific Publications.

An excellent book dealing mainly with the relationship between plant physiology, climate and production; there is a useful chapter on production in whole ecosystems.

Duvigneaud, P. (ed.) (1971), *Productivity of Forest Ecosystems*, Unesco.

An advanced research symposium suitable for reference.

IBP Handbooks, Blackwell Scientific Publications:

No. 2, Newbould, P. J. (1967) *Methods for Estimating the Primary Production of Forests*.

No. 6, Milner, C., and Hughes, R. Elfyn (1968) *Methods for the Measurement of the Primary Production of Grassland*.

No 12., Vollenweider, R. A. (1969) *A Manual on Methods for Measuring Primary Production in Aquatic Environments*.

These provide clear, detailed accounts of methods used in studying primary production.

Appendix 1 (Black)

World vegetation types

Climax vegetation types depend on the interaction of climate, terrain and geographical location. These are listed below with, in each case, a brief description of the chief characteristics, the areas where found and any major subdivisions. Remember that human interference or natural catastrophes such as fires may frequently destroy the normal climax vegetation: England is not covered by temperate deciduous forest as, left alone, it might be. Figure 16 shows the distribution of these vegetation types.

1 *Tundra*

Treeless, grassy vegetation with the soil permanently frozen just below the surface. Often wet and boggy and with a very short growing season. The tundra occurs in the northern arctic regions (Northern Canada, Siberia, Alaska) and at its southern limit dwarf scrub, about 0·7 m high, of birch and willow may develop. It also occurs on high mountains (alpine tundra).

2 *Northern conifer forest (taiga)*

A dense forest belt characterized by evergreen trees with needle-like leaves. It lies immediately south of the tundra right across north America and Eurasia.

3 *Temperate deciduous forest*

Forest characterized by autumn leaf-fall and, unlike (2), unable to tolerate extreme winter cold. There is great variation in species composition in different parts of the world and this vegetation has been one of the most severely affected by human interference. The areas included in this zone are scattered and include: the eastern United States, England, Ireland and most of Europe eastward; north-west China, New Zealand and the west coast of Australia.

4 *Temperate grassland*

Grasslands occur in the middle latitudes of both northern and southern hemispheres where rainfall is too low to support deciduous forest. Thus they are often found in the middle of continents or in the rain shadow of mountain ranges. The grasses may be from 0·16 m to 2·7 m in average height, depending on rainfall and soil type. The prairie of central USA, the pampas of Argentina, the vast steppes of central Asia and the Australian plains bordering the central desert are all grassland climax.

5 *Mediterranean or evergreen scrub (chaparral)*

In temperate regions which have a 'Mediterranean' climate (mild wet winters and hot dry summers) the climax vegetation consists mainly of rather scattered evergreen shrubs or small trees. This vegetation has been much affected by man and also by recurrent fires. It is found in many countries bordering the Mediterranean (Spain, Italy, Greece, for example), at the southern tip of Africa, along the southern coast of Australia (where *Eucalyptus* trees are dominant) and in part of California.

6 *Desert*

Deserts are usually bordered by either grassland or chaparral and are areas of low rainfall irrespective of the average temperature. The vegetation is scattered and highly specialized (see Block C). Deserts occur in central Asia, in central Australia, in the western United States and in South America (in the rain shadow of the Rockies and the Andes respectively), in the vast belt of the Sahara and Arabian deserts, and in South West Africa.

7 *Tropical grassland or savannah*

This type of grassland is characterized by scattered trees and shrubs; it occurs where there is heavy seasonal rainfall with intervening dry seasons. Fires and heavy grazing by large mammalian herbivores (both wild and domesticated)

46

exert a major influence on the vegetation. Large areas of central and southern Africa are occupied by savannah and smaller areas occur in South America and Northern Australia.

8 Tropical forest

There are three types of tropical forest: the rainforest*, which is characterized by broad-leaved evergreen trees, a very complex structure and high rainfall. There is virtually no seasonal climate change but rather erratic 'dry' periods do occur. Rainforests occur in the Amazon basin in South America and in the central American isthmus, parts of West Africa and Madagascar, and in the Far East (Burma, Malay peninsula, Borneo, New Guinea, etc.).

Tropical deciduous forest has seasonal leaf fall during clearly defined dry seasons. Monsoon forests of India, Vietnam and southern China are of this type, which also occurs in western South America.

Tropical scrub is found where the dry season is longer or more severe; it has dense shrubby vegetation, chiefly of thorn trees. There are scattered areas in America, Africa, the Arabian peninsula, India and Australia (see Fig. 16).

Figure 16 Distribution of the major types of world vegetation.

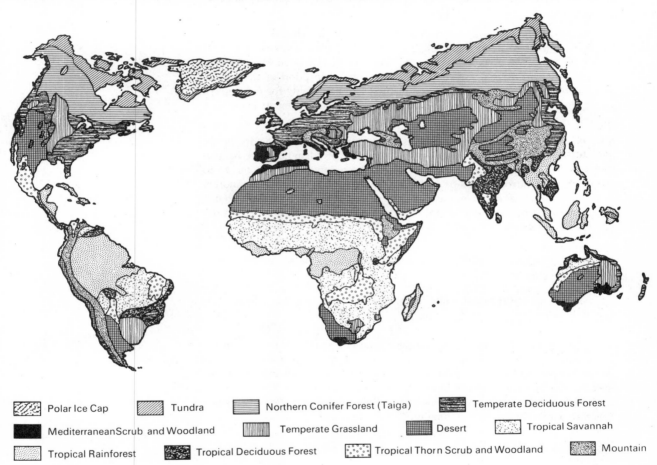

Polar Ice Cap   Tundra   Northern Conifer Forest (Taiga)   Temperate Deciduous Forest

Mediterranean Scrub and Woodland   Temperate Grassland   Desert   Tropical Savannah

Tropical Rainforest   Tropical Deciduous Forest   Tropical Thorn Scrub and Woodland   Mountain

* See TV programme, 'Tropical Forest'.

Appendix 2 (White)

Methods for studying aquatic ecosystems*

This Appendix supplements the notes given in Section 2.7.3.

Sampling

The simple method, pulling a net through a known volume of water, is of limited use for sampling phytoplankton because no nets have a sufficiently small mesh to retain the smallest species. A more useful method is to lower a container (usually between 0·5 and 5 litres in volume) to a known depth, allow to fill up and, after bringing to the surface, concentrate the enclosed phytoplankton by sedimentation, filtering or centrifugation.

Biomass estimation

Three methods are commonly used, the first two described being reasonably simple but rather inaccurate and the third reasonably accurate but very difficult and laborious.

(i) *Photosynthetic pigments* Provided that there is a reliable relationship between numbers of living algal cells and content of photosynthetic pigments (this is by no means always so), then biomass can be estimated by extracting the pigments with organic solvents and measuring absorption of the extract in a spectrophotometer. As a rule, the method is reliable only for chlorophyll a (see Unit 1, Section 1.1.2, for a list of pigments), other pigments showing a variable rate of breakdown during extraction.

(ii) *Dry weight* Phytoplankton samples can be gently dried and the dry weight or carbon content used as a measure of biomass. One problem here is to balance total removal of water during drying with loss of organic constituents: up to 20 per cent of nitrogen can be lost during oven-drying at 100 °C. Another problem is the variable mineral ash content of samples. Diatoms, for instance, may contain 50 per cent dry weight of silica and, for this reason, the ash-free dry weight is often measured when diatoms form a high proportion of the sample.

QUESTION Comparing methods (i) and (ii) above, suggest another disadvantage of (ii) compared with (i).

ANSWER In method (ii) no distinction can be made between living algal cells and dead cells or heterotrophic organisms.

(iii) *Cell counts* The best but most time-consuming method is to use a microscope and count the numbers of living algae of each species in a known volume of the sample. Knowing the relative numbers and average cell volume of each species, the total algal volume in the sample can be calculated. This method is used by research workers at the Freshwater Biological Association in England together with chlorophyll a estimation.*

Gas exchange methods

These methods are illustrated by two accounts of experimental procedures, one with the $^{14}CO_2$ method and one with the O_2 method.

(i) $^{14}CO_2$ method: A lake where the euphotic zone is about 7 m deep is sampled at three different depths, 0·5 m, 1·5 m and 5·0 m. From each depth two bottles are filled, one transparent (the 'light' bottle) and the other covered in black tape (the 'dark' bottle) and small samples of water removed for measurement of pH and total inorganic carbon content (carbonate, bicarbonate and CO_2). A standard amount of radioactive bicarbonate, $NaH^{14}CO_3$ is added to each bottle, which is then well shaken and suspended at the sampling depth for six hours. After retrieval, the water in the bottles is filtered through membrane filters which retain all phytoplankton and the filtrate dried by placing in a desiccator containing water-absorbing material (silica gel, for example). The content

* See TV programme, 'Esthwaite and the Blelham Tubes'.

of assimilated ^{14}C in the filtrate is measured in a radiation counter and, knowing the ratio of ^{14}C supplied to unlabelled C present in the water, the uptake of carbon per unit time per unit volume of water at each depth can be calculated. Assuming that all fixed carbon is converted to carbohydrate, a conversion from carbon uptake to energy fixed is possible.

QUESTION   Why are dark bottles used in this experiment?

ANSWER   As a control so that allowance can be made for any $^{14}CO_2$ fixed by non-photosynthetic 'dark' reactions.

QUESTION   Is gross production or net production measured by this method?

ANSWER   For a 6-hour incubation it is probably some intermediate quantity; there will always be uncertainty (see Section 2.7.2b for reasons, if you have forgotten) but most experimenters seem to assume that a rather low estimate of A is obtained.

QUESTION   What assumptions are made in this experiment about the light available in 'light' bottles, the behaviour of phytoplankton in the bottles and the fate of carbon fixed during photosynthesis?

ANSWER   (a) That the material of which the 'light' bottles are made does not reflect or absorb significant amounts of light. (b) That the photosynthetic rates of enclosed algae are the same as if algae were free in the water. This is often not so because natural water turbulence tends to keep algae suspended but, when enclosed in still water, the algae may sink to the bottom and self-shade each other to a large degree, thus reducing rates of photosynthesis. (c) That all the fixed ^{14}C is retained within the algae. Again, this may not be true: under conditions of high light-intensity algae may release large quantities of fixed carbon into the water as soluble products (see Unit 1, Section 1.4.2b).

(ii) O_2 method: The experimental procedure (sampling and use of light and dark bottles) is basically the same as for (i) above, but initial samples are used for measuring levels of O_2 in the water. After incubating the bottles, the accumulation or depletion of O_2 in the samples is determined, either by a chemical method or electronically, using an oxygen electrode. If it is assumed that both the product of photosynthesis and the substrate for respiration is carbohydrate (glucose) then O_2 measurements can be converted to units of dry weight.

QUESTION   What does the O_2 increase in light bottles measure?

ANSWER   Provided that heterotrophe respiration is negligible it measures net primary production. Otherwise the measurement must be regarded as equivalent to net ecosystem production as described in $W \& B$.

QUESTION   What does the O_2 decrease in dark bottles measure?

ANSWER   Combined respiration of phytoplankton and heterotrophes, $R_A + R_H$. Only if R_H is negligible is an estimate of R_A obtained. Heterotrophe content of samples, and this includes not only zooplankton but also bacteria and even fungi, is a serious source of error in this kind of experiment, and in earlier work the magnitude of the error was not fully appreciated.

QUESTION   If heterotrophe respiration is negligible, does O_2 increase in light bottles plus O_2 decrease in dark bottles provide a measure of gross primary production?

ANSWER   Yes, provided that (a) $R_{light} = R_{dark}$ and this depends on the amount of photorespiration in the light; and (b) that photo-oxidation, which occurs at high light intensity and is an oxidation process quite unconnected with respiration (Unit 1, Section 1.2.1), is not extensive.

In general these two methods for measuring primary production in aquatic ecosystems show good agreement but discrepancies occur when light-intensity is high. Under these conditions, release of extracellular products of photosynthesis and non-photosynthetic carboxylation reactions (when CO_2 is fixed without concomitant release of O_2) are greatest and photorespiration and photo-oxidation also tend to be high. The O_2 method is regarded as simpler and subject to fewer experimental errors than the $^{14}CO_2$ method, but the latter is much more sensitive and, for this reason, is nearly always used in oligotrophic lakes or any situation where phytoplankton density is low. The alternative, using the O_2 method with a long incubation period, introduces unacceptable errors: the longer an incubation the less likely are conditions inside the bottle to be remotely like conditions outside.

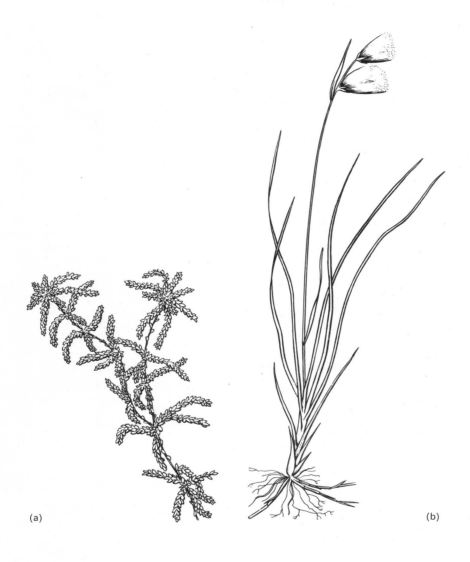

(a)   (b)

Figure 17 Examples of blanket bog plants. (a) *Sphagnum palustre*, (b) *Eriophorum vaginatum*.

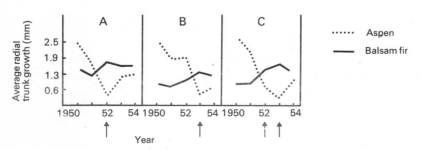

Figure 18 Radial trunk growth of aspen and balsam fir in different areas during years of heavy defoliation of aspen by the forest tent caterpillar. Areas with defoliation: (A) in 1952, (B) in 1953, (C) in 1952 and 1953.

Self-assessment questions

SAQ 1 (*Objective 3*) In an immature, planted beech wood about 50 years old, the leaf biomass is less than in a mature beech wood on the same kind of soil. Is it reasonable to assume that net primary production in the immature wood is less than in the mature wood? (Ignore production of the ground flora and shrubs because this is very low in beech woods owing to the dense shade.) Explain your answer.

SAQ 2 (*Objective 2a*) Table 14 shows the biomass and net primary production of five types of plants occuring in a North Pennine blanket bog (see also Fig. 17). (a) Calculate the $P : B$ ratio for each type of plant. (b) Compare the ratio for different plants and draw conclusions from this about the growth patterns and forms of the five types.

Note Biomass measurements for mosses include all organs, whether living or dead, which remain attached to the plants.

TABLE 14

Plant type	Biomass 10^4 J m^{-2}	Net primary production 10^4 J m^{-2} year^{-1}
Sphagnum (a moss)	3362	763
Mosses other than *Sphagnum*	920	441
Heather (*Calluna vulgaris*)	176	79
Cotton grass (*Eriophorum vaginatum*)	5·4	3·6
Lichens*	77	5·4

* Lichens are symbiotic associations of algae and fungi and form tough growths (thalli) sometimes encrusting bare rock or tree bark sometimes growing upright and branching. (See Block C for further discussion.)

SAQ 3 (*Objectives 2b and 2c*) Table 15 shows the net primary production, P, for three forests in the USA and the distribution of P between different organs.

TABLE 15

	Net production g m^{-2} yr^{-1}		
	Oak–pine forest at sea level	Mixed deciduous forest at 1310 m	Evergreen spruce–fir forest at 1800 m
Trees	1060·0	1300·0	1175·0
Shrubs	130·0	22·6	33·0
Herbs	6·0	75·0	44·0
Percentage of P for trees in:			
stem wood	14·0	33·0	31·9
stem bark	2·5	3·9	3·7
branch wood and bark	25·3	17·0	15·2
leaves	33·1	30·7	31·0
fruit and flowers	2·1	1·9	2·2
roots	25·0	13·5	16·0

(a) Can you estimate the annual increment of the forests? If so how, and if not, why not?

(b) How does the percentage of P in different organs vary between the three forests? Suggest reasons for this variation.

(c) Which forest is the most 'open' of the three (i.e. permits most light-penetration to ground level)?

SAQ 4 (*Objective 5*) In Minnesota, USA, balsam fir, *Abies balsamifera*, grows in the understorey (below the canopy) of aspen, *Populus tremula*, forests. The aspen, but not the fir, may be periodically infested with the defoliating forest tent caterpillar, *Malacosoma disstria*. In Figure 18 the effects of heavy defoliation on the radial growth of trunks of aspen and balsam fir are shown.

Describe briefly the effect of insect defoliation on radial trunk growth in the two species of trees. What factor is probably limiting primary production of the balsam fir?

SAQ 5 (*Objective 6*) In sand dunes along the west coast of Britain, where westerly winds predominate, primary productivity is consistently lower on the west side of the dunes than on the east side. Explain this in terms of the factors limiting primary production.

SAQ 6 (*Objective 6*) In a temperate region of the USA (the Smoky Mountains, Tennessee), net primary production of forests with similar species composition showed a linear decline with altitude in both wet and dry areas. Suggest an explanation.

SAQ 7 (*Objective 6*) In areas of ancient climax forest what conditions—'natural' or caused by human interference—could lead to nutrient limitation of primary production?·

SAQ 8 (*Objective 6*) Which two of the following would you expect to limit gross production of phytoplankton in the epilimnion of temperate seas during the summer months?

(a) Nutrient levels in the sea.
(b) Depth of light penetration.
(c) The rate of supply of nutrients to the euphotic zone.
(d) Zooplankton grazing and/or parasite attack.
(e) Sinking of phytoplankton below the euphotic zone.

SAQ 9 (*Objective 6*) Explain briefly:

(a) Why open tropical oceans usually have crystal clear water.
(b) Why primary productivity in open tropical water is generally low.
(c) Why the open sea off the coast of Peru is a famous fishing ground.

SAQ 10 (*Objectives 4 and 6*) Lake George in Uganda is a fairly shallow (under 10 m) tropical eutrophic lake. Because of strong winds there are normally turbulent water movements which disturb the whole body of water. Occasionally the wind drops for several consecutive days and the water becomes quite still. What will happen:

(a) to the lake water (apart from becoming still);
(b) to organisms living near the lake surface;
(c) to organisms living on or near the lake bottom?

Answer (b) and (c) in terms of the growth and productivity of the organisms during the windless period.

SAQ 11 (*Objective 7*) One way of estimating the annual increase in woody biomass of trees in temperate forests is by measuring the size of annual rings: wood produced in spring is darker in colour than summer wood and, since there is no growth in winter, the distance between two dark rings gives a measure of the annual woody increment. Could this method be used in tropical forests; if so, under what climatic conditions and in which kind of forest? (Refer to Appendix 1 for information about types of tropical forest.)

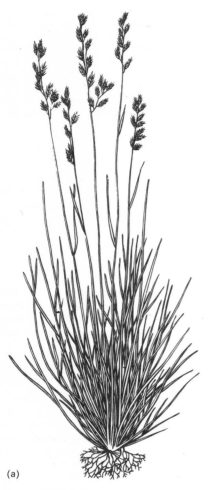

(a)

(b)

Figure 19a *Festuca ovina*, a fine-leaved grass.

Figure 19b *Agrostis tenuis*, a broad-leaved grass.

SAQ 12 (*Objectives 2 and 7*) In the Pennine hills, primary production and sheep consumption of various plant communities were investigated (Rawes and Welch (1967) *Oikos supplement* **11**, 7–72). Three of the communities examined were:

(i) Grassland containing a mixture of broad-leaved grasses (chiefly *Agrostis tenuis* and *Anthoxanthum odoratum*) and fine-leaved grasses (chiefly *Festuca ovina*)—designated A (See Fig. 19).

(ii) Grassland containing largely fine-leaved *Festuca ovina*—designated F.

(iii) Peaty areas containing chiefly species of cotton grass (*Eriophorum*, members of the sedge family)—designated E. Sheep range freely over the hills.

In one experiment the above-ground biomass was measured (a) at the start of the growing season and before grazing began (March); (b) at the end of the growing season when land had been available for grazing; (c) as for (b) but when land had been enclosed to block access of sheep. On many plants dead leaves and stems occurred and the proportion of these in the biomass was determined. Results are shown in Table 16.

TABLE 16   Standing crop (g dry wt m⁻²)

Site	Before growing season (a) Yield	% dead	After growing season (b) grazing Yield	% dead	(c) no grazing Yield	% dead
A	64	59	74	38	238	26
F	122	36	80	33	214	19
E	301	76	326	66	317	63

Sample plots were 0·5–1·5 m² and for each figure an average of 9–12 replicate plots were harvested. Harvesting was by hand-clipping at a height of 1 cm; yield can be regarded as a constant proportion of the above-ground biomass.

1   Estimate annual net above-ground production at sites A, F and E. (No elaborate transformations of the data are required.)

2   What is the major source of error in this estimation of P?

3   Calculate the apparent consumption of herbage by sheep; what assumptions must be made in order to make the calculation with the data in Table 16?

Rawes and Welch used another method to estimate above-ground production and consumption by sheep. They measured biomass for each plant species in grazed and enclosed plots; fresh plots were used for each monthly sampling and the difference in biomass (living tissue only here) of herbage species (i.e. those palatable to sheep) on the two kinds of plots gave the herbage consumed for each month. Thus by summing monthly totals, figures for net production on ungrazed and grazed plots could be obtained and the differences in herbage species (not all species were eaten) gave a figure for sheep consumption.

The results are shown in Table 17. (*Note* These are all direct measurements: consumption is not obtained by subtraction.)

TABLE 17

Site	Net above-ground production g m⁻² no grazing	grazing	Consumed by sheep g m⁻²
A	203	174	110
F	142	90	50
E	69	69	0

4   Which of the three sites is most suitable for upland sheep grazing from the point of view of palatability of the herbage and resistance of the site to damage from sheep?

SAQ 13 (*Objective 7*) List three or more possible sources of error in using the light and dark bottle method (either O_2 or $^{14}CO_2$ technique) for measurements of aquatic primary production.

SAQ 14 (*Objective 7*) A student is required to do experiments so that the production equation, $A = P + R$, can be solved for a small moderately eutrophic lake. Any two components of the equation can be measured. Time, labour and money are strictly limited, so methods requiring too much of any of these commodities are not feasible. Assume a maximum of three years for the study, starting in summer. Plan a suitable experimental approach for the student; indicate whether preliminary experiments would be necessary, which quantities are to be measured and by which experimental techniques. Give reasons for choosing the methods.

SAQ 15 (*Objectives 3 and 9*) Comment critically on the following statement: 'Tropical rainforests are enormously productive. They have higher rates of net production and grow faster than any other forest ecosystem.'

SAQ 16 (*Objective 10*) Assess the validity of the following argument:

'A comparison of primary productivity in developed and underdeveloped parts of the world indicates that the productive potential of two-thirds of the agricultural land is not fully realized. If, therefore, we devote more money to crop breeding, irrigation projects, and fertilizer, herbicide and pesticide manufacture, we shall be able to increase agricultural production by at least 200 per cent without bringing into cultivation any new land. Provided that human populations become stabilized, there need never be a shortage of food.'

ITQ answers

ITQ 1 See Figure 20 (which is the completed Fig. 2).

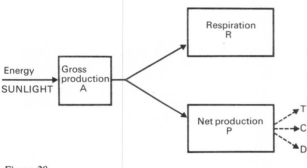

Figure 20

Note Although sunlight is the major source of energy for primary producers, you should recall from Unit 1, Section 1.6, that chemosynthetic bacteria (chemoautotrophes) can use simple inorganic compounds as a source of energy.

ITQ 2 During the day the temperature of the exposed horizontal leaf rises considerably above that of the surrounding air (Fig. 4b), reaching almost 50 °C around midday. As you saw in Fig. 3, temperatures above 25 °C inhibit net production. Only in early morning and late evening is leaf temperature sufficiently low for photosynthesis to exceed respiration.

ITQ 3 During the middle part of the day the leaf temperature of the exposed leaf is above the temperature at which net production is negative (see Fig. 3) so respiration exceeds gross photosynthesis and there is a net loss of carbon (as CO_2) from the leaf.

ITQ 4 For much of the day, exposed (or 'sun') leaves on the tree are normally in an end-on position, parallel to the incident light (Unit 1, Section 1.1.3). So less light is absorbed than for leaves at right angles to incident light, the rise in leaf temperature is less pronounced and, although net production may be reduced, it would not become negative during the middle part of the day.

ITQ 5 Yes; leaf temperature in the shaded leaf is close to air temperature. Apart from a flattening of the P curve between 12.00 and 14.00 hours, when leaf temperature reaches 35 °C, the curve is closely related to light intensity (compare Figs. 4a and 4b with 4c). For shade leaves, light rather than temperature is the major factor controlling rates of net production.

ITQ 6 (a) Silicon in the form of silica (silicon dioxide, SiO_2).

(b) No: diatoms, which often dominate the phytoplankton of small and medium sized lakes, have a hard outer shell which is composed largely of silica and constitutes about 50 per cent of the cell's dry weight. Diatom silicon requirements are, in consequence, much higher than for other algae where nitrogen and phosphorus are usually the major substances limiting primary production. Silicon is unusual among 'nutrients' in that not much is recycled. Diatom shells sink to the lake bottom and form mud; many are not decomposed and silica for new diatom growth enters the lake by weathering of silicaceous rocks.

ITQ 7 Grazing in spring is likely to cause an initial decrease in total phytoplankton production. Assuming the species of algae present are similar to those in Porter's study, then the palatable and digestible species will decline, the unacceptable species will remain constant and the gelatinous green algae will increase. If the population of digestible species were very dense then grazing could cause an initial increase in production but, since the grazers themselves are likely to increase after this, heavier grazing and a reduction in such algae would follow. After this initial decline it is likely that the numbers and production of the gelatinous green algae and perhaps some of the 'unacceptable' species would build up during the summer, resulting in a secondary peak in primary production in late summer. In fact, empirical studies have shown that an algal succession commonly occurs in lakes: edible flagellates and diatoms predominate in spring (production high) and gelatinous green algae and fiilamentous blue-green algae dominate in late summer and autumn (secondary peak of production). So the effects of grazing on primary production in lakes depends on the numbers and selectivity of the grazers and the numbers and species composition of the algae.

ITQ 8 If free CO_2 could be bubbled through the water then pH would fall and, for reasons given in (a) and (b) on p. 29, growth of green algae would be promoted at the expense of blue-green algae. If the $N:P$ ratio were increased this might also help.

ITQ 9 Before you can answer this question you must define what you mean by productive. If you mean 'has the greatest rate of net production per unit area', then the most productive ecosystems are the tropical forest (averaging both mature and immature) and the swamp and marsh. If you mean 'contributes most to world net primary production' then the answer is tropical forest (a function of net production and area occupied by the ecosystem). If you mean 'has the greatest rate of production per unit *biomass* (the highest $P:B$ ratio) then the answer is the open ocean. The word *productive*, in an ecological context, should not be used loosely.

Some of the highest figures for net primary production are for swamps or salt-marsh where reeds, *Phragmites communis*, or *Spartina* grasses are dominant: values of 150–180 kJ m^{-2} year^{-1} have been recorded (cf. values for tropical forest and the swamp average of 37.80 in Table 13).

ITQ 10 Grouping:

(1)	$P:B$ ratio high (above 3000)	Aquatic ecosystems; all marine and freshwater bodies.
(2)	$P:B$ ratio medium high (1000–3000)	Agricultural land.
(3)	$P:B$ ratio medium low (100–1000)	Deserts, tundra, grassland, savannah, swamp and marsh.
(4)	$P:B$ ratio low (below 100)	All forests.

This grouping illustrates that net production per unit biomass can be related to the size and longevity of the plants, although agricultural ecosystems, which are monocultures, stand apart as a special case. Where there are large woody perennials the $P:B$ ratio is low; where there are smaller herbaceous or shrubby plants the ratio increases; the highest ratio occurs when phytoplankton are the chief primary producers.

SAQ answers and comments

SAQ 1 No, it is not reasonable. Despite the higher leaf biomass in the mature wood, there will be a higher 'respiratory load' and possibly a reduced rate of photosynthesis per unit leaf weight (see Section 2.1). Thus there may or may not be greater net production in the mature beech forest; you cannot assume that there is.

SAQ 2 (a) The $P:B$ ratios in order from *Sphagnum* to lichens in Table 14 are: 0·23, 0·48, 0·45, 0·67, 0·07. If you got these ratios wrong, then check that you divided P by B in every case.

(b) The $P:B$ ratio tells you the net production per unit biomass. Thus, comparing the two angiosperms, heather and cotton grass, the ratio of the former (0·45) is about two-thirds that of the latter (0·67). It is unlikely that heather leaves photosynthesize so much less efficiently than cotton grass, rather, heather is likely to have a higher proportion of non-photosynthetic tissue, to be larger and have more woody supporting tissue than cotton grass (see Section 2.1, p. 8). In fact, this is true: the ratio of green shoots to woody stems and roots for heather is 0·24 while the ratio of green shoots to underground stems and roots for cotton grass is 3·9.

Mosses other than *Sphagnum* have a $P:B$ ratio which is close to heather, but *Sphagnum* is very much lower. Mosses have no true roots* and no woody tissue; virtually all tissue is capable of photosynthesis so you might expect higher $P:B$ ratios than for angiosperms. The lower ratios indicate a lower rate of photosynthesis per unit dry weight and/or a higher proportion of dead tissue, which is included in biomass measurement. This last factor is particularly relevant to *Sphagnum*, which grows in dense clumps with light excluded from the lower leaves; these leaves do not photosynthesize but are not shed and are regarded as part of the biomass. Lichens stand out in the Table (p. 51) as having an extremely low $P:B$ ratio. Knowing that they form crust-like or small branched thalli (somewhat similar in form to mosses), there cannot be a high proportion

of roots or non-productive supporting tissue and dead organs are not included in the biomass. So the low $P:B$ ratio must indicate a very low rate of photosynthesis per unit tissue, which is reasonable for an organism which is partly algal and partly fungal, i.e. non-productive. Lichens are noted for their extremely slow rates of growth. For those lichens and mosses which grow on the soil beneath heather or cotton grass, photosynthesis will be low because of severe shading.

SAQ 3 (a) No, because no data is given about litter composition (see Section 2.3.2). Even for the deciduous forest, where you could assume that all leaves fall as litter, you still do not know the woody branch component of the litter.

(b) The oak–pine forest has a much smaller proportion of P going into stem wood tissue than the other two forests and a much greater proportion of P going into roots. For other organs, the proportion is similar in all three forests.

From your reading of the Unit (e.g. Tables 2 and 5) you know that one reason for this kind of variation is the age of the forest: in fact, the oak–pine forest is only 43 years old and the others are 222 and 161 years respectively. There may also be intrinsic differences between tree species and the site (soil type, nutrient levels and water supply) could also affect apportioning of net production; much energy might be diverted to root growth when the site is poor and a large root area is needed to absorb sufficient water and nutrients. There is no evidence to suggest that elevation affects distribution of P.

(c) The oak–pine forest is the most open. You can deduce this from the much greater production here due to shrubs, which have low net production in the other forests because they are shaded out and suppressed. In fact, when light penetration to ground level is measured, it is 5·9 per cent in the oak–pine, 1·4 per cent in the spruce–fir and 0·2 per cent in the mixed deciduous forest; shrub net production reflects this. Herbaceous ground vegetation is not such a good indicator because some of these species are highly shade-tolerant (shrubs are much less so) and because a flush of spring growth may distort the picture in deciduous, but not in evergreen, forests (phenology of the ground flora is discussed in Section 2.3.1).

---

* Mosses have very simple absorbing organs called rhizoids, and some mosses lack even these.

SAQ 4 Defoliation markedly decreases trunk growth for the infested aspen. There is partial recovery in the year following defoliation but after two successive years of defoliation (Fig. 18c) the rate of recovery is much slower.

There is an inverse relationship between trunk growth for aspen and for balsam fir during defoliation periods: maxima for the fir always occurs in years of minima for aspen. Since balsam fir is an understorey plant, this suggests that growth and net primary production (as indicated by radial trunk growth) are limited by light owing to the overshadowing aspen: defoliation permits more light to reach the firs and production increases, supporting this hypothesis.

SAQ 5 Water drains through sand very rapidly and therefore water supply (Section 2.5.1b) is probably an important factor limiting primary production on the dunes (nutrients could be too). Wind affects the amount of water lost by transpiration from plants: the stronger the wind the faster is transpiration. Since, in Britain, winds blow mainly from the west, the west side of the dunes will be more exposed to the wind, with higher rates of transpiration and less water available for plant growth than on the sheltered east side. Conditions of light, temperature and nutrient supply would not be expected to vary on the two sides of the dunes. Lower temperature on the exposed side might reduce net production, but this would depend on the balance of P and R (Section 2.2.2) so you cannot be sure of this. Greater exposure to salt spray on the west side of the dunes would also contribute to reduced plant production.

SAQ 6 Average temperature declines linearly with altitude, and this is the most likely explanation for decreased net production with increasing altitude. Reduced water supply at higher altitudes, particularly if the soil remains frozen for long periods, could be a contributing factor, and increased nutrient leaching on steep slopes could be another. Temperature is the explanation usually given, but the situation is complex and still not fully understood.

SAQ 7 It is usually assumed that nutrient limitation does not occur in climax forests because efficient recycling together with rock weathering and nitrogen fixation effectively replace the small nutrient losses caused by leaching. The important feature is that roots rapidly take up soluble nutrients and so serious losses due to leaching are avoided. Conditions when nutrient limitation could occur are:

(a) Following the death of many trees (e.g. after hurricanes, by animal depredation, parasites or fire). Nutrients are no longer taken up from the soil, nutrient leaching and soil erosion increase, and regenerating forest could suffer nutrient limitation unless regeneration were very rapid.

(b) If soil conditions deteriorated (selective leaching of certain ions can make the soil more acid, for example), then conditions for microbial decomposition might become unfavourable. Nutrient release would be slow, peat could accumulate (see end of Section 2.1) and nutrient limitation could occur for the forest plants.

(c) Extensive cropping of trees by man with removal of the above-ground biomass removes large stocks of nutrients 'locked up' in the biomass. Nutrient limitation will eventually occur and it is for this reason that managed forests respond, often dramatically, to fertilizer application. The effects of clearing tropical rainforest are discussed in Section 2.5.1c.

SAQ 8 Statements (c) and (d) best describe the state of phytoplankton. These are plenty of nutrients in the sea as a whole, so (a) is wrong: it is availability to the phytoplankton above the thermocline that is important. There is usually ample light in summer in the epilimnion (see, for example, Fig. 11), so (b) is incorrect, and there is no evidence to suggest that (e) is of

major importance in summer: the euphotic zone is then deep and water turbulence is usually adequate to keep phytoplankton suspended in this zone. Read Section 2.6.1a again if you had difficulty in answering this SAQ.

SAQ 9 (a) The chief reason why tropical oceans have such clear water is basically the low numbers of phytoplankton organisms (Section 2.6.1a). This in turn means few zooplankton and little organic detritus. In the open ocean, there is little suspended inorganic sediment.

(b) If you answered (a) correctly you might deduce that low primary productivity is due to low numbers of phytoplankton organisms. This is true, but the crux of the question is why there are so few algae. The chief reason is the low levels of nutrients, particularly phosphorus and nitrogen, in the euphotic zone and this in turn is related to the permanent thermocline: nutrients in the hypolimnion can reach the epilimnion (and euphotic zone) only by slow diffusion across the thermocline. Recall from Section 2.6.1a and SAQ 8 that this may also be true for temperate seas in *summer*.

(c) As mentioned in Section 2.6.1b, the sea off Peru is an upwelling region where cold nutrient-rich water wells up into the warm lighted surface zone. Because growth and primary production in tropical seas are limited by nutrient supply (see (b) above), upwelling stimulates phytoplankton growth: herbivorous zooplankton or small fish feed on this rich crop and in turn are eaten by larger carnivorous species—the most important fish off the Peruvian coast are, in fact, anchovies, and these are the fishermen's main target.

SAQ 10 (a) In Lake George, water turbulence normally prevents formation of a permanent thermocline but, under still conditions, a stable thermocline will form. The hypolimnion rapidly becomes anaerobic owing to oxygen consumption by benthic organisms, as occurs in all stratified eutrophic lakes.

(b) Because of (a), phytoplankton in the epilimnion rapidly use up all available nutrients: remember that this is a eutrophic lake which has a large population of primary producers. Growth and multiplication of phytoplankton ceases because of nutrient limitation, and many algae may die and sink below the thermocline, so a decline in herbivorous zooplankton could follow. Larger consumers are likely to survive a temporary period of food shortage.

(c) As oxygen levels in the hypolimnion fall so all aerobic benthic organisms will die or enter a resting stage. All production will decline except for that of anaerobic decomposers and of certain mud-dwelling detritus feeders, which normally live in anaerobic bottom mud: as dead phytoplanton sink these anaerobic benthic organisms will increase in numbers. Toxic waste products of anaerobic decomposition (e.g. hydrogen sulphide) will accumulate in the hypolimnion (recall Unit 1, Section 1.6, Figure 11A) and these could kill any organisms which migrate from surface to bottom and back and tolerate short periods of anaerobiosis.

SAQ 11 The method could be used only in tropical forests with a distinct seasonal climate, i.e. with dry periods during which leaves fall and there is a reduction in wood growth. It could not be used in tropical rainforests but probably could be used in deciduous tropical forests and tropical scrub (see Appendix 1).

SAQ 12 1 An estimate of P can be obtained by subtracting (a) from (c): this gives values of 174, 92 and 16 g m^{-2} respectively. If you subtract (a) from (b) this gives only some proportion of P not consumed by sheep. You might have calculated the increase in living tissue only, by working out the amount of live tissue in (a), (b) and (c) and subtracting these: this may or may not improve accuracy (see 2 below).

2   Leaves have a limited life span (a few weeks for most grasses; see Section 2.3.2) and during the growing season may be continually lost from the plants or die and be decomposed while still attached. The yields in Table 16 include the dead component but, since we do not know the rate of shedding or of decomposition *in situ*, the value of P in (1) is likely to be seriously underestimated. Thus when allowances were made for death and decomposition of tissues by measuring the rate of weight loss or disappearance of dead tissues throughout the growing season, P at A was 203, at F 142·3 and at E 69·3.

3   By subtracting (b) from (c) an estimate of consumption can be obtained giving values of 164, 134 and —9 for A, F and E. This last figure is obviously nonsense and must mean either than sheep grazing is nil on site E and the difference between (b) and (c) is within the limits of experimental error, or that growth under grazing is greater than in enclosures and consumption cannot be detected. This gives a clue to the major flaw in this estimate of consumption; you have to assume that rates of primary production are the same in grazed and ungrazed plots. In these ecosystems the amount of photosynthetic tissue is so much greater in ungrazed plots that net production rates are likely to be higher: in fact they are higher, so this is not a valid method of estimating consumption.

4   Site A. At this site, net production is reduced only slightly (14·3 per cent) by grazing and the sheep utilize a high percentage of the vegetation ($110/174 = 63$ per cent); the site withstands grazing well and is well utilized by sheep. At F, grazing reduces P by 36·4 per cent and utilization by sheep is only 55 per cent. E is not utilized by sheep at all, presumably because cotton grass is a tough unpalatable species; it is a highly unsuitable site for grazing land.

SAQ 13   All sources of error relate to the basic problem that conditions inside bottles may differ from conditions outside.

(a)   The bottle may absorb or reflect light.

(b)   Mineral nutrients or CO_2 may be used up during incubations (especially if long).

(c)   Algae may sediment out in the bottles in the absence of normal water turbulence, and this could cause self-shading.

(d)   Herbivorous zooplankton may consume algae faster in bottles than outside, and zooplankton and bacteria also cause serious errors when using the O_2 method: they cause an overestimate of O_2 uptake by .producers in dark bottles.

SAQ 14   Preliminary investigations will be necessary:

(a)   To find out which are the major primary producers: are these exclusively planktonic algae or do attached macrophytes play an important role? Careful visual observation should answer this.

(b)   To determine the depth of the euphotic zone and the distribution of algae in the zone. Measuring light extinction at different depths and sampling water at different depths, concentrating algae and measuring chlorophyll a, or (better) observing and counting under a microscope will be necessary. Repeating this on dull and sunny days to determine if distribution varied with light intensity would be useful.

(c)   Observations in (b) could be used to give information about numbers and distribution of zooplankton: if numbers were large this could affect subsequent choice of experimental methods.

Because of time and labour shortage, the harvest methods are unsuitable for measuring P (but could be used for macrophytes).

Given that the lake is moderately eutrophic, and with information from (b) above about numbers of algae, the O_2 method is likely to be sufficiently sensitive and is less time-consuming than the $^{14}CO_2$ method. A possible series of experiments is:

(i)   Set up light and dark bottles for O_2 estimation at vertical intervals throughout the euphotic zone and determine the depth at which photosynthesis is maximal: this depth alone could be used in future and this experiment used to extrapolate results for one depth to the whole zone. These experiments give measurements of P and R.

(ii)   Measure the algal biomass in sample bottles (the chlorophyll a method is fastest) so that metabolic rates can be related to biomass. This step could be omitted, but is useful.

(iii)   If preliminary experiments reveal large numbers of zooplankton and if high bacterial numbers are suspected, then selective filtering of water samples before incubation could reduce the error. A coarse filter would remove most of the zooplankton and leave most of the phytoplankton: a fine filter would remove phytoplankton and leave bacteria. Incubating unfiltered water and the two types of filtered water would then indicate the extent of O_2 uptake by heterotrophes.

(iv)   Experiments would have to be repeated at intervals throughout the year and additional measurements of depth of the euphotic zone made to ensure that the correct depth for incubation was maintained. Average monthly (or so) values of P and R could be obtained and summed over the whole year.

(v)   So that values of P and R in terms of O_2 output or uptake could be converted to energy values, the energy content of phytoplankton would need to be measured using a bomb calorimeter (Section 2.3.1). You should have been able to answer this question, using the information in Section 2.7.3 and Appendix 2 and some common sense.

SAQ 15   In terms of total energy fixed (gross production), tropical rainforests are indeed very productive compared with other forests. Mature rainforests, however, do not have markedly higher rates of net production; they are similar to those in immature or mature beech forests, for example (compare Figs. 14 and 15 and data on p. 41), and this is because respiration rates are high in the tropics. Nor is the rate of growth (increase in biomass) particularly high in mature rainforests; compare the values for T in Figs. 14 and 15. Successional tropical rainforest, such as regenerates in cleared areas, may indeed have outstandingly high rates of P and T but it is misleading and inaccurate to claim that these are high for tropical rainforest as a whole.

SAQ 16   The argument fails to take into account the chief reason for high agricultural productivity in developed regions: energy subsidy by man (Section 2.9). With one exception, all the remedies advocated require energy expediture (for manufacturing processes, maintaining irrigation systems, etc.) and, at present, this energy derives mainly from fossil fuels—coal, oil, gas. This is the energy stored by earlier primary producers in partially decomposed plant remains and the supply is limited. Unless, therefore, a new source of energy (nuclear or solar batteries, for example) becomes available it will not be possible to sustain this kind of agriculture indefinitely. So the food problem will not be solved in the long run.

Introducing new and more 'productive' crop varieties does not, in theory, require energy subsidy, but in practice it is commonly found that 'miracle' varieties require large amounts of fertilizer to reach full productive capacity.

Acknowledgements

Grateful acknowledgement is made to the following sources for material used in this Unit:

FIGURES

Figures 3 and 4: Academic Press Inc. (London) Limited and the author for D. M. Gates in *Adv. in Ecol. Res.*, **7,** 1–35, 1968; *Figures 5a and 13:* Unesco for H. Leith and P. Duvigneaud in *Productivity of Forest Ecosystems*. Proceedings of the Brussels Symposium (27–31 October 1969). Reproduced by permission of Unesco. © Unesco 1971; *Figure 5b:* University of California Press for D. F. Westlake in C. R. Goldman (ed.) *Primary Productivity in Aquatic Environments*. Originally published by the University of California Press, reprinted by permission of the Regents of the University of California; *Figures 8a and 9:* Macmillan Publishing Co. Inc. for R. H. Whittaker, *Communities and Ecosystems* © 1970; *Figure 11:* Macmillan Publishing Co. Inc. for R. Hunter, *Aquatic Productivity; Figure 18:* Springer-Verlag for R. T. Franklin in D. Reichle (ed.), *Analysis of Temperate Forest Ecosystems*, 1970.

TABLE

Table 5: Duke University Press for M. K. Hughes in *Ecology*, **52,** 424–6, 1973.

Unit 3

Consumers in Ecosystems

Contents

Study guide

The aims of this Unit are:

1 To continue the study of ecosystems by considering energy transfer from plants (primary producers) to and among animals (consumers), and the ways in which energy is utilized by animals.

2 To consider various techniques used to measure parameters involved in secondary production, and their limitations.

3 To identify some of the factors which limit secondary production in different ecosystems.

Before reading the main text, you should work through the Pretest. The answers to the Pretest questions summarize the principles and some of the information that are assumed as prerequisites for this Unit; they include some additional information.

Consumers have an immense variety of diets and feeding mechanisms. If we wish to quantify energy flow through ecosystems, in the hope of being able to construct predictive models, it is essential to try to fit consumers into a simple system. The concept of trophic levels and categories of consumers are discussed in Section 3.0.

Section 3.1 introduces the energy flow equations applied to consumers. Methods of measuring C, F, R, and U for individual animals are summarized in Section 3.1.1; they are discussed in Appendices 1, 2 and 3 (which you could read now or later). You are required to read two set papers (see below): one describes an investigation of energy parameters for a carnivorous fish; the second describes investigations of terrestrial herbivores (caterpillars). Questions in the text indicate the information which you should extract from the papers. The Section concludes with a discussion of energy relations of mammals and birds. It is essential that you should work steadily through the parts of Section 3.1 since principles are introduced which are vital for later sections.

Section 3.2 is concerned with anabolic components of the energy equations, i.e. with growth of the body and with reproduction. Some of the effects of extrinsic factors (e.g. food and temperature) and intrinsic factors (e.g. age) are discussed, stressing the importance of general studies of animals in their environments before detailed studies of energy flow. Appendix 4, on growth rates, must be read with this Section.

In Section 3.3, consumers are considered as communities. Methods of measuring C and R for populations are described in Appendix 5, which could be read with this Section or later. Production (P) of a population is defined; Allen's graphical method for computing production is described in Appendix 6, which should be read with this Section. Some of the problems of measuring energy flow through populations are illustrated from the set paper on caterpillars. The Section ends with a discussion of energy turnover and some ratios used to compare populations.

Section 3.4 consists of five 'case studies' of varied consumers in different environments. The data from these studies and other data quoted in the Unit are brought together in Table 13 which is used as the basis for a discussion of possible generalizations for deriving some of the energy parameters for categories of consumers. Some general comments on interrelationships of plants, herbivores and carnivores conclude the Unit text.

There are many examples and values quoted in the text—do not try to memorize these, they are provided to illustrate the diversity of consumers.

If you are short of time, you could omit reading Appendices 1, 2, 3 and 5; you should try to read Appendices 4 and 6. If very short of time, postpone reading Section 3.2.

There are questions requiring you to carry out calculations both in the Main Text and in many of the SAQs—*you will waste time if you work these out to a high level of accuracy.* We expect you to use simplified calculations or a slide rule or logs to obtain approximate answers; slight differences from the printed answers (which were mostly calculated with a slide rule) should not worry you. We think that it is important that you should tackle some of these calculations but when you feel familiar with a particular type, stop repeating it—you can refer to the completed Tables if you need values for answering questions. All the examples are based on genuine values but many of them have been 'rounded' to present simplified situations.

There are two set papers to be read with this Unit:

Solomon, D. J., and Brafield, A. E. (1972) The energetics of feeding, metabolism and growth of perch (*Perca fluviatilis* L.), *J. Anim. Ecol.*, **41,** 699–718. (This is referred to in the Unit as *S & B*.)

Smith, Philip H. (1972) The energy relations of defoliating insects in a hazel coppice, *J. Anim. Ecol.*, **41,** 567–87. (This is referred to in the Unit as *PHS*.)

Objectives

After studying this Unit you should be able to:

1 Define correctly and distinguish between true and false statements concerning each of the terms and principles listed in Table A1.

2 Given appropriate information:

(a) Calculate the distribution of energy flow within the equations:

$$C = A + F + U = P + R + F + U;$$
$$R = R^1 + R^2;$$
$$P = \text{somatic growth} + \text{gonad growth}.$$

(Tested in SAQs 1, 2, 3, 5, 6, 7, 8, 12 and 13.)

(b) Derive values for instantaneous growth rates and production.

(Tested in SAQs 16, 17.)

(c) Calculate ratios: $A:C$, $P:A$, $P:C$, $R:A$, $P:B$, $R:P$.

(Tested in SAQs 1, 2, 3, 12, 13, 14 and 17.)

(d) Calculate and compare the production of herbivores and carnivores in ecosystems.

(Tested in ITQs.)

3 Assess, by compiling lists or choosing from alternatives or writing an essay, the factors which may affect energy consumption or production or biomass of consumers under different environmental conditions or in different ecosystems.

(Tested in ITQs and in SAQs 2, 4, 5, 9, 11, 12, 13 and 14.)

4 Describe and evaluate critically methods used for estimation of food consumption (C), assimilation (A), respiration (R), production (P) of somatic tissue and reproductive products, and biomass (B) of consumers.

(Tested in questions on set papers.)

5 Apply the principles developed in this Unit to make hypotheses or design experiments or draw conclusions from data relating to situations or to species not treated in the Unit.

(Tested in SAQs 8, 9, 10, 12, 13, 14 and 15.)

6 Study published papers, extracting information about energy parameters and problems of experimental methods and, in the light of principles developed in this Unit, distinguishing between valid and invalid deductions and appraising the methods used to obtain data.

(Tested in questions on set papers.)

Table A1

List of scientific terms, concepts and principles in Unit 3

Taken as prerequisites (see also Table A2)		Introduced in this Unit			
Introduced in a previous Unit	Unit No.	Developed in this Unit or in its set papers	Page No.	Developed in a later Unit	Unit No.
ecosystem	Intro. A	energy flow through herbivores and carnivores	8	ratios comparing energy flow at different trophic levels	5
trophic level	Intro. A	the energy flow equations: $C = A + F + U$;	10		
gross and net primary production	2	$A = P + R^1 + R^2$	19	integrated energy flow models for whole ecosystems	5
biomass	2	$P = $ somatic growth $+$ gonad growth	20		
phenology	2	methods of measuring rates of consumption, assimilation, respiration, excretion, growth, production of reproductive products	11, 20		
		maintenance rations and metabolism	14		
		appetite	23		
		growth efficiencies and ratios: $A:C, P:A, P:C, R:P$	29, 35		
		budgets based on study of energy turnover for individuals (poikilotherms and homoiotherms) and populations	11		
		instantaneous growth rates	47		
		Allen curve method of estimating production	49		
		$P:B$ ratios for consumers	29		
		consumption and production of consumers in selected ecosytems	30		

Table A2

Prerequisites from Science Foundation and Second Level Courses

Course	Unit	Section	Objective
S100*	18	18.1.1	Objective 1
		18.4.5	
	20	20.1	
		20.2	Objectives 1, 2, 4, 10
		20.2.1	
		20.3	
	21	21.3.3	Objectives 1, 3, 4, 10
S22–**	1	1.3	Objectives 1, 2, 5
	4	Whole Unit	All objectives
	5	5.0	Objective 1
		5.1	
	6	Whole Unit	All objectives
	8	8.3.6	Objective 1
		8.4.2	
	10	10.2	Objectives 1, 3, 7
	11	11.2	
		11.3	Objectives 1, 4, 5
		11.4	
	IS†	Whole	
S2–3‡	Block 3	Part 2	Objectives 1, 5

* The Open University (1971) S100 *Science: A Foundation Course*, The Open University Press.

** The Open University (1972) S22– *Comparative Physiology*, The Open University Press.

† The Open University (1972) S22– *Invertebrate Survey*. This forms part of the supplementary material sent to students with Course S22–.

‡ The Open University (1972) S2–3 *Environment*, The Open University Press.

5

Pretest

These questions are mostly related to S22–, Units 4, 6, 10 and 11; some require general knowledge. The answers include additional information and you are advised to read them before reading the Unit.

PTQ 1 What is the term used to describe organisms that cannot perform photosynthesis but obtain energy from other organisms?

PTQ 2 Do heterotrophes require all the various carbohydrates and amino acids which are found in their bodies to be supplied in their food?

PTQ 3 What term is used to describe amino acids which are necessary for an organism's survival and well-being and must be obtained from its food?

PTQ 4 What, if any, are the other 'essential' components of diets?

PTQ 5 Some of the nitrogen ingested as part of organic molecules may be converted into inorganic form by consumers—name the process and products involved in this.

PTQ 6 Recall the way in which animals were classified on the basis of their feeding habits in S22–, Unit 4.

PTQ 7 What differences in behaviour among herbivores and carnivores are likely to be related to feeding habits?

PTQ 8 What are the problems of digestion associated with feeding on plant material?

PTQ 9 What are the problems of digestion associated with feeding on animal material?

PTQ 10 Are plants and animals equally nutritious as diets?

PTQ 11 List the types of food supply available to fluid feeders and list some of the animals which consume these foods. Suggest advantages and disadvantages of these diets.

The answers to these questions are on p. 54.

3.0   Introduction

Study comment   Heterotrophes may be consumers or decomposers—the groups compared in this Section. Section 3.0.1 is a discussion whose point is to fit the immense variety of diets and feeding mechanisms of animals into a simple system which offers hopes of quantifying energy relations so that models of ecosystems can be constructed.

The terms 'consumers' and 'decomposers' are applied to different classes of heterotrophes. In general terms, *consumers* ingest parts of or whole organisms or ingest material produced by living organisms (such as blood, nectar, substances in solution in guts, contents of plant cells).

consumers

Decomposers attack dead organisms or dead parts or exuviae of organisms, causing the breakdown of these into smaller molecules that are absorbed by the decomposer's cells. Thus the difference between consumers and decomposers seems to be *either* the mechanism of how the food enters the body of the heterotrophe (if by ingestion, then it is a consumer) *or* the status of the food (if it is living or part of or inside or produced by a living organism, then this food is being consumed, not decomposed). We are in fact distinguishing between major divisions of the living organisms: the consumers are members of the Animal Kingdom; the decomposers are members of the Fungi or members of the Procaryota[1]*. Of course, there are 'difficult' cases such as the status of parasitic bacteria (Procaryotes) and parasitic fungi (especially as some of these continue to grow and multiply when their host has died) but the vast majority of heterotrophic organisms can be assigned easily to one or other of the two categories, consumers or decomposers.

decomposers

In ecosystems, the significant difference is the part played by the two categories of heterotrophes in the cycling of minerals, particularly nitrogen, phosphorus and sulphur. Consumers normally acquire these in their food as part of organic molecules and continue to metabolize them as part of organic molecules. Decomposers, as you will learn from Unit 4, convert much of this organic material into inorganic substances which are then available for re-cycling by the primary producers, most of which are members of the Plant Kingdom (some are green procaryotes).

mineral cycles

Recall that consumers also convert some of the nitrogen ingested as organic molecules into inorganic form.

QUESTION   What process is involved in this?

ANSWER   Excretion. See the answer to PTQ 5 for further comment.

QUESTION   Do consumers and decomposers play basically different parts in the carbon cycle?

ANSWER   No. The principal source of carbon for primary production is as CO_2. This is one of the products of *respiration*[2] in the majority of living organisms—plants, animals, fungi and procaryotes. Most organisms metabolize carbohydrates, taking up oxygen and producing carbon dioxide and water, and making available to their cells the energy so produced; this is 'used up' in living (i.e. ultimately dissipated as heat). Fats and proteins may also be substrates for respiration (see later).

The consumers, the organisms to be studied in this Unit, are thus *all* the members of the Animal Kingdom. Certain heterotrophic plants (parasites such as dodder and insectivorous plants such as butterwort, *Pinguicula*) and certain fungi and procaryotes also qualify under the definition of 'consumer', but they will be ignored because they form a very small proportion of the whole category of consumers in ecosystems.

* Superscript numbers are references to other Open University Science Courses which are listed on p. 40.

3.0.1 Categories of consumers

Among the members of the Animal Kingdom, there is great variety of methods of feeding and of foods. These are summarized in the answers to PTQs 6 and 11. Using the terms 'herbivore', 'carnivore', and 'detritivore' helps to place animals within food webs and thus to show the part they play in energy flow through an ecosystem. Herbivores, by definition, eat plants—thus they consume primary producers; sometimes the production of herbivores is called 'secondary production' to emphasize this relationship. Carnivores feed on other animals which may be either herbivores or carnivores. Detritivores typically feed on dead material in deposits—such as leaf litter in woods or detritus accumulated among stones of streams or in muddy deposits. Very often this dead material is of plant origin but it may include dead remains of small animals; usually there are live organisms present also—certainly bacteria, often fungi and often small animals such as ciliate protozoans or collembolans (minute insects) or nematode worms. Animals that feed principally on dead animals are often called scavengers; these range in size from maggots of blowflies to marabou storks and hyenas (and even lions). Animals that feed on products (exuviae) of large animals, such as dung (faeces), are another category of scavenger.

[margin: herbivores]
[margin: carnivores]
[margin: detritivores]

There is a further type of relationship, that of parasites and their hosts. Take, for example, the tapeworm and its host—how does the tapeworm fit into the classification above? It feeds by absorbing products of its host's digestive processes acting on its host's food; this implies that it could be classified in the same category as its host; thus a cow's tapeworms would be herbivores and a dog's tapeworms would be carnivores. But the tapeworm is depriving the host of its food supply and thus it appears to feed at the expense of the host and to be in the position of a predator on the host; so tapeworms of both cows and dogs would be acting like carnivores. In the few cases where the position of internal parasites in ecosystems has been discussed, they have been treated as carnivores, but this may not really be the proper way to fit all of them into the pattern. Insect 'parasitoids' are clearly carnivores since they wholly consume their insect host but take a much longer time to do this than would a predatory insect such as a carabid beetle or a praying mantis. Similarly, rabbit fleas and other blood-sucking insects are effectively carnivores. Aphids and other plant-sucking bugs are clearly herbivores, but often they are described as plant parasites; the same term is applied to eelworms (nematodes that live in plant tissues, feeding on them) which also are herbivores, as are the insect grubs that eat apples from inside.

[margin: parasites]

The concept that emerges from the discussion so far is the concept of *trophic levels*. Feeding on the primary producers are the first level of consumers, the herbivores or detritivores; feeding on these animals are the next level of consumers, the carnivores; feeding on these carnivores there may be further levels of consumers, more predatory carnivores. All these categories can be arranged in series which are food chains.

[margin: trophic levels]

Primary producer	First level consumer	Second level consumer	Third and higher level consumers
(a) live plant ⟶	herbivore ⟶	carnivores ⟶	carnivores
(b) detritus (=dead plant) ⟶	detritivore ⟶		

Examples

(a) bean plant ⟶	bean aphis ⟶	ladybird beetle ⟶	blue tit ⟶ cat
(b) dead oak leaves ⟶	woodlouse ⟶	carabid beetle ⟶	shrew ⟶ owl

Some food chains, such as the two given above, seem to fit the pattern admirably but in reality the tit may eat aphids, the shrew may eat woodlice and the owl may eat carabid beetles. The real situation is seldom simple—the organisms are linked together not as simple chains but as webs. This happens because many animal species eat a variety of food; the technical term for this is to call them euryphagous or polyphagous, in contrast to animals that eat one or very few species of food organism (these are stenophagous). Polyphagous animals may be strict herbivores or strict carnivores but some are able to feed both on plants and on animals; these are called 'omnivores'. The existence of omnivores clearly

[margin: polyphagous, euryphagous and stenophagous consumers]

[margin: omnivore]

8

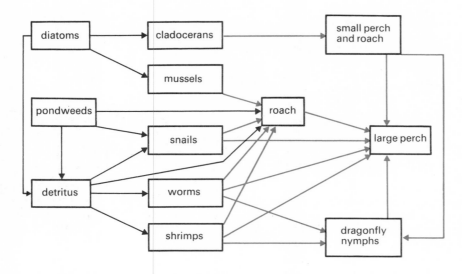

Figure 1 A food web for a small lake. The red arrows show consumers eating animal foods.

makes it difficult to analyse ecosystems in terms of trophic levels; many poly-phagous carnivores are difficult to fit in because they may function at second or higher levels at the same time, e.g. large perch in Figure 1. Many animals change their diets as they grow older; juveniles may be carnivores and adults herbivores, or vice versa. Some of the complexities of food webs are illustrated in Figure 1. Including parasites would add further interesting complications to the diagram!

Nevertheless, the idea of trophic levels is helpful in trying to follow energy flow and it can be used meaningfully up to a certain point. Really to understand an ecosystem fully in energetic terms would probably involve quantifying ALL the possible trophic interrelationships, but this task would be impossible except in a very simple system; such simple systems are very rare.

QUESTION   To which trophic level would you assign the roach in Figure 1?
_____
ANSWER   Herbivore–detritivore–carnivore. It is a euryphagous fish.

In theory, the fate of all the energy that is derived from the sunlight can be quantified and, unless some accumulates, it is all dissipated as heat by the end of the series of transfers through trophic levels. It is important to remember at this stage that the time-intervals over which energy flow is measured or estimated must be carefully considered. In a stable ecosystem, primary production, energy accumulation and dissipation at all levels should balance *if the time-interval studied is sufficiently long*. But for short intervals there may be great imbalance. Since living organisms are dynamic systems, the functioning of the ecosystem depends on the rates of all the processes involved in energy flow.

3.1   Food uptake, metabolism and excretion of individuals

Study comment The parameters that should be measured in order to quantify energy flow at the level of consumers are related to the physiology of individual animals. The basic simple equations are deduced in this Section. Methods used to measure food uptake, egesta and metabolism are given in Appendices 1, 2 and 3, which could be read with this Section or studied later or omitted if short of time; the main points made in the Appendices are given in Section 3.1.1. Section 3.1.2 introduces two research papers, the first on an aquatic carnivore, the perch, and the second on terrestrial herbivores, four species of caterpillars; from your reading of these papers and answers to questions in this text you should gain some insight into problems of experimental design and of using laboratory data to supplement field data. The papers also give values for various parameters of the energy equations; you should compare these in the two papers and with the data given in this text, both in this Section and later. Section 3.1.3 is concerned with energy studies of a special category of (mainly) terrestrial organisms, the warm-blooded birds and mammals.

It seems obvious that the amount of energy entering the primary consumer level is the amount of food eaten by all those consumers.

QUESTION But is all the 'food eaten' available as an energy source for the consumer?

ANSWER No. Much plant material is indigestible and is passed out of the body as faeces. (See the answers to PTQs 8, 9 and 10.)

So the energy entering the primary consumer level should be expressed as:

Energy taken into the body = Energy in   — Energy in
of the consumer   food eaten   faeces

or

Food absorbed   = C (consumption) − F (egesta) (see Fig. 2)

Figure 2 Food absorbed = $C - F$. In this diagram and in Figures 3, 4, 6 and 7, the area of the largest rectangle represents C (the food consumed).

The same equation can be applied to all other consumer levels; the value of F as a proportion of C is likely to vary, depending on the type of food consumed and its digestibility. Food is absorbed (after digestion) in the form of amino acids, fatty acids and sugars. Water, salts and vitamins are also absorbed, but these, although essential to the animal, can usually be neglected in studies of energy flow, although their movement through the body may involve expenditure of energy so they should not be overlooked totally.

Consider the fate of the digested food in the general metabolism of the body: some becomes involved in anabolic processes, some in catabolic processes. Anabolism includes the replacement of cell components as well as growth of the body through the production of new cells and production of gonads. Catabolism includes the breakdown of cell components and the process of respiration by which energy becomes available for all the functions of the body including movement.

The intake of amino acids usually exceeds the need of the body for amino acids in anabolic processes. The excess amino acids are deaminated forming simple nitrogenous compounds and fatty acids. If the intake of sugars and fatty acids exceeds the needs of the body for those substances at that time, the excess is usually stored, often as glycogen (in the liver of vertebrates) and as deposits of fats or oils in various parts of the body.

The nitrogenous compounds resulting from deamination are excreted from the body. It is customary to count these compounds as *not* being available as sources of energy to consumers and so to use the following equations:

Food absorbed = Food assimilated + Excreta (nitrogenous waste
                                              compounds)

          = A (physiologically useful energy) + U (excreta)

but Food absorbed = $C - F$,

so $A = C - F - U$ (see Fig. 3)

Figure 3 $C = A + U + F$.

To quantify the physiologically useful energy (A) absorbed by consumers of any trophic level, it is necessary to measure the total intake of food (C) by these consumers and to subtract from this the amount of faeces (F) and excreta (U) produced. All these quantities should be expressed in the same units—the units of energy (joules).

It is possible to derive A (the physiologically useful energy absorbed by consumers) in another way—try to think of one.

Consider how the energy is used. It is used for maintenance of the body's activities and for growth (including production of gonads as growth). Energy used in growth will appear as energy equivalent to the increase in weight either of the body or gonads. Energy used in maintenance appears as energy dissipated in the process of respiration because it is through cell respiration that energy equivalent to assimilated food or stored products is released for catabolic processes.

The use of energy is summed up in the equation:

     A = Growth + Respiration

or $A = P$ (growth of body and gonads) + R (respiration)   (see Fig. 4)

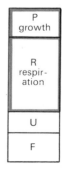

Figure 4 $C = P + R + U + F$ and $A = P + R$.

10

When there is no growth ($P = 0$), then

$A = R$ and hence $R = C - F - U$

This provides another way in which values for A or other variables may be derived from experiments.

ITQ 1 What is the equivalent to P in the equations for plant energy relations?

Read the answer to ITQ 1 (p. 55).

3.1.1 Measurement of food uptake (C), egesta (F), metabolism (expressed as respiration, R) and nitrogenous excretion (U)

The details of the methods used must clearly be related to the type of consumer studied—its habitat, its food, its size and general habits. There are certain precautions that should be taken and snags that should be avoided. These are discussed in Appendices 1, 2 and 3. You could read these now, if you wish, or proceed with this text, referring to the Appendices later. The rest of this Section is a summary of important points from the Appendices.

When quantifying C, F, R or U, the terms should be expressed as rates. These rates should be in units of energy (joules or kilojoules are the SI Units) per unit time and this involves obtaining average calorific values for all organisms, tissues and exuviae studied. Typical calorific values are given in Table 14 (Appendix 1). Since water content may vary considerably without there being variation in calorific value, it is usual to express changes or differences in weight in terms of dry weight. Calorific value and water content may vary according to age and nutritional state of organisms as well as with environmental conditions; the conditions under which observations are made should be specified in as much detail as possible.

rates

calorific values

For computing energy flow from observations on respiration, the substrate should be identified; usually this is deduced from measurements of RQ and of N in the urine. If the substrate is not known, there is less error involved in computing energy output from oxygen uptake than from CO_2 production. Heat production can be measured directly but there are technical difficulties.

RQ

The value of U is usually small compared with the other terms in the energy equation so in many energy studies, urine production is ignored. However, it is possible to compute production (P) in terms of nitrogen equivalents instead of in terms of energy; in these studies, faeces and urine are usually added together so that $F + U$ is known in terms of nitrogen. C is obtained by sampling the N content of the diet and hence A is obtained by subtracting ($F + U$) from C. A is sometimes deduced by sampling a population of animals at different times and calculating the average change in total nitrogen.

N equivalents

3.1.2 Actual values for C, A, F, R and U from laboratory and field studies

(a)   Aquatic organisms

TURN TO Solomon, D. J., and Brafield, A. E. (1972) The energetics of feeding, metabolism and growth of perch (*Perca fluviatilis* L.), *J. Anim. Ecol.*, **41**, 699–718.

This paper reports an investigation carried out while the first author was a research student. Note the arrangement of the main sections: Introduction; Methods, Experiments and Results; Discussion; Summary; References. This is typical of many papers describing original research. Most readers probably would not read the whole paper (which gives more detail than they would need) but would look at the Summary, Introduction and Discussion (probably in that order) and then other parts if they were especially interested.

The paper is chosen for you to read because it describes a well-planned investigation of all the energy parameters for a carnivorous aquatic animal; the practical problems are described and most of them are solved.

Read sections of the paper in the order given below, but *before reading each section*, first read our numbered question with prefix *S & B* (if any). Note down answers to that question *as you read the section* and then check your answers against those given in this text. Do not worry about detailed information given in the paper but not mentioned in a question.

The perch is a common British freshwater fish; it is a euryphagous carnivore. *Gammarus* is the freshwater shrimp, a common bottom-living detritus-eating crustacean.

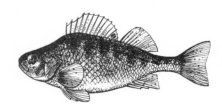

perch

INTRODUCTION Read this rapidly—answer question *S & B 1.*

S & B 1 In which two ways did the experimenters set out to improve on previous work in this field?

A 1 (a) To measure all pathways of energy through the animal concurrently.

(b) To run experiments for a sufficiently long time to avoid 'stress' effects.

Gammarus

METHODS: THE RESPIROMETER Read this rapidly—answer *S & B 2.*

S & B 2 What is the principle of measuring O_2 uptake in this respirometer? Do not give details.

A 2 To measure the O_2 content of the inflowing and outflowing water; then, knowing the rate of flow, the consumption of the fish can be calculated.

PRE-EXPERIMENT PROCEDURE Read this rapidly.

INTERPRETATION OF OXYGEN METER READINGS Answer *S & B 3.*

S & B 3 (a) List the 'oxy-calorific coefficients' (Q_{ox}) used for perch with different respiratory substrates.

(b) Give the biochemical analysis of *Gammarus*. What made up the rest of the dry weight?.

(c) Suppose that there was a constant error in measuring the oxygen concentration of the water leaving the chamber, how would this affect the validity of the experiments?

A 3 (a) Q_{ox} for protein   3·20 cal mg^{-1} (= 13·4 J mg^{-1})

for fat   3·28 cal mg^{-1} (= 13·7 J mg^{-1})

for carbohydrate   3·53 cal mg^{-1} (= 14·8 J mg^{-1})

(b) *Gammarus*—52 per cent protein; 6·4 per cent fat; no carbohydrate (all as dry weight). The rest of the dry weight (41·6 per cent) would be the 'ash' content (mainly exoskeleton which contains $CaCO_3$ and other salts). When an 'ash-free' dry weight is mentioned, this means that samples have been combusted (burnt) to remove organic matter and leave the ash, which is then weighed.

ash content

(c) This error would apply to all readings from the chart—24 such readings were made for every day and these were summed and then multiplied by the flow rate to give a figure for oxygen consumed. If the total oxygen consumed in a 24-hour period was under- or over-estimated, all calculations involving this value (e.g. Q_H) would have a systematic error. The authors' conclusions would probably stand if the error was not very large.

THE FOOD AND FAECES Answer *S & B 4.*

S & B 4 (a) What temperature was used for determining dry weights?

(b) What instrument was used for determining calorific values?

A 4 (a) 65 °C. At higher temperatures, there would be loss of weight due to breakdown of proteins and fats in addition to the loss of water due to drying.

(b) An oxygen bomb-calorimeter (Phillipson type). This is operated by placing the material in a platinum pan inside the bomb, filling the bomb with oxygen under pressure, leaving it until a steady temperature is reached and then igniting the sample with an electric current. The maximum temperature increase recorded (by a thermocouple) is a measure of energy content; this is compared with temperature changes using pellets of known calorific value.

NITROGENOUS EXCRETION Answer *S & B 5.* Do not worry about details of methods of estimation.

S & B 5 (a) What excretory products were detected?

(b) How much of the nitrogen of a meal was excreted within 48 h by a medium-fed fish?

(c) What conversion factor was used to associate O_2 consumption (and hence protein used as substrate for respiration) with excretion of NH_3 by well-fed fish so that *U* could be found by difference?

A 5 (a) Ammonia was the principal one; urea was found as traces (never more than 5 per cent of total N).

(b) About 80 per cent.

(c) 0·51 cal excreted per mg O_2 consumed (= 2·14 J mg^{-1} O_2). Note that the evidence for this is presented in another paper. Note also that 'the situation is not so straight-forward' for fish in other nutritional states.

POST-EXPERIMENT PROCEDURE Read this rapidly.

EXPERIMENTS AND RESULTS: THE ENERGY CONTENT OF GAMMARUS Answer *S & B 6*.

Note that in Table 1 the calorific values are expressed as cal/g dry weight.

S & B 6 (a) Why were the perch fed on *Gammarus* smaller than 11 mg rather than on *Gammarus* of all sizes?

(b) What was the range of energy contents for the shrimps used as food?

A 6 (a) There were consistent relationships between wet and dry weight for shrimps up to 11 mg dry weight (about 53 mg wet weight) but not for larger shrimps. To simplify the procedure, a regression was calculated relating calorific value to wet weight so that the ration could be expressed in terms of energy by simple calculation from the weights of the animals fed to the fish. Consult *ABE*, Part 2, Section 2.1.2, for a discussion of regression lines.

(b) From 793·5 cal/g (= 3330 J g^{-1}) for shrimps of 60 mg wet weight to 847 cal/g (= 3550 J g^{-1}) for shrimps of 30 mg wet weight.

LONG-TERM RESPIROMETRY EXPERIMENTS Answer *S & B 7*.

S & B 7 (a) What are the terms in Table 2 equivalent to *C*, *A*, *F*, *U* and *R* in this text?

(b) What were the calorific values of 'thin, medium and fat' fish?

(c) List the estimated maintenance requirements of the three fish R6, R10 and R12.

(d) Energy assimilation efficiency was calculated—express this in terms of *C*, *A*, *F* and *U* (or those symbols relevant to it).

(e) How did energy assimilation efficiency vary with ration?

A 7 (a) *C*, Q_I; *F*, Q_F; *U*, Q_E; *R*, Q_H. *A* is not listed in this Table.

(b) 'Thin', 4·0 to 4·5 kcal/g dry weight (= 16·7 × 10^3 to 18·8 × 10^3 J g^{-1}) 'Medium', 4·8 and 4·9 kcal/g dry weight (= 20·0 × 10^3 to 20·5 × 10^3 J g^{-1}) 'Fat', 5·0 and over kcal/g dry weight (= 20·09 × 10^3 J g^{-1} dry weight and more).

(c) R6, 4·74 kcal (= 19·8 × 10^3 J) for 28 days; this fish weighed 10·45 g (wet). R10, 6·83 kcal (= 28·6 × 10^3 J) for 28 days; this fish weighed 18·51 g (wet). R12, 4·07 kcal (= 16·8 × 10^3 J) for 28 days; this fish weighed 7·20 g (wet).

(d) Efficiency $= \dfrac{C-F}{C} \times 100$ per cent.

(e) See Figure 6 of the paper—there is an apparent trend between values of 83·5 and 87 per cent efficiency, the greater values being at the lower feeding levels—*but* the authors point out that a small systematic error in collection of faeces could result in this trend if, in fact, the efficiency remained constant at 83·5 per cent.

DISCUSSION: TOTAL ENERGY BALANCE Answer *S & B 8*.

S & B 8 What assumption made earlier in the paper is questioned in this section?

A 8 That the calorific value of perch tissues remained constant through the experiments. Discrepancies are explained if fish fed less than a maintenance ration changed in calorific value and continued to change while recovering from such low diets.

MAINTENANCE RATIONS   Answer *S & B 9*.

S & B 9   (a)   How do the maintenance rations for perch derived here differ from values derived from other authors' values for other species of fishes?

(b)   What other factor besides energy may determine a maintenance ration?

A 9   (a)   Johnson's values for pike were 5.87×10^3 J g^{-1} yr^{-1} (1·4 kcal/g/annum); the fish were of 20 to 400 g wet weight and the temperatures were mostly below 14 °C. Pentelow's value for a 10 g trout at 14 °C was 41.8×10^3 J g^{-1} yr^{-1} (10 kcal/g/annum). Perch values (25.4×10^3 J g^{-1} yr^{-1} = 6·3 kcal/g/annum) lie between those for trout and pike as would be expected from their habits.

(b)   The need for an essential component in short supply in the diet. This is illustrated by reference to work on pigs and man.

INTER-RELATIONSHIPS BETWEEN PATHWAYS   Answer *S & B 10*.

S & B 10   (a)   Figure 8 includes observations on four perch of similar size—what deductions are made from this figure concerning assimilation efficiency, excretion rate and respiration rate?

(b)   What criticism is made of Winberg's predictions on the basis of Figure 8?

(c)   What formula did Mann (1965) derive from Winberg's predictions? Express this in terms of C, A, F, U and R (or those relevant).

(d)   What do *S & B* conclude about the usefulness of Winberg's equations?

A 10   (a)   That assimilation efficiency is relatively constant at different feeding levels; that there is some nitrogenous excretion even when no food is eaten and that total excretion can be predicted from the quantity of food eaten; that the fish respired least at the lower levels of feeding and that respiration rate increased steadily as feeding level was raised above the maintenance ration.

(b)   Winberg deduced a formula: $Q = aW^b$ as cm^3 O$_2$ h^{-1}. Q is the same as R in this text; W is the weight of the fish; a is a constant depending on temperature and species (0·193 for perch at 14 °C); b is a constant (0·8) for all freshwater fish. Using an oxy-calorific value of 3·21 cal/mg O$_2$, Q can be calculated in terms of energy. 'Winberg I' is said to represent 'resting metabolism'; 'Winberg II' is twice Winberg I and represents 'natural metabolism'. Figure 8 indicates that O$_2$ consumption of perch is related to food intake and this relationship is not covered by Winberg's formula.

(c)   Mann used another Winberg formula: C (energy of ration) $= 1.25 \, (R + P)$. Since $R + P = A$, $C = 1.25 \, A$ *or* $A = 0.8C$ and $0.2C = F + U$. For perch, $A = 0.84C$.

(d)   That Winberg's formulae are not ideal for predicting metabolic rates of feeding fish since they take no account of level of feeding. Short-term respiratory experiments (up to 36 hours) give very different results from long-term experiments (several weeks). Nevertheless, Winberg's formulae set limits which included the actual values of Q for the fish in these experiments.

Study of energy flow through ecosystems must be easier if it is possible to construct generalizations.

What generalizations arise from the study of perch energetics? The importance of investigating certain variables becomes clear:

1   Whether each species should be studied separately and the validity of grouping species. Comparison of maintenance rations reveals that the three fish species pike, perch and trout form a series showing increasing maintenance rations (per unit weight) and increasing levels of general activity. So from detailed knowledge of one species, it is likely to be possible to predict general values for other species if their habits are known.

2   The validity of assuming that investigations of one group of similar individuals can define the energy relations of a given species. The size of the fish is important and this may mean that fish of different ages (sizes) have different energy relations. The previous feeding régime of the fish is important; it determines whether the fish is thin, medium or fat and the fish can change in calorific value depending on its level of feeding.

3   The validity of using results obtained under one set of conditions to define the energy relations under all conditions for that species. The type of food is important; energy relations are altered with the balance between ingredients. External conditions such as temperature may affect energy relations considerably; constant a in Winberg's respiratory formula must be corrected for temperature as well as for species.

14

But certain generalizations have come from this sort of work; Winberg, for instance, tried to extract from a great deal of data about fishes some quantitative relationships, two of which have been widely applied. These are:

(a)   The relationship between A and C: $C = 1.25A$ or $A = 0.8C$;

(b)   the relationship between R (his Q) and the species and size of fish and water temperature: $R = aW^b$, where constant a is peculiar for species and temperature.

Winberg's formulae

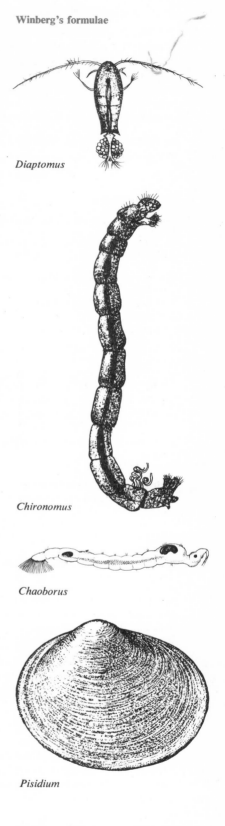

Diaptomus

Again, it is possible to group species to some extent according to systematic position. In general, metabolism is highest early in life, so that larger older individuals are more economical in energy dissipation than smaller younger individuals of that species. Metabolism is greatly dependent on temperature; the majority of animals are sluggish at low temperatures and their metabolic rates increase with increase of temperature, but there is a limit, the upper lethal temperature, above which the individual cannot survive.

Do these generalizations, derived from study of freshwater fishes, apply to other aquatic organisms?

Although there are, as you would expect, differences in the details of the relationships, the general principles derived from study of freshwater fishes apply to other aquatic animals. Here are two examples:

1   For the planktonic copepod, *Diaptomus gracilis*, the relationship between respiration and temperature is expressed by the equation:

$$R \text{ (as cm}^3 \text{ oxygen animal}^{-1} \text{ h}^{-1}) = aW^k$$

where W = dry weight in mg; $k = 0.604$ as the mean for many estimations and a averaged 0.413 at 5 °C and 9.24 at 12 °C.

2   Figure 5 shows values on semi-logarithmic plots for R against temperature for a pea mussel, *Pisidium*, a detritivorous midge larva, *Chironomus anthracinus*, and a carnivorous midge larva, *Chaoborus flavicans*. These relationships can be described by the same equation as for *Diaptomus* but with different values for the constants a and k.

Now you could attempt SAQ 1 (p. 51).

Chironomus

Chaoborus

Pisidium

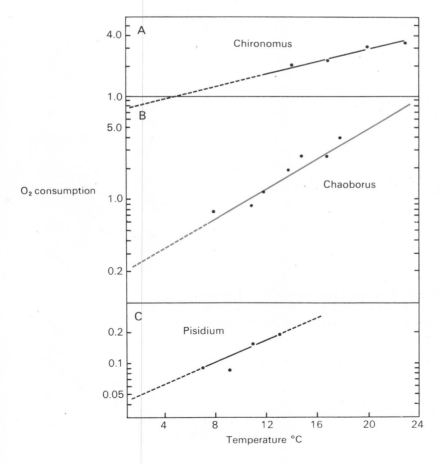

Figure 5 The oxygen consumption at different temperatures of three bottom-living organisms from a Danish lake. (Expressed as 10^{-3} cm^3 individual^{-1} h^{-1})

(b)   Terrestrial organisms

TURN TO Smith, Philip H. (1972) The energy relations of defoliating insects in a hazel coppice, *J. Anim. Ecol.*, **41**, 567–87.

This paper also is based on observations made while working for a research degree. The general layout is similar to Solomon and Brafield's paper. This paper has been chosen because it deals with small grazing herbivores and illustrates some of the problems of correlating laboratory and field data.

Note We do not expect you to read the whole of this paper *now*—you will be referred to it again later in this Unit and in Block B. Now read the Section specified below and try to answer the questions (*PHS*) relating to each.

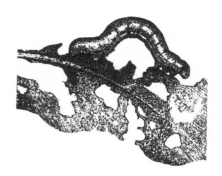

INTRODUCTION Read this rapidly to find out why the investigation was under-taken.

The 'canopy defoliators' studied were caterpillars of four genera of moth:

Operophtera brumata (L)   winter moth (family Geometridae).

Hydriomena furcata (Thunberg)   the July highflyer (family Geometridae).

Erannis spp.   the mottled umber, dotted border and scarce umber moths (family Geometridae).

Cosmia trapezina (L)—the Dunbar moth (family Noctuidae).

These all feed on young leaves of shrubs and trees between early April and mid-June.

mottled umber moth

Read: ENERGY RELATIONS: INTRODUCTION (p. 573) Answer *PHS 1*.

PHS 1   What term in the energy equation is assumed to be negligible?

A 1   *U*, the energy consumed in producing NH_3, uric acid, silk and cast skins (the exoskeleton includes chitin and protein).

FOOD CONSUMPTION AND UTILIZATION—LABORATORY STUDIES (p. 575) Answer *PHS 2*.

Note the use of logarithmic plots and of regression equations but do not worry about the method of statistical analysis (Ostle).

dotted border moth

PHS 2   (a)   What was actually measured during the feeding experiments?

(b)   Express '% assimilation/ingestion' and '% net production/assimilation' in terms of *C, A, F, U, R* and *P* (or any of these that are relevant).

A 2   (a)   Caterpillar (live) weights before and after feeding; wet weight of hazel leaves before feeding—both part of leaf to be eaten and rest of leaf as control; weight of frass and remains of leaf (dried) after feeding; weight of control part of leaf after drying. Note that the dry weight of the caterpillars was calculated from a regression based on drying and weighing many samples of caterpillars (described earlier in the paper).

(b)   % assimilation/ingestion $= \dfrac{A}{C} \times 100 = \dfrac{C - F}{C} \times 100$

% net production/assimilation $= \dfrac{P}{A} \times 100 = \dfrac{P}{C - F} \times 100$

Note that $A = 0.36$ to $0.40\ C$, about half of Winberg's general value for fishes.

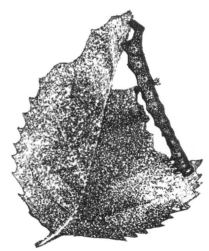

scarce umber moth

RESPIRATORY ACTIVITY (p. 576) Answer *PHS 3*.

Dunbar moth

A recording electrolytic respirometer was used—do not worry about the technical problems associated with this instrument but note the use of controls to compensate for atmospheric pressure and the need to work in settled anticyclonic weather.

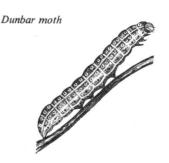

PHS 3   (a)   Over what time interval was metabolism calculated?

(b)   Why are the values in Figure 3 plotted on logarithmic scales?

(c)   How did O_2 uptake vary with caterpillar weight? Express the range of values observed as $cm^3\ g^{-1}\ h^{-1}$.

(d)   Compare the expression given as answer to (c) with Winberg's formula for fish respiration (see *S & B 10(b)*, p. 14).

A 3   (a)   Over the first 12-hour period, but allowing 2 to 3 hours for equilibration.

(b)   To give a straight line relationship instead of a curve. To obtain values for oxygen uptake, draw vertical and horizontal lines but label the intervals carefully since intervals that are equal arithmetically are not equal on the logarithmic scale.

(c)   As shown in Figure 3, conforming to the expression: $y = ax^{0.77}$, where $y = O_2$ uptake as $\mu l/h$, a is a constant varying with species, x = caterpillar dry weight (as mg). The values were of the order of $1-5$ cm^3 O$_2$ g^{-1} dry weight h^{-1} or $0.2-1$ cm^3 O$_2$ g^{-1} wet weight h^{-1}. (Conversion involved multiplying μl by 10^3 and mg by 10^3 so figures remain the same.)

(d)   The expression is similar in form to Winberg's formula: $Q = aW^b$ where $Q = O_2$ uptake, W = wet weight of fish and a and b are constants. Note that the values for the constants a and b cannot be compared directly because the Winberg constants given earlier are for wet weight of fish whereas the constants given here are for dry weight of insects.

CALORIMETRY (p. 578)   Answer *PHS 4*. Refer to *ABE*, Part 3, Section 3.3.2, for discussions of means and standard error of means.

PHS 4   *Phalera bucephala* (L) is the buff tip moth. Compare (a) the oxycalorific value of assimilated hazel leaves deduced from Evans' (1939) observations on *Phalera* and (b) the oxycalorific value derived from analysis of hazel leaves. Why were these two values different?

buff tip moth

A 4   (a)   4·89 kcal/l O$_2$ = 20·5 J cm^{-3} O$_2$

(b)   4·67 kcal/l O$_2$ = 19·6 J cm^{-3} O$_2$

If the cellulose in the leaf is all defaecated, then the food assimilated will contain a different balance of carbohydrate : fat : protein from the intact leaf, so the oxycalorific value should be higher (as observed) for the *Phalera* food intake than for the leaves.

METHODS USED TO CALCULATE ENERGY BUDGETS (p. 578).   Answer *PHS 5*. Note the use of regression lines derived from laboratory observations to obtain values for *C*, *F*, *R* and *P* and the attempts to balance the energy equations to check whether these values were consistent with each other.

PHS 5   (a)   Did the laboratory measurements give values really useful in interpreting the field results?

(b)   Compare Table 8 with Table 6—what is the difference between them?

(c)   Given that the dry weight of the *Operophtera* caterpillar was 4·70 mg, express as J mg^{-1} week^{-1} the three values for *A* calculated in this section.

(d)   Do caterpillars in the field feed continuously?

A 5   (a)   No. The caterpillars in the laboratory probably showed acceleration of feeding rate: estimates of *P* were too high, so also probably were estimates of *C* and *F*.

The utilization efficiencies (see *PHS 2*) were useful and did not appear to depend on feeding rate. These ratios were combined with field estimates of *P* (called *Pf*) to obtain values for *A* and *C* that are close to those of other workers on caterpillars. Note that Phillipson found a similar difference between laboratory and field observations on woodlice *Oniscus*.

utilization efficiencies

(b)   Table 6 is expressed in terms of dry weight of food and caterpillars, but Table 8 is expressed in terms of energy.

(c)   The values for the caterpillar are: 80·5, 25·7 and 24·4 cal/week. These become: 71·7, 23·8, 21·7 J mg^{-1} week^{-1}.

(d)   No. They probably spend about 20 per cent of their life in 'ecdysis', which is the process by which a caterpillar moults its skin and increases in volume. They rest by day and feed by night.

Now leave this paper—you should return to it in Section 3.3.2. One of the reasons for reading Smith's paper now was to allow you to check whether the generalizations based on work on perch (see p. 14) also apply to caterpillars. For these small herbivores, too, there are differences between species; size is important and temperature may be important; the type of food may be very important.

generalizations from caterpillar study

Now work through an exercise about wolf spiders, SAQ 2 (p. 51).

Great-horned owls are carnivores which feed mainly on small mammals. A study of two captive birds over a period of more than one year gave the average values in Table 1. The owls did not grow or reproduce, so $P = 0$.

TABLE 1 Daily budget of *Bubo virginianus* (Great-horned owl) of average weight 1615 g, allowed to feed on white mice, kept at 25–27 °C with a natural photoperiod (Duke *et al.*, 1973).

	C	F	U	A	R
Expressed as g dry matter kg^{-1}	26·6	2·8	6·0		17·8
Expressed as g N kg^{-1}	2·1	0·2	1·1		0·8
Expressed as kJ kg^{-1}	700	43	61		595

ITQ 2 Fill in the values of A in Table 1.

ITQ 3 Express % assimilation/ingestion in terms of energy. Compare this with values for caterpillars and fishes discussed earlier.

ITQ 4 Express R as kJ kg^{-1} yr^{-1}. Compare this value with maintenance rations for fishes, discussed earlier.
Read the answers to ITQs 2, 3 and 4.

ITQ 5 Suggest an explanation for the enormous difference in maintenance requirements between fishes and owls.
Read the answer to ITQ 5.

Great-horned owl

3.1.3 Homoiotherm energy relations

The definition of a homoiotherm is that the animal is able to maintain a relatively constant body temperature which is independent of the external (ambient) temperature. Recall that this gives the advantage of specialization of enzymes with optimum temperatures that are the body temperature; homoiothermic animals are able to remain active over a wide range of temperatures with a level of activity that is independent of the ambient temperature. For most mammals and birds, the body temperature is within the range 35–42 °C. Associated with homoiothermy are means of insulation, means of heat production and means of temperature regulation.

ITQ 6 From the point of view of energetics, what consequences are likely to arise from homoiothermy?

Read the answer to ITQ 6.

Heat is produced by muscular activity but also by resting animals—the production by resting animals is called the 'basal metabolic rate' and is conveniently calculated from measurements of O_2 uptake, CO_2 production (hence RQ) and N in the urine (from which the protein component of respiration is calculated). Another source of heat production is the metabolic processes that follow absorption of digested food; in man, there is typically a rise in heat production about 1 h after feeding, a peak about 3 h after feeding and the rate gradually falls over several hours back to the BMR of an unfed man. This action of food (called specific dynamic action or SDA) is highest with proteins and probably is related to deamination; it is nothing to do with digestion in the gut since SDA following injection of amino acids is the same as when the same quantity is taken by mouth.

BMR

SDA

You may wonder if SDA is peculiar to homoiothermic animals—the answer is *no* but SDA is generally neglected in studies of invertebrates or of fishes. But, for fishes, SDA may vary between 5 per cent and 40 per cent of the energy value of the food, depending on the proportion of protein; it can be detected as a rise in O_2 consumption after feeding although the swimming activity of the animal remains unchanged. From the point of view of movement or of growth, SDA is 'wasted' energy in poikilotherms.

QUESTION What about homoiotherms—is SDA 'wasted' energy for them?

ANSWER No. Homoiotherms must spend energy on heat production and SDA contributes heat and therefore reduces the need for other calorigenic processes (part of BMR) or for such movements as shivering.

The term R in our earlier equations thus represents two components: R^1 (the SDA of the food assimilated) $+ R^2$ (the energy used in vital activities including movement). For man, F may represent 15 per cent of C and R^1 (SDA) may be 20 per cent of A. So the energy available for P and for R^2 is about 68 per cent of C. For some fishes, F is 20 per cent and R^1 may exceed 40 per cent of C, so $(P + R^2)$ is only 40 per cent of C. Neglecting R^1 may thus lead to curious predictions of P from estimations of A, U and R^2. (See Fig. 6 and SAQ 3.)

QUESTION   What sorts of relationship are likely to be found between the size of a homoiotherm, its habits and habitat and its value for R?

ANSWER   Heat loss is roughly proportional to surface area of the body and the ratio between surface area and volume of body (hence weight) is greatest for small animals and least for large animals[3] so it is likely that R will be highest for small mammals and birds.[4] Check this in Table 2.

size and R

TABLE 2   The heat production of various fasting animals. (Recalculated from Blaxter (1967).)

Species	Body weight kg	Heat production over 24 hours	
		kJ kg^{-1}	kJ m^{-2} body surface
Horse	441	47	$3{\cdot}98 \times 10^3$
Pig	128	80	$4{\cdot}5 \times 10^3$
Man	64	134	$4{\cdot}4 \times 10^3$
Dog	15	215	$4{\cdot}3 \times 10^3$
Hen	2	296	$3{\cdot}95 \times 10^3$
Mouse	0·02	890	$4{\cdot}98 \times 10^3$

Figure 6 $C = P + R + U + F$ and $R = R^1 + R^2$.

TABLE 3   The heat production ($= R^2$) of fasting heifers of various ages. (Recalculated from Blaxter (1967).)

Age	Weight kg	Heat production kJ kg^{-1} day^{-1}
8 days	52	267
1 month	62	205
4 months	146	150
8 to 10 months	210–281	113 to 96
23 to 30 months	441–495	75

TABLE 4   The oxygen consumption of *Microtus arvalis*, all at the same temperature but in different conditions of crowding and light. (Expressed as cm^3 g^{-1} h^{-1}.) (Recalculated from Trojan (1969/70).)

Number of individuals in the group	1	3	5	6 to 9
in daylight	5·1	5·1	3·9	3·3
in darkness	4·5	4·0	3·1	X

A further implication is that young mammals will have higher values of R than adults of their species; check this in Table 3.

age and R

Microtus arvalis, the common vole, nests underground and individuals have the habit of huddling together; they come out to feed on the surface. Look at Table 4.

ITQ 7   What effect on the energy budget has the voles' habit of huddling together for part of the day?

ITQ 8   What would you expect to be the value of X in Table 4? (The oxygen consumption of a group of 6–9 individuals in darkness.)

Read the answers to ITQs 7 and 8.

common vole

The measured value of X was 3.0 cm^3 O$_2$ g^{-1} h^{-1} which is a reduction of 10 per cent of the R of 6–9 voles in daylight and a reduction of 40 per cent of the R of a solitary vole in daylight at that temperature. Huddling together greatly reduces the energy consumption of small mammals. Examine Table 5 which gives daily energy budgets for *Microtus arvalis* under typical summer and winter conditions.

ITQ 9 What would be the daily budgets in January and July if individuals spent all their time on the surface?

Read the answer to ITQ 9.

ITQ 10 Compare the daily energy budget of a vole, *Microtus*, in July under natural conditions with that of a Great-horned owl, *Bubo virginianus*, in captivity (see Table 1).

Read the answer to ITQ 10.

All this emphasizes the difficulty of using laboratory measurements of energy utilization for single animals as a guide to energy used by populations under natural conditions; animal behaviour—huddling, sheltering, hibernating, etc.— can modify greatly the energy requirements of groups of animals.

Now you could attempt SAQs 4 to 10.

TABLE 5   Daily energy budget (R) of one typical individual vole, *Microtus arvalis*, in natural conditions (expressed as kJ).

Month	Body weight g	Time spent in place at temperature h		°C	R	Total R day^{-1}
July	21	18	nest	19	23	38·4
		6	surface	20	15·4	
January	15	20	nest	0	21	36·5
		4	surface	−1	15·5	

3.2   Growth and reproduction of individuals

Study comment   Energy assimilated in excess of metabolic requirements can be measured as growth of individuals and yield of reproductive products. Patterns of growth and reproduction and their implication in terms of energy uptake are discussed first; then, in Section 3.2.1, the ratios used to express 'efficiency of growth' are defined and are applied to the data on perch and caterpillars that you studied earlier in the research papers. Section 3.2.2 discusses how the instantaneous growth rate (defined in Appendix 4, which you should read then) changes during the life span of animals and some of the factors that affect sexual maturity and reproduction. After reading this Section you should realize that it is essential to study the life history of animals before designing investigations into their production.

Where there is no growth or reproduction, then $A = R$ but, over the life of an individual animal, $A > R$ and the difference is P. P includes two different items, production of more somatic (body) tissues of the organism (i.e. growth) and production of sexual products, eggs and sperm, that are shed from the body (i.e. reproduction). (See Fig. 7.)

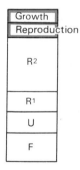

Figure 7 $C = P + R + U + F$ and $P =$ growth + reproduction.

You may wonder whether it is worth separating these two items but this can be justified on practical and on theoretical grounds. From the practical point of view, the farmer or fisherman is interested in production of edible material which is usually muscular tissue formed as a result of somatic growth; apart from those of the domestic hen, reproductive products tend to be luxury items, such as caviar, or by-products, such as soft roe of codfish. Most other carnivores also rely mainly on somatic tissues of their prey as food; a few are specialist egg predators. From the theoretical standpoint, reproduction is the essential process in the survival of a species, and the energy 'put into' reproduction yields the initial biomass for the next generation; somatic production, if not consumed by carnivores, is the transfer to decomposers from the energy consumption of the species.

In terms of energy, growth is the increase in calorific value of the body with time. But to measure its calorific value, a body must be destroyed. The simplest way to estimate P is to take a group of comparable individuals and sample it at intervals, measuring the calorific value of each sample and so obtaining an average value of P for that population. You should consider some of the statistical problems involved in this. (See *ABE*, Part 2, Section 2.1)

The more usual practice is to follow the increase in length or in weight (or both) of an individual over a period of time. This approach is similar to harvest methods and dimensional analysis used for primary producers.

The calorific value of the individual is measured at the end of the experiment, but for earlier time intervals the calorific value must be estimated using whatever information may be available about how it could have varied.

> **ITQ 11** The calorific value expressed as J g^{-1} dry weight does not remain constant through the life of an animal. Give evidence to support this statement and suggest reasons why the calorific value of an animal's body may vary.
>
> *Read the answer to ITQ 11.*

Among animals there is great variety of types of life history and pattern of growth. For many insects, including most moths and butterflies (Lepidoptera), there are four stages: egg, larva (caterpillar), pupa (chrysalis) and adult.

> **ITQ 12** During which of these stages does the insect grow?
>
> *Read the answer to ITQ 12.*

Insects are convenient experimental animals since there is not very much error in assuming that all *growth* is concentrated into the larval (e.g. caterpillar) stage; the food intake may also be concentrated in this stage but for other insects, e.g. locusts, the adult may survive for a considerable period of time and may feed a great deal—its actual increase in calorific value may be low (mature egg and sperm production) but its food intake should be taken into account when computing energy flow through its ecosystem.

For mammals, growth of young in the uterus is based on maternal food intake and the mother continues to pass on food to her young during lactation, so early growth from zygote to independent young is 'parasitic' on the mother. The young mammal is in the position of a secondary consumer, even though it may belong to a herbivorous species. A breeding female of the vole, *Clethrionomys glareolus*, requires an extra 313 kJ during her 18-day gestation period and an extra 1210 kJ during her 20-day lactation period compared with a non-pregnant female. These values represent increases of food assimilated of 24 per cent during gestation and 82 per cent during lactation over the non-pregnant feeding level; the total energy cost of a litter of bank voles is 1523 kJ spread over 38 days as extra food intake by the mother.

Female birds transfer energy to their eggs. Great tits, *Parus major*, weigh about 20 g; a breeding female lays one egg each day and generally lays a total clutch of 10 to 12 eggs. Each egg weighs about 1·7 g, so the female produces approximately her own body weight of eggs over the 12-day period. There is field evidence (which will be discussed in Block B) that food (insects) must be in good supply for tits to start laying. The female tit forages for herself but is also fed by the male, who may supply about 30 per cent of her food intake while she is laying. When the eggs hatch, the young birds may continue to be dependent on their parents until they are fledged; this happens with tits and owls and most 'garden birds'. For these fledglings, the food intake can be measured and apportioned to its source in the ecosystem (often the food consists of insects such as caterpillars) but the energy expended on gathering this food is derived from part of the parents' overall food consumption. In other bird species, e.g. grouse, the young feed themselves after they have hatched, but the parents usually expend a certain amount of energy in such activities as scratching the ground for food for the chicks and brooding them at night.

This discussion of growth in young mammals and birds has revealed some of the difficulties in apportioning energy intake of animals between growth and reproduction, two components of P in the energy equations.

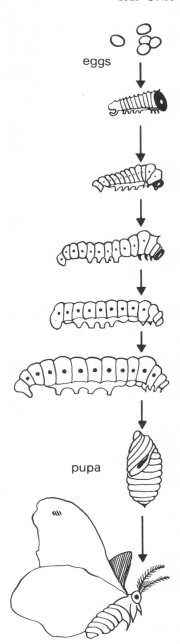

Moth development

insect life stages

ANSWER The following factors might be important:

(a)   The amount of food available in excess of the maintenance ration.

(b)   The age or stage of the animal—since there is the possibility of physiological ageing determining growth rate.

(c)   The temperature of the environment (since growth processes may well be affected by temperature). Poikilotherms are directly affected by temperature and homoiotherms need more food for maintenance at lower temperatures.

The relations between growth rates and food and age and stage of the animal are discussed in the next two Sections. As one example of the relationship between temperature, growth and life cycle, consider the data in Table 6 concerning a mirid bug (insect order Hemiptera) which sucks out the contents of plant cells. *Leptoterna dolabrata* has one generation in the year; the eggs go into diapause[5] and hatch in May of the following year. The nymphal stages are passed through rapidly (if the weather is warm) and the adults are usually able to lay their eggs in late June.

temperature and life cycle

TABLE 6   Laboratory data about length of life cycle and feeding activity of *Leptoterna dolabrata* at different temperatures. (Means of 16 individuals at each temperature (McNeill, 1971).)

Temperature °C	Time between hatching of eggs and appearance of adults (days)	Feeding rate expressed as feeding episodes insect^{-1} day^{-1}
10	eggs do not hatch	0
15	60	2·07
20	22	2·24
25	17	3·61
28	14	3·60

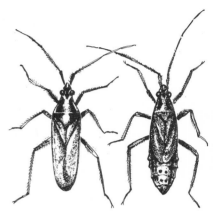

Leptoterna (male on left, female on right)

3.2.1   Growth and available food

Solomon and Brafield (1972) collected some information about the relationship between food and growth in perch; they were most interested in the maintenance ration level at which the fish put on little weight. However, their fish R2 and R3 both 'grew' more than 2 kcal in the 28-day period.

QUESTION   Calculate the values of P/C and P/A for fishes R2 and R3 from the data in Table 2 of Solomon and Brafield.

ANSWER $Q_G = P$; $Q_I = C$; $Q_F = F$; $Q_E = U$.

$$\frac{P*}{C} = \frac{Q_G}{Q_I} \quad \text{and} \quad \frac{P*}{A} = \frac{Q_G}{Q_I - Q_F - Q_U}$$

so for R2, $P/C = \dfrac{2·01}{9·84} = 0·205$ and for R3, $P/C = \dfrac{2·88}{14·88} = 0·193$

and for R2, $P/A = \dfrac{2·01}{9·84 - 1·54 - 0·81} = \dfrac{2·01}{7·49} = 0·27$

and for R3, $P/A = \dfrac{2·88}{14·08 - 2·29 - 1·07} = \dfrac{2·88}{10·72} = 0·27$

The values you have calculated are for the gross efficiency of conversion of food into fish flesh; P/C is sometimes called the 'energy coefficient of growth of the first order' (K_1) and P/A is called the 'energy coefficient of growth of the second order' (K_2). It is probably coincidence that for *both* fishes, $K_1 \approx 20$; $K_2 = 27$ per cent, but these values are within the usual range for fishes.

K_1 and K_2

If the maintenance ration is known, it is possible to calculate 'net conversion efficiency'; this is $\dfrac{P}{A - \text{maintenance ration}}$

net conversion efficiency

* These are ratios, so they are the same whether you use kilocalories or joules.

QUESTION   Why could this be an interesting value?

ANSWER   The rate of growth varies and, in computing food intake, this rate must be taken into account. An animal growing fast must consume more food per unit time than an animal on a maintenance ration.

QUESTION   Calculate 'net conversion efficiencies' for fish R2 and R3. (See *S & B*, p. 714 for an approximate MR.)

ANSWER   Assuming an approximate MR of 5 kcal for 28 days, net conversion efficiencies were:

for R2 $\dfrac{2 \cdot 01}{7 \cdot 49 - 5} = \dfrac{2 \cdot 01}{2 \cdot 49} = 0 \cdot 8$ and for R3 $\dfrac{2 \cdot 88}{10 \cdot 72 - 5} = 0 \cdot 5$.

The fish with the higher food intake had a lower net conversion efficiency. It was a smaller fish, so its real MR may have been higher, but net conversion efficiency commonly decreases at higher feeding levels; some of this fall-off may be due to increased SDA.

Recall that P. H. Smith (1972) gives values for ' % net production/assimilation' for four species of caterpillars (see *PHS*, p. 579, Table 8).

ITQ 13   Is this K_1 or K_2 or 'net conversion efficiency'?

ITQ 14   Calculate the other ratio (K^1 or K^2) for the caterpillars from the information in Table 8.

Read the answers to ITQs 13 and 14.

One factor not mentioned so far is appetite. In the perch experiments, the *Gammarus* were all eaten immediately but the caterpillars in Smith's experiments did not consume all the leaves. Had the perch been provided with a very large supply of live *Gammarus*, they would not have eaten them all—they would have revealed a limited capacity to ingest food, a limited appetite.

appetite

QUESTION   If fed *ad libitum* (as much as they could eat), would you expect 'net conversion efficiency' to be high?

ANSWER   No. See earlier.

The deduction from this, if it can be generalized, is that consumers with a superabundance of food may grow no faster than consumers with a limited food supply—and the former will 'waste' much of the energy in their food. Thus a high level of production may result from a food supply which is adequate but not very abundant. This is very important for efficient 'cropping' of domestic animals by man.

3.2.2   Growth, reproduction and age

A young animal as it grows older, grows larger—but does it continue to grow at the same rate until it dies? The answer is *no*. An exponential rate of growth[6] is maintained only for a short period of life and, in general, as the animal grows older its instantaneous growth rate decreases—see Figure 8. Turn now to Appendix 4 (p. 47) for a discussion of growth rates and a definition of instantaneous growth rate. Some animals grow at a smoothly decreasing instantaneous rate, some grow in spurts with alternating rapid and slow growth periods. The parts played by environmental factors and inherent (genetic) factors in determining growth patterns can be unravelled from experiments.

ITQ 15   Given that the food supply is adequate, what environmental factors might be expected to affect growth of vertebrates and how might they act?

Read the answer to ITQ 15.

Where environments alter seasonally, cyclical changes in growth rate are to be expected in response to changes in temperature and/or light,[5] but whether cyclical changes in growth rate also occur as a result of endogenous rhythms is controversial (see SAQ 11).

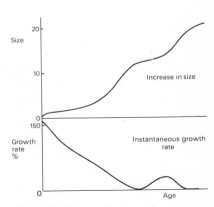

Figure 8   Changes in size and instantaneous growth rate with age.

23

If it lives long enough, an animal will become mature and, given the opportunity, will breed. From the point of view of the *species*, reproduction is the most important activity of organisms since it is essential for the survival of the species. Sexual maturity involves a diversion of energy into the gonads; typically this means cessation (or a check) in somatic growth and it may mean utilization of food reserves.

Among fishes, the weight of eggs produced is commonly about 20 per cent of the total body weight, as in brown trout, *Salmo trutta*, and pike, *Esox lucius*; it is even higher in some fish, e.g. plaice, *Pleuronectes platessa*, have eggs that make up more than 30 per cent of the weight of mature females. The growth of ovaries including ripe eggs represents 40 per cent of the total annual production of female perch in Windermere. Recall that you have already read figures related to the cost of reproduction of mammals (voles) and birds (great tits).

egg production of fishes

Mammals and birds stop skeletal growth when they reach the 'adult' size which varies only within rather narrow limits for the species.[7]

> **ITQ 16** Does the calorific value of the body of a mammal or bird become fixed when it reaches adult size?
>
> *Read the answer to ITQ 16.*

Fishes may continue to grow throughout their lives and may spawn many times. Typically growth in body size slows or stops as the breeding season approaches and is resumed in the interval between the end of that spawning and the onset of the next breeding season (see Fig. 9). Periodic changes in growth rate may be recorded in parts of the body such as scales and bones; this makes it possible to determine the age of an individual and even its past growth history (in terms of length) in some cases (see Fig. 10).

Since there are important changes in anabolism at maturity, it is necessary to consider what factors control the onset of maturity. If this happens at the same age in a variety of habitats, for that species genetic factors probably determine the timing of maturity; this is the common condition in many animals. But environmental factors may be involved to the extent that under-feeding or harsh physical conditions may delay maturity and plenty of food may advance it. At the other extreme are animals that become mature only when physical or

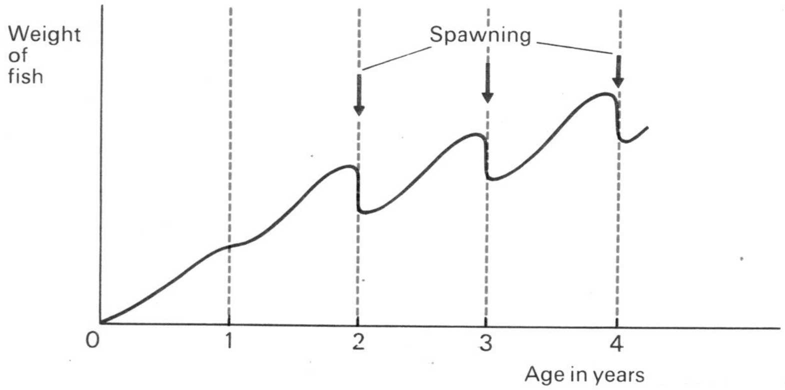

onset of maturity

Figure 9 Changes in weight of a hypothetical fish as it ages.

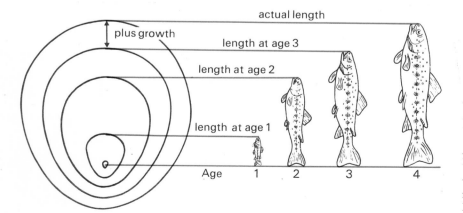

Figure 10 Diagram to illustrate how the annual rings on a fish's scales can be used to calculate the length of the fish at the end of each year of its life. Note that this is possible only when there are regular changes in growth rate as for brown trout in the British Isles.

nutritional factors have operated in a special way; thus, in Australian desert areas, birds breed only when there has been a certain amount of rain and this happens irregularly and at intervals of several years.

The majority of fish species spawn more than once in their lives and grow between each spawning season; larger fish have larger gonads, so females produce more eggs on each spawning occasion as they grow older. Some species, such as Pacific salmon, *Oncorhynchus*, mature all their eggs or sperm at the same time— so they spawn once only and die soon afterwards. Most insects behave in the same way as Pacific salmon—the adults all breed within a limited period and then die. Most mammals and birds are able to breed on more than one occasion but, unlike the fishes, they do not show skeletal growth between their breeding seasons; the number of offspring produced does not depend on the age or size of the female but is characteristic of the species. Whales represent a compromise; they grow between pregnancies but only one offspring is produced each time, however large the mother.

The type of life history (the extent to which growth is affected by maturity and the number of breeding events and number of offspring produced) is very important when considering energy flow in ecosystems and population dynamics and the management of resources. This type of study in animals is comparable with phenological studies of plants (Unit 2, Section 2.3.1).

Now you can attempt SAQs 11, 15 and 16.

3.3 Energy parameters of populations of consumers

Study comment This is the first Section to consider the problems of measuring energy flow for communities instead of for single individuals. There must be a decision, based on preliminary observations, of how to group consumers and which groups to study in detail. Methods are described in Appendix 5, which could be read now or later. Section 3.3.1 discusses how production of a population is defined and measured; the details of Allen's graphical method are given in Appendix 6, which should be read at this stage. For Section 3.3.2 you are referred again to the research paper by P. H. Smith, which illustrates some of the problems of working with populations in the field and gives comparative figures for wild populations of caterpillars, grasshoppers and spittle-bugs. Section 3.3.3 discusses some factors that affect production and some ratios by which the turnover of energy can be compared in different communities or at different trophic levels.

So far we have considered the various parts of the energy flow equations in terms of individuals, but in ecosystem studies the 'consumers' are many individuals, often of many different species, and the problems of evaluating their respiration, consumption and production are not quite the same as for individuals. Sometimes it is possible to distinguish between types of herbivore and to relate them to types of primary producer—herbivores that live on phytoplankton or on higher plants in aquatic ecosystems, for instance; sometimes it is possible to distinguish a group of carnivores which are the 'top' carnivores.

Usually each type of consumer includes individuals of several different species— the caterpillars that eat hazel leaves can be considered as one group of herbivores, but there are differences in physiology between them, so treating them as a single group means making approximations. Ideally, each species should be studied independently, but this would make drawing up energy balances for even simple ecosystems an impossible task. Study of the most abundant species will usually give an acceptable approximation. There are many inherent errors in calculating energy flow through populations, and treating all consumers of one particular category as though they were of one species may not add greatly to the error of the estimates. A study to identify the most abundant species and their feeding habits and phenology is an essential prerequisite to a study of energy flow in a community. Compare the situation in studying primary production, discussed in Unit 2, Section 2.3.1.

Refer to Appendix 5 for an account of methods of measuring C and R for populations.

3.3.1 Production (*P*) of populations of consumers

Production of an individual is measured as the growth in energy content of that individual over a period of time. For a population, the energy content at any time is the biomass multiplied by the average energy content of individuals.

Production is defined as the total elaboration of tissue during any time interval and it may be measured in terms of weight (wet or dry) or energy content.

QUESTION   If B_{t2} is biomass at time t_2 and B_{t1} is biomass at time t_1 (and t_2 is later than t_1), does $(B_{t2} - B_{t1}) = P$?

ANSWER   Only if there have been no deaths or emigration or immigration between time t_1 and time t_2.

Production includes elaboration of tissues by individuals that die before the end of the period as well as that by individuals that survive; it also includes elaboration of tissues by individuals that come into the population as a result of reproduction unless these are specifically excluded, for instance, by considering the production of a particular age group (called a cohort or age class) of a population of consumers. Production can be related to biomass:

$$P = G\bar{B}$$

when $\bar{B}$ is the average biomass during a time-interval, t, and G is the instantaneous rate of growth in weight. This formula works well over short periods or when G and mortality are both small or both vary exponentially; otherwise its usefulness as an approximation is variable and must be assessed, and the values may not be very close to the truth. Probably the simplest method of computing production is 'Allen's graphical method', first used for a trout population in New Zealand (Allen, 1951). This is described in Appendix 6 (p. 49), which you should read now.

Allen's graphical method

For all methods of computing production, simultaneous estimates of population numbers and of mean weight are required and as frequently as possible. But it is usually difficult and time-consuming to estimate population size and sometimes it is sufficient to have a few good estimates of numbers and to assume patterns for mortality from which to derive the numbers between these periods; mean weights are usually easy to determine and so can be obtained for many more dates than the good estimates of numbers. Under some conditions, e.g. in fish ponds, there are few deaths and the production is simply the difference between biomass at the beginning and end of a period.

It is generally true that production of populations of very young and small individuals is extremely difficult to estimate accurately. Often these young individuals are subject to high mortality, which may not be exponential but may operate heavily at definite stages. The rate of growth is usually exponential early in life. Production of young stages is sometimes computed from estimates of numbers and weight of eggs produced by females of the population and from estimates of numbers and mean weight of young individuals at some later date by assuming that both growth rate and mortality rate are exponential; often this is the best estimate possible.

3.3.2 Energy budgets of caterpillars

TURN TO Smith, Philip H. (1972) The energy relations of defoliating insects in a hazel coppice, *J. Anim. Ecol.*, **41**, 567–87. Recall that you have already read parts of this paper (see Section 3.1.2b). The object of this investigation was to provide energy budgets for certain caterpillars in Monks Wood, and it provides a good example of how energy budgets are constructed for wild populations by a combination of field and laboratory observations.

INTRODUCTION   (You have read this before.)

THE STUDY AREAS   Note the choice of old and young coppice to give contrasts but the similarity in soil and other vegetation (do not worry about details of these).

DEFOLIATOR SPECIES STUDIED   (Refer back to Section 3.1.2b for common names of these caterpillars.)

SAMPLING METHODS Note that there were practical and theoretical problems of sampling. The current year's leaf-bearing shoot was chosen as basic sample unit because the number of leaves does not increase during the year. 'Unit ground area conversion' is applying a formula relating the shoots to the area of coppice floor in m^2.

For the following sections, try to answer the numbered questions.

RESULTS OF SAMPLING:

1 LEAVES AND SHOOTS Answer *PHS 6*.

PHS 6 (a) Were more leaves per shoot produced by the older or younger coppice?

(b) Were the numbers of leaves per shoot similar in the two years (1965 and 1966)?

A 6 (a) By the younger coppice (the black circles in Fig. 1).

(b) No. The maximum values were higher in 1965 for both sorts of coppice but the values at the end of the growing season were higher in 1966 (comparing old with old and young with young).

2 LARVAL POPULATIONS The following statistical concepts are dealt with in *ABE*: mean in Part 2, Section 2.1.2; variance and standard error in Part 3, Section 3.3.2. Do not worry about statistical tests not given in *ABE*. Answer *PHS 7*.

PHS 7 (a) What were the ranges of mean densities per 100 shoots in 1965 and 1966? Was the standard error high or low?

(b) In Figure 2, what sort of scale is used for the ordinates?

(c) Was mortality similar in older and younger coppice?

A 7 (a) In 1965, from 21 to 0·27 (0·3) larvae per 100 shoots; in 1966, from 1·86 to 0·07 larvae per 100 shoots. The standard error was high—up to 30 per cent of the mean.

(b) A logarithmic scale. This allows the values to be plotted in a reasonable space; a further advantage is that the slope is related to the rate of decrease of numbers.

(c) Yes. There was a lag of about one week in the younger coppice at the beginning of the season but less difference at the end.

ENERGY RELATIONS:

1 INTRODUCTION (You have read this earlier.)

2 TISSUE PRODUCTION—FIELD ESTIMATES Note the use of regressions to convert wet to dry weights. Answer *PHS 8*.

PHS 8 (a) How was production of caterpillars defined?

(b) Which of the four species of caterpillar contributed most to the seasonal production?

(c) Were there differences in production between the two sites and the two years?

A 8 (a) As gain in dry weight of the larval population per season.

(b) *Operophtera brumata* (the winter moth)—see Table 4.

(c) The differences between old and young coppices in the same year were small but the differences between the two years were large (three times or more higher in 1965 than in 1966).

You have already read ENERGY RELATIONS (3, 4, 5 and 6).

Read 7 CONSTRUCTION OF FIELD ENERGY BUDGETS.

Refer back to *PHS 5* (p. 17) and its answer; then answer *PHS 9*.

PHS 9 Did feeding rates derived from laboratory experiments give useful estimates of assimilation in the field?

A 9 No. The net production/assimilation ratios were used to compute seasonal assimilation, intake and egestion parameters because these gave the most consistent estimates (given in Table 10).

PHS 10 (a)   Are feeding estimates of defoliators based on % defoliation likely to be accurate?

(b)   How good is the agreement between % defoliation and calculated energy ingested by caterpillars for 1965?

A 10 (a)   They are likely to be inaccurate because holes caused by caterpillars feeding become larger as the leaf itself grows in area and also because caterpillars may bite off bits of leaf that fall to the ground.

(b)   Fair—percentage values of 7·2 and 4·04 for old coppice and 5·5 and 4·41 for young coppice.

DISCUSSION: ENERGY RELATIONS   Answer *PHS 11.*

PHS 11 (a)   Is it easy to work out caterpillar energy budgets in terms of area of ground?

(b)   Smalley (1960) worked on grasshoppers (*Orchelimum*) living on a salt-marsh grass (*Spartina*)—how do values for these insects compare with the defoliators? *Note* a misprint in Table 12: read Ingestion instead of Infestion.

(c)   Wiegert (1964, 1965) worked on spittle-bugs (frog-hoppers, order Hemiptera) and grasshoppers in alfalfa fields and in fields that had gone out of cultivation (old-fields)—how do values for these insects and localities compare with the defoliators on hazel?

A 11 (a)   No. A hazel coppice consists of clumps (stools) with a variable area of canopy, so estimates should be based on detailed surveys. It is better to express production in terms of land area (to make it comparable with grassland studies) than of leaf area, and it is land area that is used here.

(b)   Net production was higher for the grasshoppers and so were all the other parameters estimated, but the ratio of % net production/ingestion of grasshoppers was about half that for the caterpillars and grasshopper metabolism/net production was about three times that of the caterpillars. The explanation for these differences is that all stages of the life history of grasshoppers were included in the study but only the larval (growing) stage of the caterpillars.

grasshoppers and bugs

(c)   All the values for energy budgets of spittlebugs on alfalfa were much higher than those for the caterpillars; there was less difference for the grasshoppers on alfalfa. The values for insects of old-field communities were lower than for the caterpillars. The other insects had markedly higher metabolism/net production ratios and markedly lower % net production/ingestion ratios than the caterpillars. The reason for this is given in the answer to (b).

Net production values from Table 12 converted into J m^{-2} are (reading down the column): 28·4, 31·7, 9·6, 7·5, 45, 67, 19, 0·21, 2·5, 0·42, 1·67.

EFFECTS OF DEFOLIATION ON PRIMARY PRODUCTION   Answer *PHS 12.*

PHS 12 (a)   What were the increases in leaf production in 1966 as compared with 1965?
(b)   What were the changes in defoliator pressure between 1965 and 1966?

A 12 (a)   Leaf production was 75 per cent higher in old coppice and 35 per cent higher in young coppice in 1966.

caterpillars and tree production

(b)   The loss of leaf was 1–2 per cent in 1966 compared with 4–6 per cent in 1965 (a change of 3–4 per cent); the energy flow through the defoliators was 49–54 J m^{-2} in 1965 and 14·6–16·7 J m^{-2} in 1966.

Note that other authors also have found that caterpillars reduce primary production of trees by a factor much greater than the actual assimilation or production of the insects.

Turn to Smith's Table 13 (p. 584); Figures are given here for K_1 and K_2 for field populations of various insects. (Look at the second (K_2) and third (K_1) columns.) Note the contrast between the caterpillars (the hazel defoliators) and the spittlebugs and grasshoppers; the two latter groups included adults feeding but not growing as well as larvae feeding and growing. Note that the figures for the caterpillars are not exactly the same as those given earlier since this Table is based on field data.

3.3.3 Production, biomass and total energy turnover

'Production' as defined here is not the same as 'productivity' used in ordinary speech, when it is generally equated with 'yield'. This yield is usually thought of in terms of units that are useful to man (e.g. tonnes of fish landed) or of value in some way (e.g. the number of adult lions or large elephants in a national park). Sometimes 'terminal production' is used to describe yields of interest to man.

When considering the functioning of ecosystems, production at one trophic level is a limiting factor for the production of the trophic level above it—total carnivore production cannot exceed total herbivore production; it must be less or the herbivores would become extinct and it is likely to be much less since the carnivores have K less than 100 per cent. One of the relationships which is considered in Unit 5 is that between the production of adjacent trophic levels, since this has been the subject of much argument since Lindeman's original statement of the theory of trophic levels in 1942.

Production is not the only important parameter when considering the flow of energy through ecosystems. For each trophic level, $A = P + R$ and the relationship between P and R may vary widely. R represents the consumption of energy (food) that is not being transformed either into new flesh or into gonadal products—a 'loss' to the ecosystem. Where P represents a resource of use to man, clearly it is desirable to make R as small as possible so that P becomes a higher proportion of A (so that K is high). The relationship between annual P and annual R is discussed in Section 3.5.

P:R

Another relationship of great interest is that between P and B.

P:B

> ITQ 17 What relationship would you expect to find between P and B?
>
> *Read the answer to ITQ 17.*

In populations of fish, the growth rate (and hence P) may be very low because many individuals (high B) are sharing a limited food supply. Reduction of B, by cropping some of the population, may lead to increase in growth rate of the survivors and hence to increase in P—yet the total consumption of food (C or A) may remain the same. High values for B in an ecosystem do not necessarily mean high values of P; low values of B may be associated with either high or low values of P—hence it is necessary to try to estimate P and R as well as B and C (or any three of these four parameters) to gain an accurate picture of energy turnover within a particular population or trophic level of the ecosystem.

Refer back to Unit 2 if you need to recall a similar discussion of $P:B$ ratios of primary producers. The values generally considered are annual values for both plants and animals.

One of the difficult problems about $P:B$ ratios is deciding what value of biomass to use. Generally authors state that they use 'average or mean biomass' over the period for which production was estimated.

QUESTION Does this imply adding up values of biomass and taking the arithmetic mean?

ANSWER This is sometimes done but really the average value should be computed from the instantaneous rates of growth and of mortality, which may have changed during the period. Derivation of average biomass from an Allen curve is probably a good approximation. If production of gonads is not involved and mortality is low the $P:B$ ratio is really the same as the instantaneous rate of growth in energy content; this is high, typically, for young stages, when biomass is small, and falls as biomass increases.

Various ratios have been used to express the relationship between energy turnover and production at different tropic levels. Some of these are discussed in Unit 5. One commonly used ratio is called '*food chain efficiency*' and is defined as:

food chain efficiency

$$\frac{\text{energy of prey consumed by predator } (= C_{n+1})}{\text{energy of food supplied to prey } (= Y_{n-1})} \times 100\%$$

where the prey is at level n, the predator at level $(n + 1)$ and the prey's food at level $(n - 1)$. Y_{n-1} may equal P_{n-1}.

Another commonly used ratio is '*gross ecological efficiency*' (which is the same as Ivlev's 'energy coefficient of growth of the first order'). It is defined as:

$$\frac{\text{energy of prey consumed by predator } (= C_{n+1})}{\text{energy of food consumed by prey } (= C_n)} \times 100\%$$

The highest food-chain efficiencies occur when all the prey's food is consumed, that is, when food-chain efficiency = gross ecological efficiency. One of the principal thinkers in this field has been Slobodkin (1959, 1962, 1964) working on laboratory populations of *Chlamydomonas* (an alga), *Daphnia* (a herbivorous crustacean) and Man (cropping the *Daphnia* and thus acting as predator) and also on *Artemia* (a crustacean that feeds on minute algae), *Hydra* (a cnidarian that feeds on *Artemia*) and Man (a higher order predator cropping *Hydra*). For the *Daphnia* experiments, the maximum ecological efficiency attained was 13 per cent but for the *Hydra* experiments it was 7 per cent. Slobodkin suggested that as a general rule gross ecological efficiency in natural ecosystems should be of the order of 10 per cent.

Tilapia

If you have retained *Ecological Energetics* from S100 (Phillipson, 1966) you can read about the *Daphnia* experiments in sections 2.5 and 2.6 of that book. *This is black-page reading.*

Now you can attempt SAQs 12–15.

Ctenopharyngodon

3.4 Consumers in natural ecosystems

Study comment This Section consists of a series of 'case studies' of different types of consumers in different environments. You should work carefully through the ITQs and should note the contrasts between the actual values of energy parameters and the ratios between them for the different populations of animals.

Table 13 on p. 35 has spaces which you should try to fill in as you read through the sub-sections of Section 3.4; this Table will be discussed in Section 3.5.

3.4.1 Herbivores in aquatic ecosystems

Fishponds with herbivorous fish which are completely harvested present a simple system for studying energy flow with man acting as consumer at the level of first carnivore. Table 7 gives figures for ponds in Malaysia, stocked with a *Tilapia* hybrid, which feeds on algae, and grass carp, *Ctenopharyngodon idella*, which feeds on angiosperms. The values in the Table are for 24 weeks of fish growth:

Uganda kob

> **ITQ 18** What sort of efficiency is the conversion value of net plant production to fish production? Comment on the value of this ratio.
>
> *Read the answer to ITQ 18.*

3.4.2 Herbivores in terrestrial ecosystems

You have already studied one category of these, the defoliating caterpillars of Smith's paper.

As a contrast, consider the figures in Table 8 for large mammals in East Africa. The kob ingested about 10 per cent of the net plant production in the National Park area; the elephants and grazing mammals in another National Park in Uganda actually ingested about 60 per cent of the annual net production of plants.

> **ITQ 19** Calculate the food chain efficiency for the kob, assuming that the whole production is consumed by a predator (man or lions). Calculate the gross ecological efficiency on the same assumption.
>
> *Read the answer to ITQ 19.*

A study of small mammals in a desert area of Arizona, USA, where the principal plants were creosote bush *Larrea tridentata* (covering about 21 per cent of the ground surface) and grasses (covering about 2 per cent of the surface) revealed

African elephant

that the most abundant were kangaroo rats, *Dipodomys merriamus*. The jack rabbit, *Lepus californicus*, had a slightly higher biomass because the animals were much larger; a third species of interest was the grasshopper mouse, *Onchomys torridus*, because it feeds on arthropods as well as on plants. Table 9a gives information about the community of mammals. The food of the small mammals was worked out in detail as shown in Table 9b.

> **ITQ 20** Compare the proportion of the total herb and shrub production consumed by the small mammals with the proportion of total seed production consumed.
>
> *Read the answer to ITQ 20.*

Dipodomys

Onchomys

The kangaroo rats may have assisted the germination of some seeds through their habit of stripping off the fruit coats and burying the seeds, whereas the rabbits destroyed an equal quantity of shoots to that which they ate—but even this may have contributed to plant production by stimulating growth of dormant buds.

TABLE 7 Fish production in ponds in Malaysia over a period of 24 weeks. The solar radiation available for photosynthesis was $13 \cdot 8 \times 10^5$ kJ m^{-2}. (Recalculated from Prowse (1972).)

Pond	Primary gross production kJ m^{-2}	Primary net production kJ m^{-2}	Fish production kJ m^{-2}	Conversion efficiencies plant gross production solar radiation %	fish production plant net production %
B3	8×10^4	$2 \cdot 1 \times 10^4$	$3 \cdot 7 \times 10^2$	5·8	1·8
B21	$9 \cdot 6 \times 10^4$	2×10^4	3×10^2	7	1·3
B15	$5 \cdot 4 \times 10^4$	$1 \cdot 7 \times 10^4$	$2 \cdot 4 \times 10^2$	4	1·4

TABLE 8 Annual budgets for large herbivorous mammals in East Africa. (Recalculated from Buechner and Golley (1967) and Weigert and Evans (1967).)

	Consumption kJ m^{-2}	Assimilated food kJ m^{-2}	Respiration kJ m^{-2}	Production kJ m^{-2}	Average biomass kJ m^{-2}
Kob (antelope) in Uganda	310	262	257	3·47	13
Elephants in Uganda	300	98	96	1·42	30
Other large mammals with the elephants	1570	—	—	—	158
Large grazing mammals in Tanzania	880	660	650	13	62

TABLE 9a Mammals of a desert creosote bush community. All values m^{-2} yr^{-1}. (Recalculated from Chew and Chew (1970).)

Species	Numbers	Average biomass mg	Production J	Maintenance J	Ingestion J	Assimilated J
Dipodomys	$11 \cdot 5 \times 10^{-4}$	45·3	$12 \cdot 6 \times 10^2$	228×10^2	299×10^2	242×10^2
Lepus	$0 \cdot 2 \times 10^{-4}$	45·5	$5 \cdot 1 \times 10^2$	92×10^2	192×10^2	97×10^2
Onchomys	$1 \cdot 83 \times 10^{-4}$	4·0	$1 \cdot 5 \times 10^2$	28×10^2	—	29×10^2
Others (10 spp.)	$4 \cdot 1 \times 10^{-4}$	18·5	$4 \cdot 9 \times 10^2$	70×10^2	150×10^2	75×10^2

TABLE 9b Food sources of small desert mammals. All values as kJ m^{-2} yr^{-1}. (Recalculated from Chew and Chew (1970).)

	Seeds*	Herbs and low shrubs	Tall shrubs browsed	Cactus	Arthropods	Vertebrates
Dipodomys	25·8	3·6	0·6	0	0·75	0
Lepus	0·3	4·4	13·8	0·7	0	0
Onchomys	0·2	0·15	0	0	3·35	0·15
Other spp.	3·6	0·75	0·4	0·3	1·8	0·05
Total available	34·5	315	640	13·7	?	?
Total eaten by small mammals	30	8·9	14·8	1	5·9	0·2
Total metabolized by small mammals	24	5·5	6·3	0·5	4·5	0·15

* Seeds were available through the whole year.

31

3.4.3 A terrestrial ecosystem with herbivorous and carnivorous arthropods

Sericea lezpedeza is a hardy deep-rooted leguminous plant growing to a height of up to 1m. E. F. Menhinick (1967) studied the arthropods living in an almost pure stand of this legume; he divided them into herbivores of several categories, carnivores of several categories, and detritivores (not numerous in this study). Table 10 gives estimates for A, R and P.

The figures for R are all taken from laboratory experiments and Menhinick states that probably they are half the real values; it is possible that the P values also are only half the real values. The A values are obtained by adding P and R, so they may be underestimated by 100 per cent. A is likely to have been 30–50 per cent of C (cf. the caterpillars).

The net production of the legume was 9.8×10^3 kJ m^{-2} and this was 34 per cent of the gross plant production; the production values are comparatively low, similar to those for forest heaths and about half that of beech woods.

TABLE 10 Energy budgets for arthropods living on *Sericea lezpedeza*. All values kJ m^{-2} yr^{-1} (Recalculated from Menhinick (1967).)

	A	R	P
HERBIVORES*			
grazing herbivores (grasshoppers, beetles, caterpillars)	7·9	5·5	2·3
sucking herbivores (plant bugs and aphids)	5	3·8	1·2
nectivores (bumble and solitary bees)	7·2	7·2	**
all herbivores	20	16·4	3·6
CARNIVORES			
chewing carnivores (mantids, dragonflies)	0·59	0·51	0·08**
sucking carnivores (bugs, flies, spiders)	1·64	1·42	0·23**
all carnivores	2·23	1·93	0·31
DETRITIVORES (beetles)	0·09	0·09	**

* 80 per cent of all species collected were herbivores.

** Production was not measured from species that fed outside the area as well as in it.

ITQ 21 Calculate the ratios of herbivore consumption to net plant production and carnivore consumption to herbivore consumption.

ITQ 22 What is the gross ecological efficiency of the herbivore to carnivore link?
Read the answers to ITQs 21 and 22.

moose

3.4.4 Mammalian herbivores and carnivores on an island

Isle Royale is an island, 544 km^2 in area, in Lake Superior (North America). Moose reached this island in 1908 and wolves crossed to it on the ice in 1948. In a later Unit, the population changes will be discussed in detail but here we will assume that in the 1960s there was a steady state, so that the extent and production of the vegetation, the size and composition of the moose population

TABLE 11 Data from Isle Royale study. (Jordan *et al.* (1971).)

Moose biomass	in August	386 000 kg	average biomass	6·76 kg ha^{-1}
	in March	349 000 kg		
Increment in live weight of moose		91 000 kg yr^{-1}		1·67 kg ha^{-1} yr^{-1}
Biomass transfer of moose to wolves		68 000 kg yr^{-1}		1·24 kg ha^{-1} yr^{-1}
Wolf biomass in January		812 kg		0·015 kg ha^{-1} yr^{-1}
Increment in live weight of wolves		141 kg yr^{-1}		0·0026 kg ha^{-1} yr^{-1}
Number of individuals of moose in May		about 1000		
Number of calves produced each year		about 440		
Number of wolves in March		about 24		

and the size and composition of the wolf population remained stable from year to year, meaning that the system was in balance. The wolves are the only predators on moose, and most moose that die are killed by wolves or eaten by wolves after death; in midsummer, however, some calves may die and not be found by wolves until too much decomposed. Moose make up 85 per cent of the animal food of wolves; the rest is mainly beavers.

wolf

The figures in Table 11 were generated by a computer programme using data from Isle Royale supplemented by other data about moose and wolves in captivity.

ITQ 23 Calculate (a) the increment in live weight of moose (P) as a percentage of average moose standing crop (B); (b) P for wolves as a percentage of B for wolves; (c) B for wolves as a percentage of average B for moose; (d) P for wolves as a percentage of P for moose; (e) B for wolves as a percentage of biomass transfer of moose.

ITQ 24 Assuming that the heat production of wolves is the same as that for dogs (see Table 2), calculate the annual R of wolves.

ITQ 25 Assuming that moose have a similar calorific value to deermouse and voles (take it to be 20 kJ g^{-1} of dry weight, and the wet weight to include about 60 per cent by weight of water), calculate how much moose the wolves should eat to provide energy for R.

Read the answers to ITQs 23, 24 and 25.

The computer programme gives values of biomass (standing crop), annual increment and transfer to wolves for a 'cohort' (groups of individuals born in the same year) followed through time until the last surviving member dies at the age of 17+ years. These are shown in Figure 11.

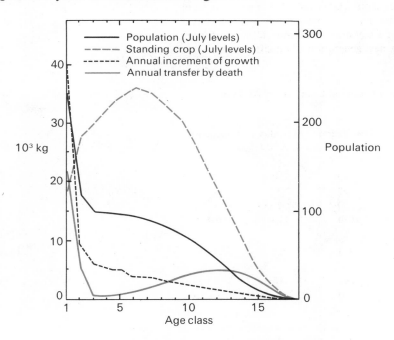

Figure 11 Numbers and biomass computed for each year class of the Isle Royale moose herd. The population is the number present in July; the standing crop is the biomass of that population; the annual increment is the total of live-weight gains in the year; the annual transfer is the total weight of moose dying in the year.

ITQ 26 From the curves, answer the following:

(a) At what age is the biomass of the cohort greatest?

(b) At what age is the annual increment greatest?

(c) At what age is the transfer to predators greatest?

(d) At what age does the annual transfer first exceed the annual increment?

Read the answer to ITQ 26.

33

A moose cohort survives for 18 years and this means that a large portion of its biomass is maintained for many years before being harvested by the wolves. The turnover is slow as indicated by the low proportion of wolf B to moose B in the community. But consider the environment—in the Canadian winter, plants die back and the herbivorous moose is faced with many months when food is sparse and probably of low quality. Almost certainly the moose stops growing and is able to lower its basal metabolic rate during the winter. The wolves are in a more fortunate position, since their food supply is available all through the year; probably they eat relatively more in winter—wolves in a Canadian zoo consume $1\frac{1}{2}$ times as much food in winter as in summer. So the seasonal fluctuations affect the primary producers very drastically and the primary consumer population shows physiological adjustments; the carnivores do not suffer food diminution in winter but do, of course, suffer from direct effects of climate on their physiology. But the biomass and production of the carnivores are very much lower than the biomass and production of the herbivores. This is an example of a fairly simple system that has been observed over many years and latterly has seemed to be in balance.

3.4.5 Benthic consumers in a productive lake

The values given in Table 12 are the result of many years study of Lake Esrom in Denmark; the insolation on average is 367×10^4 kJ m^{-2} yr^{-1}. Gross phytoplankton production is 1.02×10^4 kJ m^{-2} yr^{-1}, and net production is probably 6.8×10^3 kJ m^{-2} yr^{-1}. Some of this is consumed by zooplankton which has a production of 500 kJ m^{-2}yr^{-1} and possibly respires 750 kJ m^{-2} yr^{-1}. Probably, up to half the phytoplankton production sediments and so becomes available for detritivores in the benthos. This is the main source of energy for the benthos but a certain amount of detritus comes from plants near the shore and from wind-blown leaves. There are three main detritivores in the mud and two predatory insect larvae. The insect larvae metamorphose into adults that leave the lake—but lay eggs that hatch into a new generation of aquatic larvae.

TABLE 12   Energy budgets for benthic invertebrates in Lake Esrom. All kJ m^{-2} yr^{-1}. (Recalculated from Jónasson (1972).)

	Production	Respiration	Mortality	Emergence
DETRITIVORES				
Chironomus anthracinus (midge)	314	1510	150	164
Ilyodrilus (worm)	25	30	?	—
Pisidium (pea mussel)	6·3	20·2	?	—
Total detritivores	345	1570	150	164
CARNIVORES				
Chaoborus flavicans (midge)	60	213	11	48·5
Procladius pectinatus (midge)	12	30	5·5	7
Total carnivores	72	243	16·5	55·5
DECOMPOSERS (=microbenthos)	?	880	—	—

Chironomus and *Pisidium* grow very slowly, suggesting that much of what they ingest is indigestible whereas *Chaoborus* and *Procladius* grow quickly.

ITQ 27   Calculate the total assimilated energy for detritivores as a proportion of net production of phytoplankton.

ITQ 28   Calculate the ratio of carnivore consumption to detritivore consumption (assuming that A is the same proportion of C for both groups—is this likely to be true?).

Read the answers to ITQs 27 and 28.

3.5 General principles about the energetics of consumers in ecosystems

Study comment A full study of energy flow through an ecosystem requires a great deal of time and research resources. The effort could be reduced if there are consistent relations between some of the energy parameters. The $A:C$ ratio, the relationship of R to A and R to P and the $P:B$ ratio are discussed from this point of view. The Section concludes with general comments on the inter-relationships of primary producers, herbivores and carnivores.

Fill in the empty spaces in Table 13; the second column (Source) indicates where the information is to be found in this Unit.

Consider the steps that must be taken to work out the energetics of a group of consumers:

data necessary in energetics study

1 A preliminary study to gain information about their distribution in the habitat, feeding habits and phenology (life history), and about their food organisms and predators.

2 Laboratory studies (probably) of: wet to dry weight and calorific value of animals and their food; $A:C$; R under various conditions; perhaps growth rate under various conditions.

TABLE 13 Some ratios of energy parameters for animals mentioned in this Unit.

Animal	Source	Type of consumer	$A:C$ %	$R:A$ %	$P:B$ %	$P:C$ % (K_1)	$P:A$ % (K_2)	$R:P$* actual
perch	S & B fish R2, R3	carnivore	83·5	—	—	21	27	—
bullhead	SAQ 1 fish 5	carnivore	82	61	1·1	31	38	(1·6)
	SAQ 15		—	—	3·2, 3·8	—	—	—
trout	SAQ 3 fish 4	carnivore	86	65	4·8	30	35	(1·8)
	SAQ 15		—	—	0·8 to 2·7	—	—	—
winter moth caterpillar	PHS	herbivore			—			
Orchelimum	PHS	herbivore	27	62	—	10	37	1·7
alfalfa grasshopper	PHS	herbivore	37	65	—	13	34–38	1·9
alfalfa spittlebug	PHS	herbivore	39	59	—	16	42	1·4
old-field spittlebug	PHS	herbivore	58	92	—	4	8	11
Leptoterna	SAQ 13	herbivore			—			
grazing insects	3.4.3	herbivores	—		—	—		
sucking insects	3.4.3	herbivores	—		—	—		
chewing insects	3.4.3	carnivores	—		—	—	—	—
sucking insects	3.4.3	carnivores	—		—	—	—	—
wolf spider	SAQ 2	carnivore						(2·1)
Chironomus	3.4.5	detritivore	—		3·8 yr 1 / 0·4 yr 2	—		
Ilyodrilus	3.4.5	detritivore	—		0·7	—		
Pisidium	3.4.5	detritivore	—		0·2	—		
Chaoborus	3.4.5	carnivore	—		1·7	—		
Procladius	3.4.5	carnivore	—		1·9	—		
Diaptomus	SAQ 12	herbivore			—			
owl, Bubo	3.1.2b	carnivore			—	—	—	—
Uganda kob	3.4.2	herbivore						
elephant	3.4.2	herbivore						
Tanzanian mammals	3.4.2	herbivores						
Dipodomys	3.4.2	herbivore						
Lepus	3.4.2	herbivore						
Onchomys	3.4.2	omnivore	—			—		
moose	3.4.4	herbivore	—			—	—	—
wolf	3.4.4	carnivore	—	(>45)			—	—

* These are based on annual values except those in brackets, which are for shorter periods.

Note that — indicates that no information is available.

3   Field estimates at intervals of: population numbers; weights of individuals (to give mean weights for the population); food intake; state of reproductive maturity (and weight of gonads); respiratory activity if possible.

This adds up to a formidable research programme, so it is not surprising that most studies have gaps in the information collected and very few studies are continued for more than two years (i.e. the 'life' of a research student on a grant which is two to three years). To cover more than a small number of species of consumers and more than a very small number of ecosystems will only be possible if the actual workload can be cut down by making assumptions based on the detailed observations now available for a few species.

Clearly field data must be obtained for population numbers and average weight at intervals; from these, biomass and production can be derived by construction of Allen curves. State of maturity can be observed when weight data are collected so production can be portioned between somatic growth and gonad growth. Field data of food consumption also can be obtained when weight data are collected, but this may involve careful timing based on the preliminary study of feeding habits (e.g. it is no good always sampling at midday and expecting to measure food consumption accurately if the animals only feed at dusk). Tracer studies using labelled P or C have been very helpful in some environments.

field data

> **ITQ 29**   Given that values of B, P and C are available from field studies, what other energy parameters are needed for fitting the consumer into an ecosystem energy-flow model?
>
> *Read the answer to ITQ 29.*

Turn to the completed version of Table 13.

> **ITQ 30**   Consider the $A:C$ ratios—try to suggest generalizations based on these.
>
> **ITQ 31**   Consider the $R:A$ and $R:P$ ratios—try to suggest generalizations based on these.
>
> *Read the answers to ITQs 30 and 31.*

McNeill and Lawton (1970) have plotted $\log P$ against $\log R$ for 53 determinations of annual values of P and R and have found that it is possible to draw three straight lines representing three sets of regression equations. The categories of animals involved are:

$\log R : \log P$

1   Homoiotherms, all with high $R:A$ and $R:P$ ratios.

2   Poikilotherms with short lives (less than two years) with low $R:P$ ratios.

3   Poikilotherms with long lives (more than two years) with intermediate $R:P$ ratios.

Category 3 includes most fishes, and most insects belong to category 2, which can be subdivided into those animals with resting stages which have very low respiratory rates, such as eggs or pupae in diapause, and those which do not have such resting stages. The insects with low-energy-cost resting stages have lower $R:P$ ratios than the others.

McNeill and Lawton give regression equations relating $\log P$ and $\log R$ for their three categories. If these equations prove to be well-founded, this offers the possibility that R values can be derived from observed P values (or vice versa, using R values deduced from laboratory experiments and knowledge of temperatures in the field).

From earlier discussions, it is not surprising that homoiotherms should have a different $R:P$ ratio from poikilotherms since the maintenance of constant body temperature imposes an energetic cost. Among invertebrates, a contrast between herbivores and carnivores might have been expected but this is not apparent in our figures nor is it mentioned by McNeill and Lawton.

It would be convenient to be able to relate production and biomass so that measurement of one could be used to forecast the other. Table 13 shows a wide dispersion in values of $P:B$, the five highest (17–27 per cent) being for ungulate mammals (kob, moose and Tanzanian mammals), the wolf spider and the wolf. The other values are 5 per cent or less but the Table has many gaps. On general

$P:B$

grounds it is likely that the ratio should be high for organisms with short life histories and therefore with a rapid turnover; it should be very high for large animals with short average life span.

This Unit has been concerned more with the problems of estimating the energy parameters for individual consumers and populations of consumers than with the impact of consumers on each other and on primary producers. This topic will be discussed in Unit 5, but it seems appropriate to end this Unit by considering some relevant information.

Two ratios comparing energy turnover and production at different trophic levels were stated in Section 3.3.3: food-chain efficiency and gross ecological efficiency. Since this Unit has discussed very few food chains, there is not enough evidence to draw conclusions about the values for these ratios.

Two simple questions can be asked:

consumers and their food resources

1 To what extent do herbivores exploit their food resources?

2 To what extent do carnivores exploit their food resources?

Question 1 can be answered in general terms for the British Isles from the fact that much of the vegetation remains green throughout the summer until autumn, when leaves fall from trees and herbs die back as a result of hormonal changes

TABLE 13 (completed) Some ratios of energy parameters for animals mentioned in this Unit.

Animal	Source	Type of consumer	$A:C$ %	$R:A$ %	$P:B$ %	$P:C$ % (K_1)	$P:A$ % (K_2)	$R:P*$ actual
perch	S & B fish R2, R3	carnivore	83·5	—	—	21	27	—
bullhead	SAQ 1 fish 5	carnivore	82	61	1·1	31	38	(1·6)
	SAQ 15		—	—	3·2, 3·8	—	—	—
trout	SAQ 3 fish 4	carnivore	86	65	4·8	30	35	(1·8)
	SAQ 15		—	—	0·8 to 2·7	—	—	—
winter moth caterpillar	PHS	herbivore	41	43	—	24	59	0·6
Orchelimum	PHS	herbivore	27	62	—	10	37	1·7
alfalfa grasshopper	PHS	herbivore	37	65	—	13	34–38	1·9
alfalfa spittlebug	PHS	herbivore	39	59	—	16	42	1·4
old-field spittlebug	PHS	herbivore	58	92	—	4	8	11
Leptoterna	SAQ 13	herbivore	16 to 36	41 to 52	—	15 to 20	48 to 59	0·7 to 1·1
grazing insects	3.4.3	herbivores	—	70	—	—	29	2·4
sucking insects	3.4.3	herbivores	—	76	—	—	24	3·2
chewing insects	3.4.3	carnivores	—	86	—	—	—	—
sucking insects	3.4.3	carnivores	—	87	—	—	—	—
wolf spider	SAQ 2	carnivore	91 or 76	68	18	29	32	(2·1)
Chironomus	3.4.5	detritivore	—	83	3·8 yr 1 0·4 yr 2	—	17	4·8
Ilyodrilus	3.4.5	detritivore	—	55	0·7	—	45	1·2
Pisidium	3.4.5	detritivore	—	77	0·2	—	23	3·2
Chaoborus	3.4.5	carnivore	—	78	1·7	—	22	3·6
Procladius	3.4.5	carnivore	—	72	1·9	—	28	2·5
Diaptomus	SAQ 12	herbivore	35 to 60	44 to 81	—	8 to 34	30 (19 to 56)	2·3
owl, Bubo	3.1.2b	carnivore	85	100	—	—	—	—
Uganda kob	3.4.2	herbivore	85	98	27	1·1	1·3	74
elephant	3.4.2	herbivore	33	98	5	0·5	1·4	67
Tanzanian mammals	3.4.2	herbivores	75	98	21	1·5	2	50
Dipodomys	3.4.2	herbivore	81	94	3·5	4·2	5·2	18
Lepus	3.4.2	herbivore	50	95	1·4	2·6	5·3	19
Onchomys	3.4.2	omnivore	—	93	4·8	—	5·2	19
moose	3.4.3	herbivore	—	—	25	—	—	—
wolf	3.4.4	carnivore	—	(>45)	17	0·2	—	—

* These are based on annual values except those in brackets, which are for shorter periods.

Note that — indicates that no information is available.

within the plants. Clearly the edible parts of the primary producers are not fully consumed during the season of production; much primary production passes to the decomposers. Some herbivores may be limited by their food supply—they may be able to feed only on young leaves or only on a certain plant species. That many plants produce substances distasteful to animals[8] is an interesting evolutionary development which limits herbivore consumption, which in general is a small fraction of primary production.

It is much more difficult to answer question 2 from general observations. Many carnivores are euryphagous and turn to a different prey species if one species of prey becomes rare. As you will read in Block B, food shortage may lead to few or no young being produced in some years but adults can survive on low rations.[9] The normal excess of plant production over herbivore consumption may be the result of carnivores keeping the herbivore populations at levels such that the plants are not over-exploited. Removal of carnivores may lead to such increase in number of herbivores that they eat out their food supply—examples of this will be discussed in Block B.

It seems a reasonable assumption that observations over a sufficient period of time would show that an ecosystem is in a state of balance in which herbivores do not over-exploit primary producers and carnivores do not over-exploit herbivores or other carnivores.

Summary

The diets and feeding methods of consumers are very diverse so that it is difficult to assign consumers to definite trophic levels unless they are strict herbivores. Any study of energy flow through consumers in an ecosystem must be preceded by general studies of the food, feeding habits and life histories of the animals; methods and timing of procedures to measure energy flow can then be planned to cover the principal species (those with the highest numbers or greatest biomass or highest rate of energy turnover).

The equations used to follow the fate of energy entering a consumer trophic level are:

$$C \text{ (consumption of food)} = A \text{ (physiologically useful food absorbed)} + F \text{ (faeces)} + U \text{ (urine or nitrogenous excretion)}$$

and $A = P$ (production) $+ R$ (respiration)

and $P =$ somatic growth $+$ gonad growth

and $R = R^1$ (specific dynamic action of food absorbed) $+ R^2$ (energy used in vital activities)

These equations can be applied to studies of individuals in the laboratory or to populations under field conditions. Methods of measurement are given in the Appendices. The research paper by Solomon and Brafield is an example of a competent laboratory study of a carnivorous fish. It is seldom, if ever, possible to measure all energy parameters under field conditions, so values derived from laboratory investigations are used to supplement values obtained in the field. The research paper by P. H. Smith illustrates some of the problems involved in this procedure when applied to caterpillars in a wood.

Study of consumers in ecosystems would be easier if it were possible to make generalizations about their energy relations. Study of a variety of consumers reveals the following possible generalizations:

The ratio of A to C is often of the order of 80 per cent for carnivores and for mammalian herbivores with symbiotic bacteria or eating highly digestible food, such as some seeds. For other herbivores, the $A:C$ ratio is often of the order of 40 per cent, presumably because of the large amount of indigestible material present.

There is a contrast between homoiotherms and poikilotherms in the proportion of absorbed energy which is spent in respiration. The $R:A$ ratios for birds and mammals are usually over 90 per cent, whereas for most cold-blooded animals these ratios are much lower, especially if the animals have short lives and spend part of this time in low-energy-cost resting stages such as the pupae of insects.

An implication of this is that $R:P$ ratios are high for homoiotherms and low for poikilotherms and that a greater proportion of the food intake of poikilotherms can be devoted to production.

For many species, there is a relationship between size and R of the type of: $R = aW^b$, where R is oxygen consumption, W is weight and a and b are constants which may be related to temperature and to the type of organism. (Winberg proposed such a relationship for fishes.)

Metabolism and production are usually highest early in life; older individuals are more economical in the use of energy but also grow more slowly and may stop growing and divert excess energy into reproduction, a process which often imposes a considerable energetic cost.

The relationship between P and the biomass present is very variable, but is likely to be high early in life and for organisms with short life spans. A simple way of computing production and biomass and the changes in these is by the use of Allen curves.

The Unit concluded with two general statements:

Herbivore consumption is usually a small fraction of primary production, perhaps because many herbivores are selective; they eat few species of plants and usually special parts of these.

Carnivores are often euryphagous and can turn to alternative prey species if preferred foods become rare. Their reproduction may be limited by food shortages.

References to other Open University Courses

1   S22–, Unit 1, Section 1.2
2   S100, Unit 15
    S22–, Unit 5, Section 5.0
    S22–, Unit 6, Section 6.0
    S323, Units 1 and 2
3   S100, Unit 18, Section 18.1.1
4   S22–, Unit 6, Table 1, Figures 3 and 4
5   S22–, Unit 11, Section 11.3
6   S100, Unit 20, Section 20.3.1
7   S22–, Unit 11, Section 11.2.3
8   S22–, Unit 11, Section 11.4.1
9   S100, Unit 20, Appendix 1
10 S323, Unit 1
11 S22–, Home Experiment 7
12 S22–, Unit 10, Section 10.2
13 S2–3, Block 3, ITQ 19

Publications cited in text

Allen, K. R. (1951) *New Zealand Marine Dept. Fish. Bull. No. 10 1–231. The Horokiwi Stream. A Study of a Trout Population*. New Zealand Marine Department.

Blaxter, K. L. (1967) *The Energy Metabolism of Ruminants*. Hutchinson.

Buechner, H. K. and Golley, F. B., Preliminary estimations of energy flow in Uganda kob (*Adenota kob thomasi* Neumann), in Petrusewicz, K. (ed.) (1967) *Secondary Productivity of Terrestrial Ecosystems*, pp. 243–54, Institute of Ecology, Polish Academy of Sciences.

Chew, R. M. and Chew, A. E. (1970) Energy relationships of the mammals of a desert shrub (*Larrea tridentata*) community, *Ecol. Monogr.*, **40**, 1–21.

Duke, G. E., Ciganek, J. G., and Evanson, O. A. (1973) Food consumption and energy, water, and nitrogen budgets in captive Great-horned Owls (*Bubo virginianus*), *Comp. Biochem. Physiol.*, **44A**, 283–92.

Jónasson, P. M. (1972) Ecology and production of the profundal benthos in relation to phytoplankton in Lake Esrom, *Oikos Suppl.*, **14**, 1–148.

Jordan, P. A., Botkin, D. B. and Wolfe, M. L. (1971) Biomass dynamics in a moose population, *Ecology*, **52**, 147–52.

Kibby, H. V. (1971) Energetics and population dynamics of *Diaptomus gracilis*, *Ecol. Monogr.*, **41**, 311–27.

Lindeman, R. L. (1942) The trophic-dynamic aspect of ecology, *Ecology*, **23**, 399–418.

Mann, R. H. K. (1971) The populations, growth and production of fish in four small streams in southern England, *J. Anim. Ecol.*, **40**, 155–90.

McNeill, S. (1971) The energetics of a population of *Leptoterna dolabrata* (Heteroptera: Miridae), *J. Anim. Ecol.*, **40**, 127–40.

McNeill, S. and Lawton, J. (1970) Annual production and respiration in animal populations, *Nature*, **225**, 472–4.

Menhinick, E. F. (1967) Structure, stability and energy flow in plants and arthropods in a *Sericea lezpedeza* stand, *Ecol. Monogr.*, **37**, 254–72.

Moulder, B. C., and Reichle, D. E. (1972) Significance of spider predation in the energy dynamics of forest-floor arthropod communities, *Ecol. Monogr.*, **42**, 473–98.

Phillipson, J. (1966) *Ecological Energetics*, Edward Arnold.

Prowse, G. A., Some observations on primary and fish production in experimental fish ponds in Malacca, Malaysia, in Kajak, Z., and Hillbricht-Ilkowska, A. (ed.) (1972) *Productivity Problems of Freshwaters*, pp. 555–61. Polish Scientific Publishers (Państwowe Wydawnictwo Naukowe).

Slobodkin, L. B. (1959) Energetics in *Daphnia* populations, *Ecology*, **41**, 232–43.

Slobodkin, L. B. (1962) Energy in animal ecology, *Adv. Ecol. Res.*, **1**, 69–101.

Slobodkin, L. B. (1964) Experimental populations of *Hydrida*, *J. Anim. Ecol.*, **33** (Suppl.) 131–48.

Trojan, P., An ecological model of the costs of maintenance of *Microtus arvalis* (Pall.), in Petrusewicz, K., and Ryszkowski, L. (ed.) (1969/70) *Energy Flow through Small Mammal Populations*, Polish Scientific Publishers (Państwowe Wydawnictwo Naukowe).

Weigert, R. G., and Evans, F. C. Investigations of secondary productivity in grasslands, in Petrusewicz, K. (ed.) (1967). *Secondary Productivity of Terrestrial Ecosystems*, pp. 499–518, Institute of Ecology, Polish Academy of Sciences.

Recommended general reading

In addition to the general textbooks, the following are particularly relevant to this Unit:

Gerking, S. (ed.) (1967) *The Biological Basis of Freshwater Fish Production*, Blackwell Scientific Publications. (This includes a selection of interesting papers.)

Hardy, R. N. (1972) *Temperature and Animal Life*, Arnold. (This is an introductory text. Chapters 3 and 4 deal with calorimetry, energy balance and heat relations, especially of homoiotherms.)

Watson, A. (ed.) (1970) *Animal Populations in relation to their Food Resources*. Blackwell Scientific Publications. (Some of the papers refer to food selection; most are more relevant to Block B than to this Block.)

Methods of measuring food uptake (C) and egesta (F)

Consider a caterpillar eating a leaf: it bites portions of the leaf cleanly away and swallows them and at intervals it produces solid 'frass' (faeces). It is possible accurately to weigh: (a) the leaf before and after the caterpillar has fed on it; (b) the caterpillar before and after it has fed on the leaf; (c) the frass produced by the caterpillar. The time involved should be recorded so that the terms can be expressed as rates; they should all be expressed as units of energy (joules) per unit time so the weights of leaf and frass and caterpillar (before and after eating the leaf) should all be convertible into joules. This means making a series of observations to obtain average calorific values for leaves, caterpillars and frass. The instrument used is the bomb calorimeter[10]; the material to be assayed is dried and ground to a powder and made into pellets before being put into the instrument. Only a small quantity can be ignited at a time so the whole process is laborious and time-consuming.

You should consider the statistical problems involved—how many samples should be ignited to give reliable calorific values? What are likely to be the limits of probability when using such average calorific values in any single experiment? Look at *ABE*, Part 2, Section 2.0.

Notice that the material to be assayed is dried before ignition. There can be large differences in water content and these lead to weight differences which are not relevant to measurements of energy flow—hence it is essential to work in *dry weight equivalents*. Again this leads to the problem of sampling and using average values when quantifying experimental observations. You must assume that the leaf is an *average* leaf of that species—but the water content and calorific value (and digestibility) of leaves varies with their age and possibly with their position on a tree—it may be necessary to specify that the leaf is an *average young shade leaf* of that species of tree growing at a specified season on a specified type of soil and in a region with a specified type of climate. Similarly, the average water content and calorific value of frass may vary with the age and nutritional state of the caterpillar and with the type of plant being eaten. The caterpillar, too, may vary in its water content and calorific value according to age, nutritional state, humidity of the air and so on.

Because of limitations of time, money (apparatus) and personnel, most investigators of food uptake (especially under field conditions) use averaged calorific values, often obtained from different species of plants and animals and under different conditions (see Table 14 for example). It is fairly general for dry weight or water content to be estimated for that particular set of experimental conditions, since this is a simple task involving only an accurate balance and a drying oven.

The example of one caterpillar eating one leaf is a simple system which could be managed wholly under experimental conditions. Plants could be grown under carefully controlled conditions, caterpillars reared with a similar degree of care, and all operations carried out in sterile laboratories under constant conditions. The results obtained should then be reproducible with a high degree of probability.

Many animals feed less tidily than caterpillars and produce faeces that are much less easy to handle, so that there are problems of measuring food uptake and faeces production even in terms of wet weights. The use of radioisotopes may simplify the situation.

If the plant has incorporated labelled ^{14}C into its leaves, then a caterpillar feeding on it will take up the ^{14}C in the bits of leaf it eats and some of this will be assimilated and the rest will pass out in the faeces. Using a counter to estimate the quantities of ^{14}C in the remains of the leaf, in the caterpillar and in the frass (and making allowance for background radiation and for the loss of activity due to passage of time) can given an accurate picture of the uptake of plant material by the caterpillar. The compounds in which the ^{14}C will be present at any time can be extracted and identified. To quantify energy flow, it is necessary to assume that the ^{14}C labelled compounds behave in the same way as the bulk of

use of ^{14}C

TABLE 14   The energy content of various organisms and parts of organisms (all as kJ g^{-1} dry weight).

Chlorella (alga)	21·8 (ash-free 24·2)	*Microtus pennsylvanicus* (vole)	19·2
Ankistrodesmus (alga)	22·6 (ash-free 24·4)	*Peromyscus maniculatus* (deermouse)	18·8
Nitschia (alga)	16·4 (ash-free 23)	*Mus musculus* (mouse)	26·2
Hazel leaves	19·6	another estimate	16·5
Plant stems	18	*Cottus perplexus* (bullhead or sculpin)	22·1
Plant roots	19·6	*Salmo gairdneri* (rainbow trout)	22
Seeds	.20·3	*Cichlasoma bimaculatum* (tropical fish)	21·5
Litter	18	*Operophtera brumata* (caterpillar)	24
Sphaerotilus (bacteria)	17·6	*Philaenus spumarius* (spittlebug)	
Tubifex (aquatic worm)	23·2	egg	25·3
Ilyodrilus (aquatic worm)	21·5	larva	22·1
Pisidium casertanum (pea mussel) (shell-free)	14·3	adult	23·8
Modiolus (horse mussel) (shell-free)	19·2	adult	24·7
Succinea (water snail) (shell-free)	22·5	*Tenebrio molitor* (mealworm)	
Schizocosa (spider)	22·7 (ash-free) 23·8)	larva	26·4
Xysticus (spider)	25 (ash-free 26·7)	beetle	20·9
centipede	25·1 (ash-free 26·4)	*Musca domestica* (housefly)	
cockroach	23 (ash-free 24)	maggot	25·6
carabid beetle	25 (ash-free 25·2)	adult	20
Acheta (cricket)	24 (ash-free 25·4)	*Ephemerella* (mayfly nymph)	21
Diaptomus gracilis (copepod)		*Nemoura* (stonefly nymph)	22·3
eggs	23·6	*Rhyacophila* (caddis larva)	25·3
nauplius	21	*Chironomus anthracinus* (midge larva)	24·5
copepodids	22	*Chaoborus flavicans* (midge larva)	20·6
adult	23·9		
Daphnia (cladoceran)	18·4		

the substances in the plant which form the food of the caterpillar. The use of isotopes in this way has been helpful in studying uptake of phytoplankton by zooplankton and by suspension feeders such as bivalve molluscs.

Following a labelled meal through the gut, partly into the body and partly into faeces gives information about rates of assimilation and evacuation. It is essential to know these rates if the main information about feeding comes from examination of gut contents of samples of animals collected and killed in the field. From these samples are derived 'fullness of gut' indices or actual weights of food in the stomach for different animals; these indices or weights can be turned into 'quantities eaten per day' (*C*) if rates of passage from the stomach to the rest of the gut are known. Comparison of contents of the rectum and the stomach can give a measure of *F* compared with *C*. You should consider the statistical difficulties inherent in this quite common type of calculation of *A* from *C* and *F*.

fullness of gut

Methods of measuring metabolism, expressed as respiration (R)

The methods to be used must depend on the size of the consumer and the habitat in which it lives. Students of S22 will have done an experiment on the metabolism of fly maggots.[11] Recall the principle underlying this experiment and the assumptions on which it was based.

The principle of the experiment is to hold a given number of maggots in a limited volume of air from which carbon dioxide is removed by absorption with soda-lime (Figure 12) and to measure changes in the volume of air over a period of time. It is assumed that the maggots absorb oxygen and give out carbon dioxide; all the CO_2 is absorbed by the soda-lime so the changes in volume of the air are a measure of the oxygen absorbed by the maggots. It is assumed that there are no other processes that affect the volume of air round the animals (the experiments were conducted in a water bath to give constant temperature and control tubes without maggots were used to monitor changes in volume of air in tubes with soda-lime only). Students convert maggot volume into dry weight using graphs provided in the *Home Experiment Notes*; thus they can express maggot metabolism in terms of volume of oxygen absorbed per unit dry weight of maggot per unit time for the temperature used. The apparatus used is a simple *respirometer*.

respirometer

For computations of energy flow, the uptake of oxygen must be turned into a figure representing the energy made available for metabolism as a result of cells respiring that volume of oxygen.

Consider the substrates for cellular respiration: these may be carbohydrates or fats or proteins (amino acids).

With carbohydrate as substrate, the situation is summed up by the equation:

$$C_6H_{12}O_6 + 6O_2 \rightarrow 6CO_2 + 6H_2O$$

The respiratory quotient (RQ), which is ratio of O_2 absorbed to CO_2 given off, is 1·0.

With fats as substrate, the RQ is less than 1·0. Taking the saturated fat tripalmitin, the equation is:

$$C_{51}H_{98}O_6 + 72.5O_2 \rightarrow 51CO_2 + 49H_2O$$

The RQ is $51/72.5 = 0.70$.

It is not possible to give a representative equation for proteins but the RQ is typically about 0·8. Some of the carbon and oxygen in the protein (or amino acid) remains combined with nitrogen and is excreted. On average, 1 g of urinary N represents the catabolism of 6·25 g of protein and means that:

111 kJ of energy has been made available, 5·94 l O_2 has been consumed and 4·76 l of CO_2 has been given off (RQ 0·80).

TABLE 15   Energetics of respiratory substrates.

	carbohydrate	saturated fat	protein
RQ (ratio of O_2 to CO_2)	1·0	0·71	0·8
Energy liberated (as J) during:			
combustion of 1 mg of food	23·6	39	17
uptake of 1 cm³ of O_2	21·2	19·2	19·2
production of 1 cm³ of CO_2	21·2	27·2	24·4
Liberation of 1 J of energy involves:			
uptake of O_2 in cm³	0·048	0·052	0·052
production of CO_2 in cm³	0·093	0·078	0·081

When the substrate is not known, energy output can be computed with less error from measurement of O_2 uptake than from measurement of CO_2 production (compare the last two lines of Table 15). For really accurate estimations, the substrate should be identified, and this is often done by measuring the RQ and the output of urinary N and then calculating the amount of protein respired (and the volumes of O_2 and CO_2 involved in this) and then the balance between fats and carbohydrates respired.

QUESTION It is generally assumed that the principal substrate for respiration is carbohydrate. Under what conditions is the principal substrate likely to be (a) fats (or oils), (b) proteins?

ANSWER (a) Many animals store fats (or oils) which are likely to be the chief substrate when they are using food reserves, i.e. when they are not assimilating enough food to provide for their metabolic requirements. Animals that eat diets containing much fat (e.g. some seeds) are also likely to use fats as principal respiratory substrate. (b) Animals that are starving and have used up all food reserves are likely to use protein as principal substrate. Animals living on a high protein diet also may use protein as principal respiratory substrate.

The average adult European has an RQ of 0·82 indicating that the respiratory substrate is *not* exclusively carbohydrate!

The rate of metabolism is usually estimated by measuring the rate of oxygen uptake. The CO_2 may be removed from the system (as in the maggot experiment and when using Warburg manometers) or oxygen concentration may be measured in the inflow and outflow of an apparatus and the consumption found by difference. The latter method is very common when dealing with aquatic organisms; sometimes oxygen content is sampled at the beginning and end of an experiment, using a closed chamber. Automatic oxygen recorders are now available.

In some studies, the output of CO_2 is measured by absorbing the gas in alkali and then titrating against acid; there are instruments, such as infrared gas analysers, that are sufficiently sensitive to be very useful in CO_2 studies.

A direct way of estimating metabolism is to measure heat production in a calorimeter. There are operational snags, but the method can be used for large animals as well as for small ones (down to 6 mg weight). If respiration is wholly or partly anaerobic, studies of heat production are likely to be the best method of measuring metabolism.

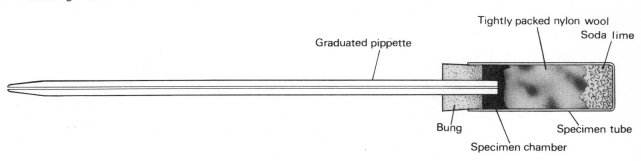

Figure 12 A simple respirometer used for maggots.

Methods of measuring nitrogenous excretion (*U*)

Recall from S22–, Unit 10[12], the principal excretory products of animals: many aquatic animals excrete mainly ammonia and the amount of this in the water can be monitored by using chemical methods. Fishes excrete ammonia via the gills and may also excrete other nitrogenous substances via the kidneys—since these are all soluble, the total nitrogen excreted can be estimated by chemical methods but this value may include some soluble nitrogenous compounds in faeces. Terrestrial animals may produce liquid urine, often with urea as the main excretory product, or urine may be semi-solid or wholly solid (as with birds and many insects) with uric acid as the main excretory product; it may be difficult to separate semi-solid urine from faeces.

Having estimated the rate of loss of nitrogenous products in urine, it is necessary to convert this into terms of energy dissipated. For fishes producing ammonia, the figure is 17 J of energy for every mg of NH_3 excreted. For caterpillars, 0·3 per cent by weight of the dried frass (faeces + urine) represents uric acid and ammoniacal nitrogen; the value for energy involved in excretion of uric acid is proportionally higher than for ammonia. Caterpillars also lose nitrogen in their cast exoskeletons and secrete nitrogen in silk—but normally the caterpillars swallow this material so all the nitrogen is not lost to the body. In many studies, energy dissipated by urine production is ignored since the value is usually small compared with other terms in the energy flow equation. For fishes, ignoring *U* probably means less than 3 per cent error in calculating *A*.

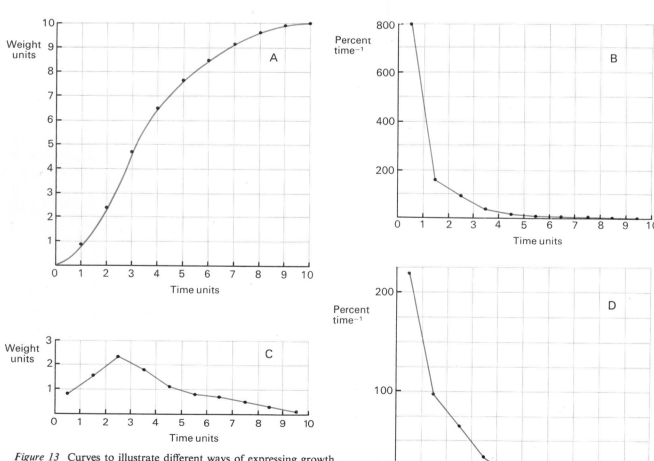

Figure 13 Curves to illustrate different ways of expressing growth. A The weight at different times; B The weight increments for equal time-intervals; C The weight increments expressed as percentage of initial weight for that time-interval; D The instantaneous rate of growth in weight.

Appendix 4 (White)

Growth rates (G)

An organism increases in size (grows) by a combination of increase in size of individual cells and increase in number of cells. Some of the tissues formed by growth do not themselves grow but, in animals, a large proportion of cells can grow and multiply through the growth period of the animal, which may be its whole life (as in fishes and whales) or a limited period of time. Early in life the proportion of cells that grow and multiply actively is close to 100 per cent but the proportion falls later.

In computing growth rates, the information available is usually the weight at given intervals of time. Where measurements were taken of lengths or other dimensions, these are generally turned into weights for studies related to energetics (and the weights are transformed into calorific values using appropriate ratios). In Figure 13, A, B, C and D show four different ways of dealing with size/time data given in Table 16. In A, the weight at each interval of time is plotted—giving a *growth curve*. Look at it and decide when the animal was growing at the fastest rate. Curve B shows the *increment* of growth in weight for equal time-intervals plotted against time—there is a peak between the second and third measurements. Curve C shows values for the *increment in weight expressed as a percentage of the initial weight* for that time-interval plotted against time—the highest value is in the first interval and values fall off for the rest of the time. Curve D shows the *instantaneous growth rate* plotted against time—this rate is calculated from the formula:

$$G = \frac{\log_e Y_T - \log_e Y_t}{T - t} \times 100$$

or

$$G = \frac{\log_{10} Y_T - \log_{10} Y_t}{T - t} \times 2 \cdot 3026 \times 100$$

where G is instantaneous growth rate as per cent unit time^{-1},

Y_T is size at time T,
Y_t is size at time t,
T is later than t
$2 \cdot 3026$ in the second expression converts $\log_{10}$ to $\log_e$.

These formulae are transformations of the formula:

$$Y_T = Y_t e^{g(T - t)} \qquad \text{(where } 100\,g = G\text{)}$$

The assumption is that all the tissue in the body is growing at the same rate and

TABLE 16   Data used in constructing Figure 13, A, B, C and D.

Time units	Weight units	Weight increment for interval units	Weight increment as percentage of initial weight for time interval % time^{-1}	Instantaneous growth rate % time^{-1}
	A	B	C	D
0	0·1			
		0·8	800	220
1	0·9			
		1·5	160	98
2	2·4			
		2·3	96	67
3	4·7			
		1·8	40	32
4	6·5			
		1·1	20	16
5	7·6			
		0·8	10	10
6	8·4			
		0·7	8	8
7	9·1			
		0·5	6	5
8	9·6			
		0·3	3	3
9	9·9			
		0·1	1	1
10	10			

all newly formed tissue starts to grow at that rate as soon as it is formed—the formula is a 'continuously-paid-compound-interest' type. Compare curve D with curve C (the actual values are given in Table 16)—the values are very different for the first five time-intervals but after that are almost the same. Curve C is based on a 'simple interest' type of calculation. The instantaneous growth rate comes closest to describing how an organism grows, but there is little loss of accuracy in using 'increment as percentage of starting weight' (curve C) where the increments are relatively small. Note that when size is changing rapidly (and growth rate may be changing) the time-intervals should be as short as possible even when instantaneous growth rates are used.

As an exercise, do SAQ 16 now.

Appendix 5 (White)

Measurement of consumption (C) and respiration (R) of populations of consumers

Sometimes it is possible to measure the disappearance of a food source—as when caterpillars are eating leaves, leaving holes that can be measured. It is more usual to estimate the food uptake of a population by extrapolating from laboratory studies of the relationship between food consumed and growth rate; the growth rates of wild individuals are estimated and from this their food consumption is deduced by using laboratory estimates of K (the energy coefficient of growth *or* conversion rate of food eaten into animal flesh). The reliability of this type of estimate must depend on how reliable K is—how it varies with time of year, with external and internal factors, with type of food available and so on.

Three other methods of estimating food consumption in nature are:

1   To collect a large sample of the wild consumers, hold them under controlled conditions and measure the quantity of food in the stomachs of samples killed at the time of capture and at intervals thereafter. From the average rate of disappearance of the food, the average amount consumed per day can be estimated; the procedure must be repeated for different times of year, different types of environment, and so on.

2   To collect individuals from the wild population and measure the rate of nitrogen loss through excretion and defaecation for a short time after removal from natural conditions. The average nitrogen gain through growth of wild individuals is estimated by analysing samples at intervals. Adding the nitrogen loss to nitrogen gain per unit time gives a figure for total intake of nitrogen; this is converted into total food consumption by estimating the nitrogen available in the food source. This 'nitrogen balance' method is much used in studies of fish in USSR. The principal snag is that animals brought into the laboratory may suffer from stress and have an abnormally high loss of nitrogen for several days.

3   To measure the growth in nature (in terms of energy) and add to it an energy equivalent to the metabolism of the animal calculated from laboratory studies. Thus Winberg's formulae have been used for fish: the energy equivalent to growth (P) is added to twice the routine metabolism (measured in the laboratory) to give A and it is assumed that $A = 0.8 \, C$.

The respiration of samples of the wild population can sometimes be measured under field conditions—otherwise respiration is estimated from laboratory observations extrapolated for the measured environmental conditions in the field.

Notice how the field worker is often dependent on laboratory studies for estimates of energy utilization and uptake; many values for field situations are therefore dependent on the reliability of laboratory studies and on the error involved in transposing deductions from laboratory estimates to field conditions. You should remember these possible errors when comparing figures for different types of consumers and different ecosystems.

Appendix 6 (White)

Allen's graphical method of estimating production (*P*) and biomass (*B*) of populations

The number of individuals at successive times are plotted against the mean weights of the individuals at those times (Allen, 1951). Typically the number of individuals falls and the mean weight increases as in Figure 14. For any interval of time, the production is the area under the curve between the points representing the beginning and end of that period of time. Biomass at any time can

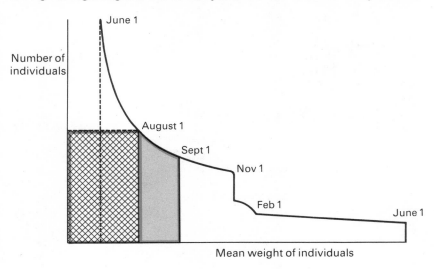

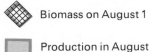

Figure 14 An Allen curve to illustrate this method of computing biomass and production.

also be deduced from the curve by constructing a rectangle (note that the abscissal scale must begin at 0 for this to be possible). If the curve is plotted on graph paper, the areas can be measured by counting squares. Allen curves are based on actual counts and weights of individuals from the population, hence their accuracy varies with the errors of sampling for both numbers and mean weights. (See *ABE*, Part 3, Section 3.3.2.) Another problem arises when drawing curves through these points.

QUESTION   Will the curves be more accurate if the estimates of population are made at regular intervals or at irregular intervals?

ANSWER   This depends on how the population numbers and mean weights change with time—whether there are periods when the former suddenly decreases or the latter suddenly rises (or decreases, e.g. after spawning).

In practice it is usual to work from two curves, one showing changes in numbers and the other showing changes in mean weight, both with time (see Fig. 15, A and B). The Allen curve is constructed by reading points off the two other curves.

Now carry out the exercise on this in SAQ 17.

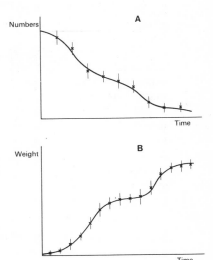

Figure 15 The two curves from which an Allen curve would be constructed. A The change in population numbers with time; B The change in mean weight of individuals with time.

TABLE 17 Values for various energy parameters for individual bullheads *Cottus perplexus* fed on midge larvae and kept in separate tanks at two different temperatures. All the energy values are in J fish^{-1} week^{-1}.

Fish mean energy content	C	A	P	R	F	A:C %	R:A %
at 11 °C							
5385	34·8	30·5	4·8	25·7	4·3	88	84
4990	40·4	33·1	8·5	24·6			
5805	40·8	33·5	6·1	27·4			
5510	80·9	66·3	18·0		14·6		
6235	209·4	171·8	65·8		37·6		
at 7 °C							
6600	24·9	20·8	−6·0	26·8	4·1	84	129
5925	37·3	30·6	0		6·7		
6260	73·2	60·0	13·2		13·2		
6440	126·6	104·2	19·7	84·5			
5350	78·2	62·5	10·5	52·0			

TABLE 18 Data for five trout held in tanks at 8 °C; four were fed on maggots. The values are in J trout^{-1} week^{-1}.

Fish mean energy content J	C	A	P	R (total)	R^1 (SDA)	A:C %	R^1:C %
14 360		0	−430	430		—	
14 185		980	385	595		85	
17 870		1945	835	1110		86	
18 220		2480	870	1610		86	
20 160		1830	790	1040		85	

TABLE 19 Rounded figures based on observations on the population of *Diaptomus* in Queen Elizabeth Reservoir in 1968; all values are expressed as mJ* copepod^{-1} day^{-1}. (Recalculated from Kibby (1971).)

	C	A	R	P	A:C %	P:C (K_1) %	P:A (K_2) %
March	14	5	4	1	35	7	20
April	50	22	17	5			23
May	79	42	25	17			
June	92	54	35		59		
July	122	74	33		61		
August	92	36	29			8	
September	92	41	27			15	
October	65	24	16				33

* mJ = 10^{-3} J

50

Self-assessment questions

SAQ 1 (*Objective 2, a and c*)   (a)   Fill in the blank spaces in Table 17.

(b)   Compare the mean amount of food assimilated (*A*) and the mean respiration (*R*) of the two sets of fish at different temperatures—what are the differences between the two groups? How meaningful is this comparison?

SAQ 2 (*Objectives 2 a and c, 3*)   Data for the wolf spider, *Lycosa rabida*, kept at 20 °C and offered crickets, *Acheta domesticus*, as food. The values were obtained from 10 spiders, each kept for 10 days. (Recalculated from Moulder and Reichle (1972).)

Mean wet weight of spiders	284·5 mg
Mean calorific value of spiders	2·3 J
Quantity of crickets attacked	205 J spider^{-1} day^{-1}
Quantity of remains of crickets*	33 J spider^{-1} day^{-1}
Quantity of spider faeces**	16 J spider^{-1} day^{-1}
Increase in weight of spiders	2·2 mg day^{-1} = 50 J spider^{-1} day^{-1}

* Spiders suck the juices out of their prey, leaving behind the exoskeleton of insects.
** This includes urine (solid guanine).

1   Calculate (a) *C*, (b) *A*, (c) *R* (all expressed spider^{-1} day^{-1}).

2   What are the values of the following ratios for the spiders:

(a) *A*:*C*; (b) *R*:*A*; (c) *P*:*A*?

3   Compare the ratios of *A*:*C* (per cent assimilation to ingestion) and *P*:*A* (per cent net production to assimilation) for spiders with those of winter moth caterpillars (See *PHS*, Table 8, p. 579). Suggest explanations for differences.

SAQ 3 (*Objective 2, a and c*)   (a) One of the five trout (Table 18) was starved and the value obtained for *R* was taken as a measure of standard metabolism. Assuming that all the other fish would have the same value for standard metabolism and that all increase in respiration above this value was due to SDA (and therefore was *R*^{1}), fill in the values of *R*^{1} in the table and work out the ratios of *R*^{1}:*A*. Comment on these ratios.

(b)   Given the ratios of *A*:*C* observed in this experiment, calculate the values of *C* and fill them into Table 18.

SAQ 4 (*Objective 3*)   The four values *W*, *X*, *Y* and *Z* are for the total energy consumption (a) for a cow of weight 454 kg (1) inside a cowshed and (2) outside on pasture, and (b) for a sheep of weight 45 kg (1) in a pen and (2) outdoors on a hillside. Identify which value was obtained for which animal and give reasons for your choices.

$$W = 50·8 \times 10^6 \text{ J day}^{-1}$$
$$X = 10·5 \times 10^6 \text{ J day}^{-1}$$
$$Y = 6·1 \times 10^6 \text{ J day}^{-1}$$
$$Z = 41·8 \times 10^6 \text{ J day}^{-1}$$

SAQ 5 (*Objectives 2d and 3*)   Which will need the greatest weight of food daily—a dog of weight 40 kg, fed on raw meat, or a sheep of weight 40 kg, fed on oat straw?

SAQ 6 (*Objectives 2a and 3*)   The vole, *Microtus arvalis*, in summer is much the same weight as a mouse. Compare the values for *R* for the mouse in Table 2 and for *Microtus* in Table 5. Explain the difference between the values for these two animals of similar weight.

SAQ 7 (*Objective 2a*)   The Great-horned owl, *Bubo virginianus*, weighs slightly less than a hen. Compare the values for metabolism for the owl in Table 1 and the hen in Table 2. Explain the difference between the values for these two animals.

SAQ 8 (*Objectives 2a and 5*)   The hummingbird, *Eulampis*, sips nectar from flowers; this nectar is the main source of energy for its activities. When provided with 0·25 M sucrose solution (equivalent to 1·4 kJ cm^{-3}) the hummingbird can attain a foraging efficiency of 80. (Foraging efficiency = energy value of food ingested (*C*) divided by energy cost of hovering while feeding (*R*^{H})). Given that *R*^{H} is 8·7 kJ h^{-1} and that the resting metabolic rate is 2·2 kJ h^{-1}, calculate how long in each hour (on average) a hummingbird *must* spend foraging for nectar and approximately how much sucrose solution it would need for the hour. All the values given are genuine values for a bird of weight 10 g.

SAQ 9 (*Objectives 3 and 5*)   The heat production of a fasting, resting hummingbird of weight 0·01 kg is at the rate of 3120 kJ kg^{-1} day^{-1}. Assume that the ratio between heat production and surface area is similar to that for the hen (Table 2). What is the body area of the hummingbird and of the hen? What are the ratios between surface area and weight of the body for the hen and for the hummingbird? Do you expect these two ratios to be the same?

SAQ 10 (*Objective 5*)   The root vole, *Microtus oeconomicus*, weighs on average 26 g in autumn and has a daily food requirement of 2·08 $\times$ 10^3 J g^{-1} day^{-1}. In 1966, there were 91 voles per hectare. The standing crop of plants was 9·4 $\times$ 10^9 J ha^{-1}. Assuming that all the plant material is palatable to voles and that the digestibility is 85 per cent, calculate what proportion of the standing crop of plants would be consumed by voles in the three months of autumn (take this as being 90 days).

SAQ 11 (*Objective 3*)   Write a brief outline to explain how you would investigate whether animals of a given species had an endogenous growth rhythm.

SAQ 12 (*Objectives 2a and c, 3 and 5*)   *Diaptomus gracilis* is a planktonic copepod which feeds mainly on planktonic algae. In the Metropolitan Water Board's reservoirs near London, it overwinters as adults but there are eggs produced throughout the year and several overlapping generations. The numbers of individuals vary through the year as do their respiration and their rates of feeding and assimilation. The biomass varies between about 1·3 and 29 kJ m^{-2}; the total annual respiration has been estimated as 510 kJ m^{-2} and the total annual production as 217 kJ m^{-2}, of which about 23 per cent is production of adults.

Fill in the blanks in the columns: *P*; *A*:*C*; *P*:*C*; *P*:*A*, in Table 19. Consider whether each of the statements (a) to (d) are likely to be true or not:

(a)   The respiration of *Diaptomus* depends on the temperature of the water and increases as the water temperature increases.

(b)   The rate of feeding of *Diaptomus* is probably affected by temperature, being faster at higher temperatures.

(c)   The rate of feeding of *Diaptomus* is probably affected by the type of phytoplankton organisms present.

(d)   Variations in production during the summer may be related to the balance between the different stages present—e.g. whether there is a larger or smaller proportion of adults compared with copepodids.

TABLE 20 Rounded figures based on annual populations of *Leptoterna* near Ascot. All values are expressed as J m^{-2} year^{-1}. (Recalculated from Mc Neill (1971).)

Year	C	A	P	R	A:C %	P:C %	P:A %
1	3480	1010	590	420	29	17	58
2	1450	520	250				
3	2140	760	400				
4	1900	640	380				
5	3450	900	530				

TABLE 21

Year	*Holcus* production kJ m^{-2} year^{-1}	*Holcus* P to *Leptoterna* C	*Leptoterna* P to *Holcus* P
1	2700	780	$2\cdot2 \times 10^{-4}$
2	3900		
3	3360		
4	3020		
5	7750		

TABLE 22

Year	Total eggs laid J m^{-2} year^{-1}	Eggs laid as % reproductive effort	Eggs laid as % total P of *Leptoterna*
1	50	21	8·5
2	70	64	
3	110	52	
4	120	88	
5	90	36	

TABLE 23 Biomass of fish in small streams.

Stream	Biomass of fish present in summer			Annual production of fish		
	trout	bullhead	Total	trout	bullhead	Total
Walla Brook	13·3	*	13·3	12·6	*	12·6
Docken's Water	6·5	—	7·5	12·1	—	14·0
Tarrant	4·4	13·5	19·8	12·0	43·1	59·6
Lower Bere	17·1	3·9	26·7	12·9	15·0	35·1

* Means present in very low numbers.
Note Not all the fish present are listed in this Table.

TABLE 24 Data used in Figure 16.

Time units	Weight units	Weight increment for interval	Weight increment as percentage of initial weight for interval % time^{-1}	Instantaneous growth rate % time^{-1}
0	0·1			
2	1·3			
4	1·4			
6½	6·6			

SAQ 13 (*Objectives 2a and c, 3 and 5*) *Leptoterna dolabrata* is a mirid bug (order Hemiptera) which sucks out the contents of plant cells; when it feeds on grass blades (leaves) the emptied mesophyll cells show up as white patches which can be measured. *Leptoterna* has one generation in the year. A population was studied with the grass *Holcus* as principal food resource. The cell contents of *Holcus* leaves have a calorific value of 18·1 kJ g^{-1} and represent 52 per cent of the total calorific value of the leaves.

Fill in the blanks in Table 20.

Consider whether statements (a) and (b) are true or not:

(a) The $A:C$ ratio is of the order that is to be expected from a herbivore.

(b) The $P:A$ ratio is surprisingly high considering that it is based on all the stages of the life history and that the animal is a herbivore.

Now fill in the blanks in Table 21.

Consider whether statements (c) and (d) are true or not:

(c) *Holcus P*:*Leptoterna C* is a measure of the 'resource utilization' of the bug; the values suggest that the bug's feeding is closely adjusted to the production of the plant, so that the bug would be in danger of over-exploiting its food supply were its feeding level to be increased only slightly.

(d) The ratios of production of bug to production of grass indicate that the two are closely linked.

Now fill in the blanks in Table 22.

Consider whether statements (e) and (f) are true or not:

(e) The proportion of P which is channelled into laying eggs is approximately constant from year to year,

(f) The proportion of P which is channelled into laying eggs depends on the level of P; it is greater when the total production of the population is smaller and less when the total production is larger. This system imples that the population in one year is regulated by the production of the previous year.

SAQ 14 (*Objectives 2c, 3 and 5*) The values in Table 23 (all expressed as g m^{-2}) are for trout and bullheads (if present) in small streams in southern England. (Data from Mann (1971).) Calculate the $P:B$ ratios for the trout and bullheads in these streams.

Consider each of the statements (a) to (c) and decide whether it is justified from the information available to you.

(a) The annual production of trout in these four streams is almost the same but the $P:B$ ratios are very different; probably Walla Brook and Lower Bere stream contain a greater proportion of old fish than do Docken's Water and the River Tarrant.

(b) The annual production of bullheads in the Lower Bere and Tarrant is very different but the $P:B$ ratios are similar; probably the population structure is the same in the two streams but there are relatively fewer living spaces for bullheads in the Lower Bere stream than in the River Tarrant.

(c) The presence or absence of bullheads seems to have no effect on the production of the trout populations, even though the production of bullheads is greater than that of the trout; probably these two species do not compete for food.

SAQ 15 (*Objective 5*) The calorific values of some animals vary from time to time. Suggest how you would investigate the hypothesis that the variation is seasonal.

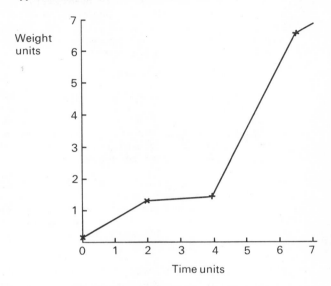

Figure 16 The data in Table 24 plotted as a growth curve.

SAQ 16 Examine Figure 16 which is based on the values in Table 24. Was the organism growing faster between time-intervals 0 and 2 or between time-intervals 4 and 6½? Fill in the spaces in the Table 24 and calculate approximately the ratio between the growth rates in the two periods.

SAQ 17 Using the values in Table 25, construct an Allen curve. Then answer the following questions:

(a) What was the change in biomass between June of year 1 and September of year 1?

(b) What was the change in biomass between September of year 1 and December of year 1?

(c) What was the change in biomass between June of year 2 and September of year 2?

(d) What was the total production between June of year 1 and June of year 2?

(e) What is the ratio between the total production between June in year 1 and June in year 2 (the answer to (d)) and the biomass in June of year 1?

TABLE 25 Data for construction of Allen curve

Date	Mean numbers m^{-2}	Mean weight of individuals g
March of year 1	900	0·5
June of year 1	400	5
September of year 1	200	20
December of year 1	150	18
March of year 2	75	22
June of year 2	50	27
September of year 2	20	40

Pretest answers

PTQ 1 Heterotrophes. Their 'key' characteristics are that they cannot build up (1) carbohydrates from CO_2 and water and (2) amino acids from carbohydrates and 'mineral salts'. Heterotrophes are dependent on other organisms for the supply of carbohydrates and some amino acids in their food. Refer back to S100, Unit 20, Section 20.1.

PTQ 2 No. Heterotrophes can transform some carbohydrates into others and some amino acids into others; they can also transform amino acids into carbohydrates (the processes of deamination followed by gluconeogenesis). They also transform carbohydrates into fats and vice versa.

PTQ 3 Essential amino acids. See S22–, Unit 4, Section 4.1.1.

PTQ 4 Vitamins and trace elements are substances essential for well-being that cannot be synthesized within the body of the organism and must be included in the diet. Most organisms require water either as a liquid or as part of their food. Some animals have a very low requirement for water; these produce 'metabolic water' from dietary constituents such as fats.

PTQ 5 Excretion. Amino acids surplus to the requirement of the body are deaminated, producing carboxylic acids and nitrogen compounds such as ammonia, urea or uric acid; these nitrogenous substances are voided from the body (usually as urine but ammonia may diffuse, e.g. from the gills of fishes). See S22–, Unit 10, Section 10.2.

PTQ 6 S22–, Unit 4, followed C. M. Yonge, who divided animals into three major groups: microphagous feeders—those that feed on relatively small particles; macrophagous feeders—those that feed on relatively large particles; fluid feeders—those that take up or suck up fluids.

Microphagous feeders were further subdivided into those that filtered their food from aquatic environments, called suspension feeders—e.g. *Chaetopterus, Ostrea, Sabella, Calanus*—and those that fed on particles forming deposits, called deposit feeders—e.g. *Amphitrite, Arenicola.*

The macrophagous feeders studied were: *Hydra* (a cnidarian carnivore) and gastropod molluscs (especially the carnivores *Natica* and *Conus*). There were also references to various mammals and some insects.

The fluid feeders studied were: aphids and coccids (plant-sucking bugs) and *Glossina* (the blood-sucking tsetse fly).

Note that this way of classifying feeding methods does not indicate whether the animal is a herbivore consuming plant material or a carnivore consuming animal material.

PTQ 7 Whereas most plants are rooted, most animals move about and many have behavioural mechanisms which lead to avoidance or repulse of predators. Herbivores and carnivores must all be able to tackle their food—to seize it, bite it, swallow it whole if necessary—but a carnivore feeding on active prey is likely to expend more energy in capturing it than a herbivore browsing on plants. The carnivore may then rest for a long period, digesting; herbivores usually feed for long periods.

Prey organisms are likely to survive in greater numbers if they have defensive mechanisms against predators. Herbivorous animals may expend much energy in response to the presence of predators, such as fleeing away, or they may lose valuable feeding time by taking up protective postures. Plants also display defensive mechanisms such as spines, distasteful inclusions and poisonous constituents (see S22–, Unit 11, Section 11.4.1).

PTQ 8 Plant cells typically have walls of cellulose or of other complex carbohydrates (e.g. lignin); very few animals possess the enzymes cellulase or xylase. Usually the cell walls must be broken in some way before the contents can be digested; this breakage is often the result of mechanical treatment such as grinding by teeth or plates in the gut. Some herbivores have, living in part of their guts, symbiotic micro-organisms with enzymes that digest cellulose or lignin. (See S22–, Unit 4, Section 4.9.) The gut of herbivores is usually relatively long and generally they produce massive faeces which consist of undigested parts of the plant food and also bacteria from the gut. Often these faeces provide a food supply for specialist consumers (dung beetles and dung flies on land, some marine deposit feeders) as well as substrate for decomposers (see S323, Unit 4).

PTQ 9 Animals with exoskeletons made of chitin, especially arthropods, may present problems since few (if any) animals have chitinases; some method by which the consumer pierces the exoskeleton makes the rest of the body digestible. Animal cells are generally easy to digest. Carnivores typically have short guts often with a bag-like stomach where protein digestion begins.

PTQ 10 No. Plant material usually includes a high proportion of fibrous material that is indigestible; the problem of getting at the contents of plant cells may mean that potentially digestible material is not used. Different parts of plants have very different nutritive values; the concentration of proteins and soluble carbohydrates is highest in young leaves and the proportion of structural carbohydrates (wood, etc.) is highest in stems. Animal food may also include indigestible parts (shells, exoskeletons, bones, teeth, tough ligaments) but in relatively small amounts.

Since the range of amino-acids in animal proteins is very similar in all groups of animals, carnivores have little trouble in obtaining a balanced intake of amino acids, including sufficient of those that are essential. Plant proteins are very different from animal proteins and this may create problems for herbivores; if an essential amino acid is relatively rare in its food plant, a herbivore will have to consume a great deal of material to obtain its requirement. Some amino acids will be assimilated in great excess of requirements; these must be deaminated and this may cause excretory problems. In general, plant proteins are short of methionine and cystine, both amino acids containing sulphur.

PTQ 11 (a) Blood and body fluids of animals are consumed by blood-sucking insects and ticks; some secrete anti-coagulants and digestive enzymes before sucking. Spiders are a special class of fluid feeder since they pierce their prey and secrete digestive enzymes into it and then suck up the digested material, leaving an empty shell of exoskeleton. These fluids are likely to contain sugars, amino acids and fatty acids and to present a balanced, pre-digested food supply.

(b) Substances in solution in gut contents are consumed by gut parasites such as tapeworms. Since the soluble gut contents are the food about to be assimilated by the host, the nutritive value is high. These parasites have no need for digestive processes of their own but they require a protective mechanism against the host's digestive enzymes.

(c) Plant juices are consumed by plant-sucking bugs such as aphids. Those that feed on cell sap, e.g. in mesophyll cells of leaves, may secrete enzymes and digest a full range of cell components; those that suck up the phloem contents may acquire mainly sugars and amino acids without need for digestion. Plant-sucking consumers suffer the general disadvantage of all herbivores, that the balance of amino acids may be such that they must consume a great deal more material than they actually require. Some aphids pass quantities of sugar solution through their guts, producing 'honey dew'.

(d) Nectar is consumed by a variety of animals including many insects and humming birds. The main growth of the insects has occurred in the larval stage when the animals have often been herbivorous macrophages (caterpillars); the nectar consumed by the adults may be principally a source of energy for flight which could be powered from carbohydrates alone. The nectar may also contain amino acids, which are important if the animals are growing or producing eggs and so require organic nitrogen.

ITQ answers

ITQ 1 Recall from Unit 2 that for plants:

Gross production = Net production + Respiration

If gross production can be taken as equivalent to assimilation (A), then net production is the equivalent of P, since $A = P + R$. Consumption (C) of animals can be taken as equivalent to absorption of light energy by the chloroplasts of plants; the amount of absorbed energy that is not converted into gross production then is equivalent to $F + U$ of animals.

Net production of plants may appear as somatic growth or as reproduction in just the same way as P of animals. For both, some of the production may be consumed by animals and some may die and pass to the decomposers; this can be expressed as the equation:

$$P = T + Y + D$$

where T is the increase in biomass, Y is the yield to consumers and D is the amount that dies and passes to decomposers. The time-interval must be specified, since some of the T may eventually die and pass to D, as when the woody tissue of plants eventually decays.

ITQ 2 $A = C - (F + U)$. But also $A = P + R$. In this case $P = 0$ so the values for A are the same as those for R. Note that these values are maintenance rations.

ITQ 3 $\frac{A}{C} \times 100 = 85$ per cent. This is much higher than Smith's values for caterpillars ($A = 36$ to 40 per cent C) but similar to the values for perch ($A = 84$ per cent C).

ITQ 4 $R = 595$ kJ kg^{-1} day$^{-1} \equiv 2 \cdot 17 \times 10^5$ kJ kg^{-1} yr^{-1}.* Values for fishes were from $5 \cdot 87$ to $41 \cdot 8 \times 10^3$ J g^{-1} yr^{-1};* the owls' maintenance requirements were of the order of 10 times the maintenance requirements of perch.

*(kJ kg$^{-1} \equiv$ J g^{-1})

ITQ 5 Part of the difference may be due to the higher energy expenditure of flight compared with swimming; however, owls spend most of their time perched on branches and captive owls fly very seldom. The major difference is because fishes are poikilotherms and owls are homoiotherms. Refer to S100, Unit 18, Section 18.4.3, if you need to remind yourself about 'cold-blooded' and 'warm-blooded' animals.

ITQ 6 In most environments, the ambient temperature is less than 35 °C and often it is much lower, so homoiotherms must usually be in the position of maintaining a body temperature that is higher than ambient; this implies that homoiotherms will need to produce heat. The amount of heat needed will depend on the efficiency of the insulation as well as on the difference in temperature between body and surroundings. The source of the energy for heat production is the food.

ITQ 7 From these figures, huddling in a group of 5 or more reduces R by more than 20 per cent of the rate in daylight. A group of 5 in darkness shows reduction of R by 20 per cent compared with a similar group in light.

ITQ 8 If the decrease in darkness compared with light is the same as for a group of 5, then X should $=$ about $2 \cdot 6$ cm^3 g^{-1} h^{-1} (which is 80 per cent of $3 \cdot 3$).

ITQ 9 Assuming no change in temperature during the 24 hours: for July, $4 \times 15 \cdot 4 = 61 \cdot 6$; for January, $6 \times 15 \cdot 5 = 93 \cdot 0$ (both kJ day^{-1}). This represents an increase of 60 per cent in July and of 15 per cent in January.

ITQ 10 The owl (weight 1615 g) respired approximately 600 kJ kg^{-1} whereas the vole (weight 21 g) respired a total of $38 \cdot 4$ kJ, which represents approximately 1800 kJ kg^{-1}. So the vole respired about three times as much energy as the owl on a unit weight basis; the owl was about 80 times the weight of the vole. Since this comparison is between animals which spend much of their time inactively under conditions where energy loss is kept low, these figures support the conclusion that smaller homoiotherms have relatively higher energy requirements than larger ones.

ITQ 11 You have already met an investigation in which this value was not constant—the perch on maintenance rations almost certainly changed in calorific value. The laying down and depletion of reserves of fat or oil is one very likely reason; there may be marked seasonal changes in calorific value. It may or may not be true that the body of a young animal has the same balance of constituents as that of an old one—the young animal may have more live cells and less 'ash'—skeletal components of various types. Eggs and sperm may have different compositions from average body tissues—so animals ready to reproduce may have a different calorific value from immature and non-breeding animals.

ITQ 12 First we must define 'growth'. The insect develops during the egg stage from a zygote to a small caterpillar—but there is a decrease in total calorific value as a result of respiration. The caterpillar feeds and grows in volume and in total calorific value and there are changes in its detailed anatomy. The pupa is a stage during which the caterpillar turns into the adult insect—there is a great deal of rearrangement of tissues—and the total calorific value decreases. The adult may already contain eggs or sperm ready to mature without further feeding so in this stage the calorific value falls (result of respiration) at first slowly and then (result of shedding eggs or sperm) rapidly and the insect soon dies. Some adult insects must take food either as a supply of energy for flight and other activities—often this food is nectar (mainly carbohydrate)—or it may need a source of protein before eggs mature. Thus measuring growth in terms of total calorific value means that there is negative growth in egg and pupa, positive growth in the caterpillar stage and either negative or positive growth in the adult stage.

ITQ 13 This is K_2. Note that the values range from 39 per cent to 71 per cent.

ITQ 14 Multiply the two percentages together to get $P/C = K_1$. *Operophtera*, 23 per cent; *Hydriomena*, 16 per cent; *Erannis*, 31 per cent; *Cosmia*, 22 per cent.

ITQ 15 Temperature and light are likely to affect growth, acting through the hormonal system. (Refer to S22–, Unit 8, Section 8.4, and Unit 11, Section 11.3, to remind yourself of this.) Interactions with other individuals could lead to stress and other effects.

ITQ 16 No. The calorific value of the body may vary considerably depending on the laying down or dissipation of fat and other food reserves. Thus there can be positive and negative values of P in the energy equation for an adult.

ITQ 17 Very variable. From earlier statements, you might expect high P in populations of very young individuals whose B would be small and lower P in populations of old large individuals whose B might be high. Look at Figure 14 (Appendix 6).

ITQ 18 This is food chain efficiency ($C_{n+1}: Y_{n-1}$) since $P_n = C_{n+1}$. The values are lower than expected probably because not all the algae in the pond were digestible. Note that the primary production was comparatively low, probably as a result of autoshading by dense growths.

ITQ 19 Food chain efficiency $= \dfrac{C_{n+1}}{Y_{n-1}} \times 100$ per cent

$$= \frac{3\cdot47}{310 \times 10} \times 100 \approx 0\cdot1 \text{ per cent*}.$$

Gross ecological efficiency $= \dfrac{C_{n+1}}{C_n} \times 100$ per cent

$$= \frac{3\cdot47}{310} \times 100 \approx 1 \text{ per cent}.$$

* The symbol $\approx$ means 'approximately equal to'.

Note that predation is an important source of mortality for kob, so that the given production value is in addition to an unknown amount consumed by predators; the real efficiencies are therefore higher than the calculated values.

ITQ 20 Of 955 kJ m^{-2} production of herbs, low shrubs and shrub browse, only 23·7 kJ were consumed—this is about 2·5 per cent. Of 34·5 kJ m^{-2} yr^{-1} of seeds produced, 30 kJ were consumed—this is about 85 per cent.

ITQ 21 For herbivores, A was estimated as 20 kJ but might have been 40 kJ. If $A = 50$ per cent C, then C would be 40 to 80 kJ; if $A = 30$ per cent C, then C would be 65 to 130 kJ. Thus the ratio of herbivore consumption to net plant production could be between 20 and 130 to $9\cdot8 \times 10^3 = 0\cdot2$ to 1·3 per cent (a very low value).

ITQ 22 The value of carnivore consumption (C_{n+1}) to herbivore consumption (C_n) cannot be worked out exactly since figures are available for A but not for the $A:C$ ratios. A for carnivores: A for herbivores $= 2\cdot2 : 20 = 11$ per cent. So the gross ecological efficiency is of the order of 10 per cent.

ITQ 23 (a) About 25 per cent; (b) 17 per cent; (c) 0·22 per cent; (d) 0·15 per cent; (e) 1·2 per cent.

ITQ 24 Total $215 \times 812 \times 365$ kJ $\approx 6\cdot4 \times 10^7$ kJ; *or* $0\cdot015 \times 215 \times 365$ kJ ha^{-1} yr$^{-1} \approx 4\cdot5 \times 10^3$ kJ ha^{-1} yr^{-1}.

ITQ 25 20 kJ g^{-1} dry weight $= 8$ kJ g^{-1} wet weight. R of $4\cdot5 \times 10^3$ kJ ha^{-1} yr^{-1} represents 0·56 kg ha^{-1} yr^{-1} of moose biomass. This value is about 45 per cent of the biomass transfer value of moose to wolves. So the calculation gives a figure of the right order, which is gratifying since the value for R is taken for a fasting dog under conditions that must be very different from those facing wolves on Isle Royale.

ITQ 26 (a) $5\frac{1}{2}$; (b) first year; (c) first year; (d) 8.

ITQ 27 $A = P + R$. For detritivores, this is 1915 kJ so the ratio to net phytoplankton production is $\dfrac{1915}{6800} = 28$ per cent.

ITQ 28 No, probably the proportion of A to C will be higher for the carnivores than for the detritivores but all we can do is to use the ratio of values of $A = \dfrac{315}{1915} = 16$ per cent.

ITQ 29 $F + U$ measures energy passed to decomposers (or detritivores) from ingested food; knowing the $A:C$ ratio allows deduction of $F + U$ from C. R measures energy dissipated as heat and so 'lost' to the ecosystem; R can be deduced from $A - P$ or derived from laboratory studies.

ITQ 30 (a) The carnivore $A:C$ ratios seem to be consistently high, of the order of 80 per cent or more. Recall that Winberg deduced this from study of many fish species, typically carnivores (Section 3.1.2a).

(b) The ratios for invertebrate herbivores (insects, *Diaptomus*) are much lower than 80 per cent but vary between 27 and 60 per cent—perhaps 40 per cent would be a useful value to assume if a detailed study had not been made.

(c) The five ratios for mammalian herbivores include three high ones (85, 81, 75) and two low ones (50, 33). Note that two of the three high ratios are for ungulates (mammals that ruminate—chew the cud) which have bacterial breakdown of plant material; the third value is for *Dipodomys* which eats mainly seeds, a food source which is much more digestible than leaves or stems. So perhaps it would be legitimate to assume $A:C$ ratios of 80 per cent for mammalian herbivores with special digestive arrangements (such as ruminants) or which feed on seeds, and to assume ratios of about 40 per cent for other herbivorous mammals (i.e. a similar ratio to that suggested for invertebrate herbivores).

ITQ 31 There appears to be a contrast between the warm-blooded mammals (and the owl) on the one hand, with $R:A$ ratios over 90 per cent and $R:P$ ratios of 18 and over, and the fishes and invertebrates on the other hand, with lower ratios of both types. The old-field spittlebugs have an $R:A$ of 92 and $R:A$ ratios of some other insects exceed 80. The $R:P$ ratio of the spittlebugs was 11 and the $R:P$ ratios of the other insects are all less than 10.

TABLE 17 (completed)

Fish mean energy content	C	A	P	R	F	$A:C$ %	$R:A$ %
at 11 °C							
5385	34·8	30·5	4·8	25·7	4·3	88	84
4990	40·4	33·1	8·5	24·6	7·3	82	74
5805	40·8	33·5	6·1	27·4	7·3	82	82
5510	80·9	66·3	18·0	48·3	14·6	82	73
6235	209·4	171·8	65·8	106·0	37·6	82	62
at 7 °C							
6600	24·9	20·8	−6·0	26·8	4·1	84	129
5925	37·3	30·6	0	30·6	6·7	82	100
6260	73·2	60·0	13·2	46·8	13·2	82	78
6440	126·6	104·2	19·7	84·5	22·4	82	81
5350	78·2	62·5	10·5	52·0	15·7	80	83

SAQ answers

SAQ 1 (a) See Table 17 with figures filled in. Recall that $R = A - P$ and $F = C - A$. Notice that the ratio $A:C$ is 82 per cent for 7 out of the 10 fish; the extreme values are 80 and 88 per cent. The ratio $R:A$ varies much more, with extremes of 62 per cent and 129 per cent.

(b) You should have noticed that the two sets of fish are of different sizes so that for a meaningful comparison you must express A and R in terms of units of calorific value of fish. The simplest calculation involves finding the mean energy content of each set of fish and then expressing the mean A and mean R in terms of kJ of fish energy content. The values are:

	in experiment at 11 °C	in experiment at 7 °C
Mean energy of fish (as J)	5585	6115
Mean assimilation A (as J fish week^{-1})	67	55·6
Mean assimilation (as J kJ fish^{-1} week^{-1})	12	9
Mean respiration (as J week^{-1})	46·4	48·1
Mean respiration (as J kJ fish^{-1} week^{-1})	8·3	7·8

On the basis of this calculation, the fish at the lower temperature assimilated relatively less food and respired at a relatively lower rate, but this latter represented a higher proportion of the food assimilated (about 70 per cent at 11 °C and about 87 per cent at 7 °C).

The values for A and R show a wide scatter for both groups of fish, so comparison of average values is not meaningful unless some test of significance is applied.

SAQ 2 1 (a) $C = 205 - 33$ kJ $= 172$ kJ.

(b) $A = 172 - 16$ kJ $= 156$ kJ.

(c) $R = A - P = 156 - 50 = 106$ kJ.

2 (a) 91 per cent; (b) 68 per cent; (c) 32 per cent.

3 $A:C$ was 91 per cent for spiders but only 40·5 per cent for winter moth caterpillars; $P:A$ was 32 per cent for spiders but 57 per cent for caterpillars. The difference in $A:C$ could be because the caterpillars are herbivorous (eating food with indigestible fibres) but the spiders are carnivores; spiders also increase their efficiency by sucking up contents of their prey's bodies and so avoid taking into their bodies a mass of indigestible material. The ratio of A to $(C + $ remains of crickets$) = 156:205 = 76$ per cent, and this is still nearly twice as high as the ratio $A:C$ for caterpillars. The difference in $P:A$ ratio implies that caterpillars are able to transform more of their 'useful' food into new body cells than can spiders; it also implies that spiders 'spend' relatively more of their 'useful' food energy in respiration. This is to be expected if spiders seek a mobile food organism (as these wolf spiders do) whereas caterpillars attack leaves.

SAQ 3 (a) The calculated values for R and for R^1 are given in the completed Table 18. R^1 was obtained by subtracting 430 from R. The ratio $R^1:A$ could be related to the actual amount of food assimilated; it increases as the value of A increases and for two similar values of A the ratios are very similar (1945, 35 per cent; 1830, 33 per cent). Of course many more observations would be necessary before a firm conclusion could be reached. Since the fishes were of different sizes (energy contents from 14 360 to 20 160 J), it is unlikely that all would have a standard metabolism of 430 J week^{-1} so the values for SDA must be recognized as approximations. However, with food of high protein content (maggots) it is reasonable that SDA should increase with increase in the amount of food assimilated.

(b) The values are given in the completed Table 18.

SAQ 4 The cow is larger than the sheep, so values for the cow should be higher than those for the sheep. The animals will be more active out of doors than in a cowshed or a pen and will probably be exposed to a lower temperature. Hence the values are likely to decrease in the following order: cow in pasture (W) > cow in cowshed (Z) > sheep on hillside (X) > sheep in pen (Y). Notice that the cow weighs about 10 times the sheep but $W \approx 5X$ and $Z \approx 7Y$; the increase in size is associated with economy in use of energy.

SAQ 5 The sheep will need more because its food contains a less satisfactory 'mix' of amino acids than that of the dog and a higher proportion of indigestible 'fibre'. In fact, a sheep fed on straw needs about twice the weight of food of a dog fed on meat.

SAQ 6 First you must manipulate the two values so that they can be compared. The value of 890 kJ day^{-1} for the mouse is expressed kg^{-1} of body weight. The value of 38·4 kJ day^{-1} for the vole in July is the total requirement for an animal of 21 g body weight. Expressing the vole requirement in similar terms to that of the mouse gives a value of 1830 kJ kg^{-1} day^{-1}; this is more than twice the mouse value. Differences in shape between the two animals and differences in activity are not likely to be great enough to give differences in surface area that would explain this discrepancy. The principal reason for the difference is that the value for the mouse is R^2 (*fasting* metabolism) whereas the vole under natural conditions would have fed; its value is for R which equals $R^1 + R^2$. The SDA of the food assimilated is represented by R^1. If R^2 for the mouse and the vole are similar, then SDA for the vole is of the order of 50 per cent of the total metabolism.

TABLE 18 (completed)

Fish mean energy content	C	A	P	R (total)	R^1 (SDA)	$A:C$ %	$R^1:A$ %
14 360	0	0	−430	430	0	—	—
14 185	1145	980	385	595	163	85	17
17 870	2270	1945	835	1110	680	86	35
18 220	2900	2480	870	1610	1180	86	48
20 160	2140	1830	790	1040	610	85	33

SAQ 7 These values can be compared directly:

owl, 595 kJ kg^{-1} day^{-1};

hen, 296 kJ kg^{-1} day^{-1}.

The hen at 2 kg is larger than the owl at 1·6 kg but this difference is not enough to account for the owl's R value being about twice that of the hen. The hen was fasting and the owl was allowed to feed, hence R for the hen is R^2 only whereas R for the owl is $R^1 + R^2$. If R^2 for the two is similar (but probably it is higher for the (smaller) owl), then SDA for the owl is of the order of 50 per cent of the total metabolism.

TABLE 19 (completed)   Values as mJ copepod^{-1} day^{-1} or as percentages

	C	A	R	P	$A:C$ %	$P:C (K_1)$ %	$P:A (K_2)$ %
March	14	5	4	1	35	7	20
April	50	22	17	5	44	10	23
May	79	42	25	17	54	22	41
June	92	54	35	19	59	21	35
July	122	74	33	41	61	34	56
August	92	36	29	7	39	8	19
September	92	41	27	14	44	15	34
October	65	24	16	8	37	12	33

TABLE 20 (completed)   Rounded figures based on annual populations of *Leptoterna* near Ascot. All values are expressed as J m^{-2} year^{-1}.

Year	C	A	P	R	$A:C$ %	$P:C$ %	$P:A$ %
1	3480	1010	590	420	29	17	58
2	1450	520	250	270	36	17	48
3	2140	760	400	360	35	19	52
4	1900	640	380	260	34	20	59
5	3450	900	530	470	26	15	59

TABLE 21 (completed)

Year	*Holcus* production kJ m^{-2} year^{-1}	*Holcus* P to *Leptoterna* C	*Leptoterna* P to *Holcus* P
1	2700	780	$2 \cdot 2 \times 10^{-4}$
2	3900	2700	$0 \cdot 6 \times 10^{-4}$
3	3360	1600	$1 \cdot 2 \times 10^{-4}$
4	3020	1600	$1 \cdot 2 \times 10^{-4}$
5	7750	2300	$0 \cdot 7 \times 10^{-4}$

TABLE 22 (completed)

Year	Total eggs laid J m^{-2} year^{-1}	Eggs laid as % reproductive effort	Eggs laid as % total P
1	50	21	8·5
2	70	64	28
3	110	52	27·5
4	120	88	31·5
5	90	36	17

SAQ 8 If the foraging efficiency of the hummingbird is 80, then hovering to feed for one hour should yield 80×8.7 kJ = 696 kJ. This represents 11·6 kJ for one minute of hovering to feed, which is approximately 0·2 kJ for one second of hovering to feed. The resting metabolic rate is 2·2 kJ h^{-1} which should be satisfied by about 11 seconds of hovering to feed. Hovering for 11 seconds and resting for the remainder of the hour represents a total expenditure of energy of about 2·5 kJ, which should be satisfied by less than 2 cm^3 of the sucrose solution. This calculation has left out the energy that the bird may have to expend in flying to the source of nectar and back to its perch; this in natural conditions probably increases the cost of feeding by a factor of 4. Hummingbirds observed in Dominica spent about 10 per cent of their time foraging for nectar, about 87 per cent of their time resting on perches and the other 3 per cent on fly-catching, changing perches and chasing off other hummingbirds. The flowers vary in their nectar composition and content and the foraging efficiency is usually less than 80 and may be as low as 10.

SAQ 9 To calculate surface area, work out the heat production over 24 hours (multiply the value given as kJ kg^{-1} by the weight in kg) then divide this by the value given for heat production per body surface (3.95×10^3 in this case). The answers are:

hummingbird surface area is 0·008 m^2;
hen surface area is 0·15 m^2.

The ratios of surface area to body weight for the two birds are: hen 0·075 m^2 kg^{-1} and hummingbird 0·08 m^2 kg^{-1}.

Knowing (1) that the hen is much larger than the hummingbird and (2) that as size of a spherical organism increases, its area increases proportionally to the square of its linear dimension (radius) whereas its volume (or weight if it remains the same density) increases as the cube of the linear dimension, you should expect that the ratio of surface area to weight would be smaller for the hen than for the hummingbird—the difference calculated here is less than you would expect from applying first principles which assume that both birds are spherical in shape—which clearly they are not.

SAQ 10 To obtain the amount of food eaten by the voles, multiply $26 \times 91 \times 2.08 \times 10^3 \times 90$ which will give A, the amount that must be assimilated in the 90 days to provide the energy requirement; multiply this by 100/85 to obtain C, the food consumed. Express this as a percentage of the standing crop value.

Hence the answer is:

$$\frac{26 \times 91 \times 2.08 \times 10^3 \times 90 \times 10^4}{85 \times 9.4 \times 10^9} \text{ per cent of standing crop}$$

$$= \frac{4.42 \times 10^{12}}{8.0 \times 10^{11}} \approx 5.5 \text{ per cent.}$$

Thus if there is no increase in the amount of plant material, this population of voles (which is a high population) will eat approximately 5·5 per cent of the living plant material present at the end of the summer. The daily consumption of the voles would be 0·06 per cent approximately of the standing crop of plants.

SAQ 11 Endogenous rhythms express themselves when animals are kept under environmental conditions that are constant, so the basic experiment would be to maintain some of the animals under the same environmental conditions for long periods of time. It would be necessary to control the temperature, the duration and intensity of lighting, the type of food and relative amount offered (the actual amount must increase if the animal grows). Under these conditions, two-year-old trout displayed changes in instantaneous growth rate, with faster rates in spring, slowing down through the summer and little growth in winter; these trout matured in autumn as they would have done under natural conditions. Endogenous rhythms are often triggered by external changes. Refer to S22–, Unit 8, Section 8.4.2, for a further discussion.

SAQ 12 See the completed Table 19 for values of P, $A\!:\!C$, $P\!:\!C$, $P\!:\!A$. ($P = A - R$.)

(a) The value for R is least in March and highest in June and July; this supports an hypothesis that respiration rate is related to temperature and is higher at higher temperatures. The fact that R is less in August than in July should be investigated since water temperatures are often higher in August than in July.

(b) The value for C is least in March and highest in July (like the values for R); again, it seems reasonable that feeding rate may be higher at higher temperatures. In filter-feeding organisms, such as *Diaptomus*, the limbs may be moved more frequently at higher temperatures and this would lead to more rapid filtering of the water.

(c) This statement seems eminently reasonable, but it is difficult to comment on it from the values in the table. Actually, the rate of filtering varied from 0·1 cm^3 copepod^{-1} day^{-1} when bacteria were the chief substrate to 2·54 cm^3 copepod^{-1} day^{-1} when the water contained large numbers of the alga *Diplosphaeria*. Assimilation also varied with the substrate and the higher values of $A\!:\!C$ (e.g. June and July) probably indicate periods when certain algae were present rather than others.

(d) This statement also is eminently reasonable but cannot be supported or rejected on the evidence available. Production was very high in July and fell dramatically in August—more information about the balance between different stages of the life history in these months would be helpful. Production was very low in March when probably most of the population consisted of adults.

SAQ 13 See the filled-in Tables 20, 21 and 22 for the values.

(a) The $A\!:\!C$ ratio varies between 26 and 36 per cent and this is as you might expect from the figures you have met for herbivorous insects. In fact, however, the $A\!:\!C$ ratio changed during each season, starting at about 10 per cent and becoming about 50 per cent for young adult bugs. It seems likely that the small nymphs were unable to cope with some of the cell organelles, such as chloroplasts. The sucking habit means that bugs do not ingest cell walls, so you might expect their $A\!:\!C$ ratio to be higher than for chewing insects such as caterpillars and grasshoppers. (Compare the spittlebugs in Table 13 of Smith's paper with the other insects in that Table and with these bugs.)

(b) The $P\!:\!A$ ratio varies between 48 and 59 per cent (again this varies through the life cycle, being about 20 per cent for small nymphs and up to 70 per cent for young adults). These ratios are of the same order as those for the caterpillars in Smith's paper (Table 13) but that was production of larvae only and the same amount of food had to cover adult stages, so that total production ratios would be much lower. The *Leptoterna* ratios are markedly higher than for the spittlebugs and grasshoppers in Smith's Table 13. It is suggested that *Leptoterna* is a very sedentary insect and makes use of a food source (cell contents of mesophyll) which is likely to be particularly good value. Having a low value for R, the values for $P\!:\!A$ should be high.

(c) *Leptoterna* C is of the order of one-thousandth of *Holcus* P so there is no indication that the bug is in danger of over-exploiting its food supply. The values of *Leptoterna* C show no indication of being adjusted to *Holcus* P.

(d) These values vary from 0.6×10^{-4} to 2.2×10^{-4}, making it very unlikely that there is any link between bug P and grass P.

(e) Eggs laid as percentage of bug P vary from 8·5 to 31·5, so this statement is clearly not true.

(f) This statement is true. The two lower values for egg production as a percentage of bug P are for the two years with highest P values (years 1 and 5). This relationship would tend to regulate the population about an intermediate level of numbers and production (see Block B for further discussion). Actually this is not a very common bug; its peak numbers vary between about 2·4 and 7·1 m^{-2}.

SAQ 14 The $P:B$ ratios are:

Walla Brook	trout	0·95		
Docken's Water	trout	1·9		
Tarrant	trout	2·7	bullheads	3·2
Lower Bere	trout	0·75	bullheads	3·8

(a) The observation is true. If the greatest production is in the first year of life, the implication is that there are plenty of young fish in the Tarrant and Docken's Water, giving a low biomass but high $P:B$ ratio. The available food is channelled into many young fish rather than into fewer older fish with lower production.

(b) The observation is true. The similarity of $P:B$ ratios suggests that the population structure and growth rates are similar and this means that the difference in total production of bullheads is related to the biomass present. Bullheads are small fish that live on the bottom of rivers with stony gravelly substrata[13] and it is possible that the River Tarrant has a greater area of suitable bottom than the Lower Bere. There could be other explanations of the difference, so this suggestion is one possible hypothesis that should be investigated.

(c) The observation is true but it is based on only four sets of figures so would need much more support before being accepted as a general rule. If it is true that high production of bullheads does not lead to reduced production of trout, this suggests that bullheads are not reducing the potential food supply of the trout. The two species eat an overlapping range of foods but trout feed on organisms that fall on the water surface; these are not available to the bottom-living bullhead.

Note that the total fish production value for the River Tarrant is one of the highest ever recorded for fish populations—and the major contribution to it is from the bullhead, a small species of no sporting or culinary value.

SAQ 15 You would need to establish that the variation existed by sampling through the year at regular intervals. You should collect data on changes in sizes of parts of the animal (especially the gonads) and on changes in level of feeding, since it is likely that a seasonal change (if demonstrated) would be the result of either of a variation in feeding level or of a physiological variation related to breeding. Having established that there was a change, you could then proceed to investigate the cause by a series of experiments varying food, light, temperature, etc., and/or by modifying conditions in the field (e.g. by adding food) or modifying the physiology (e.g. by injecting hormones).

SAQ 16 The instantaneous growth rate is approximately twice as high in the earlier period (between time-intervals 0 and 2) as in the later period (between time-intervals 4 and $6\frac{1}{2}$). See the completed Table 24 for the actual values.

SAQ 17 The Allen curve should resemble Figure 17. The biomass values can be read off the graph or (more easily) can be calculated by multiplying numbers by mean weight:

June of year 1, 2000 g m^{-2}; September of year 1, 4000 g m^{-2};

December of year 1, 2700 g m^{-2}; June of year 2, 1350 g m^{-2};

September of year 2, 800 g m^{-2}. So the answers are:

(a) an increase of 2000 g m^{-2};

(b) a decrease of 1300 g m^{-2};

(c) a decrease of 550 g m^{-2}.

(d) The answer to this is the shaded area in Figure 17 expressed as g m^{-2}. It is made up of three rectangles of areas:

$200 \times (18 - 5) = 2600$; $75 \times (22 - 18) = 300$;

$50 \times (27 - 22) = 250$ plus four triangles of areas:

$\frac{1}{2}(200 \times (20 - 5)) = 1500$; $\frac{1}{2}(50 \times (20 - 18)) = 50$;

$\frac{1}{2}(75 \times (22 - 18)) = 150$; $\frac{1}{2}(25 \times (27 - 22)) = 62.5$.

So the total production between June of year 1 and June of year 2 was:

$2600 + 300 + 250 + 1500 + 50 + 150 + 62.5 = 4912.5\,\mathrm{g\,m^{-2}}$ (i.e. 4.9×10^3 g m^{-2}).

(e) The ratio of production to initial biomass was 4912·5 : 2000 which equals 2·46. (2·5).

TABLE 24 (completed)

Time units	Weight units	Weight increment for interval	Weight increment as percentage of initial weight for interval % time^{-1}	Instantaneous growth rate % time^{-1}
0	0·1			
2	1·3	1·2 (2 time units)	600	128
4	1·4	0·1 (2 time units)	4	4
6½	6·6	5·2 (2½ time units)	150	62

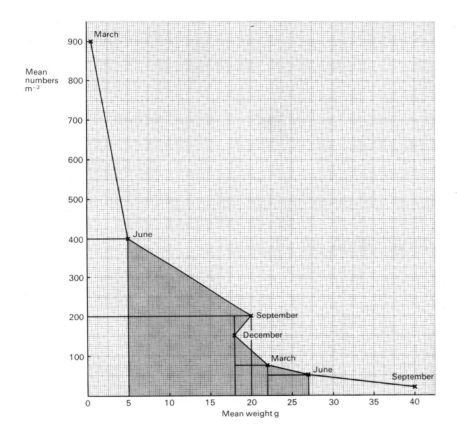

Figure 17 The Allen curve plotted from the data in Table 25.

Acknowledgements

Grateful acknowledgement is made to the following sources for figures used in this Unit:

Figure 5: Oikos for P. M. Jónasson, Ecology and production of the profundal benthos in relation to phytoplankton in lake Esrom in *Oikos Suppl.*, **14**, 1972; *Figure 11:* Duke University Press for P. A. Jordan, D. B. Botkin and M. L. Wolfe, Biomass dynamics in a moose population in *Ecology*, **52**, 1971.

S323 ECOLOGY

Bindings are arranged as follows:

Introduction to Block A, Units 1–3
Units 4 and 5
Introduction to Block B, Units 6–9
Introduction to Block C, Units 10 and 11
Units 12–14, Discussion of Blocks A, B and C
Units 15 and 16
The Analysis of Biological Experiments: Parts 1–4